Preface

The time seems ripe for a modern statement of the division of knowledge we have called "behavior genetics." During the last two decades there have been chapter-length reviews of the area (Hall, 1951, Caspari, 1958), but no comprehensive treatment. This book is intended to fill the gap. It is not presented as a definitive work, because that would be impossible in a field of study which is in a dynamic stage of growth.

At present there are few courses labeled "behavior genetics" in American college and university curricula. Nevertheless, this book is written for a readership of advanced undergraduates and graduate students in biology and psychology. Teachers of courses in genetics and in experimental, physiological, or comparative psychology may find useful supplementary material here. We have also considered matters of concern to psychiatrists, clinical psychologists, educators, and others who must cope with individual differences among human beings. Even animal breeders may find material pertaining to their work, for selection for behavioral traits is often an important part of a breed-improvement program.

We have divided our book into three sections. Chapters 1 through 4 provide a general introduction to the viewpoints and techniques of behavior genetics. Chapters 5 through 9 are a survey of the literature of behavior genetics. In the final chapter, behavior genetics is successively considered as a division of population genetics and as a series of physiological-developmental problems. An attempt is made to present a theoretical framework which can serve as a guide to new areas for research.

We have had some difficulty in limiting the study of behavior genetics because of its wide range, which extends from biochemistry, through various branches of biology, to psychology, psychiatry, social science, and statistical methods. Since we could not hope to qualify as experts in all of these fields, we trust we have not erred seriously in relating our particular subject to other scientific disciplines.

v

Another difficulty has been in selecting suitable materials for citation, especially when these fell short of exacting scientific standards. This has been particularly true of studies dealing with human beings. We considered omitting human studies completely, but did not do so because of the primary interest of many readers in human problems. Furthermore, there is increasing realization of the need for better techniques in this area, and some excellent research has been done. The juxtaposition of animal and human studies also has value, we believe, in the search for general laws of behavior.

Certain studies have been reported with a statement of the original author's conclusions, even though we have reservations concerning them. This procedure has been used when the investigator was obviously at grips with an important but difficult problem—one in which it was impossible to achieve all desirable controls with the available facilities and concepts. Pioneers must use the tools they have.

A word, perhaps, is needed concerning our choice of the term "behavior genetics." Other designations are "psychological genetics" and "psychogenetics" (Hall, 1951). The latter term has been used as a synonym for "genetic psychology," which has at times been rather antagonistic to heredity. Since behavior is of interest to biologists as well as to psychologists, "behavior genetics" seems to be the most general and acceptable name, although a case can be made for "psychological genetics" when the data analyzed are derived from psychological tests.

We hope this book will stimulate increased interest in behavior genetics research. The measure of its success will be the rapidity with which it becomes outdated.

JOHN L. FULLER
W. ROBERT THOMPSON

May 24, 1960

Behavior Genetics

JOHN L. FULLER

Roscoe B. Jackson Memorial Laboratory

WILLIAM R. THOMPSON

Wesleyan University

New York · London · Sydney   *John Wiley & Sons, Inc.*

Behavior Genetics

Acknowledgments

Both authors wish to express their gratitude to the John Simon Guggenheim Foundation for fellowship grants which assisted them in the preparation of this book. We are also grateful to the authors and publishers who generously granted permission for the reproduction of credited tabular and graphic material. All sources are cited fully in the bibliography.

Portions of the text were read critically by Jerry Hirsch and Everett R. Dempster, and many of their suggestions were adopted. However, the authors are fully responsible for all conclusions and for any errors which remain.

We are grateful to the typists, Jennie Jenkins and Helen Ehlinger, who labored over our manuscripts, and especially to Bernice Sylvester, who combined editorial surveillance with the tasks of typing and indexing. Ruth Fuller also assisted substantially with indexing and bibliographic research.

Finally, we are very appreciative of the many services and courtesies accorded to us by the publisher.

J. L. F.
W. R. T.

Contents

1

The scope of behavior genetics

Behavior genetics is a science which has aroused more than its share of controversy. Some disputation is inevitable in a developing field of knowledge, for scholars in all honesty interpret the same facts in different ways, but in the field of behavior genetics a more important source of conflict arises from the social and political implications of the subject. Pastore (1949a) has persuasively argued that the attitudes of scientists on the issues are affected by their liberal or their conservative social views. It is not a coincidence that genetics has been the biological science most prostituted in both Fascist and Communist states. Men are different, but man has not always been open-minded in seeking for the source of these differences.

The vigor of the nature-nurture controversy has declined in America since the 1920's; thus fewer scientists can be classified as "hereditarians" or "environmentalists." Exaltation of Nordic man (Grant, 1921), violent anti-heredity positions (Kuo, 1924), arbitrary ratios in the order of 5:1 for the relative importance of heredity to environment (Hirsch, 1930); all these are now of historic significance only. Even in midcentury, however, discourses on heredity and behavior between men trained in different disciplines often uncover disagreements. Several fairly recent series of polemics in the scientific press are ample evidence that some biologists and social scientists still hold unreconciled views (Dice, 1944; Herskovits, 1944; Strandskov, 1944a,b; Ashley-Montagu, 1944; Pastore, 1949b, 1952; Hurst, 1951, 1952). A beginning student of psychology might well be confused to read in one journal that ". . . at the present time practically all responsible workers in the field recognize that conclusive proof of the heritability of mental ability is still lacking where no organic or metabolic pathology is involved" (Sarason and Gladwin, 1958) and to find in the same year an eminent psychologist publishing a table showing that

1

more than half the variability in intelligence is attributable to heredity (Burt, 1958).

The Nature-Nurture Problem. Perhaps at this time there is no one who classifies behavior into two categories, innate and learned. The dichotomy, carried to its logical conclusion, would define innate behavior as that which appeared in the absence of environment, and learned behavior as that which required no organism. Verplanck (1955) has exposed the absurdities of slightly less extreme positions. The dichotomy is not in the kind of behavior studied (the dependent variable), but in the independent variables which are manipulated or observed. Here a clear distinction can be made between genetic factors which are transmitted from parents to offspring in the gametes and non-genetic factors which are not. This distinction, of course, limits the genetic contribution to extremely small packets of molecules in the nucleus of sperm and ovum.

Three kinds of questions may be raised with respect to the nature-nurture relationship (Anastasi, 1958b). What are the effects of heredity upon behavior? How large are these effects? What mechanisms are involved? Answers to the last question span the fields of genetics, physiology, and psychology. The purpose of this book is to present current thought on these three problems.

The development of any trait always involves genetic and environmental determinants. The *variation* between individuals is sometimes almost entirely due to one or the other type of factors. In common speech and in many genetic investigations a threefold classification of the characteristics of an organism has been used (Dahlberg, 1953).

1. A trait is called hereditary if most of the variation within a population is associated with differences in genetic endowment. As an example the agglutinogens of red blood cells are directly controlled by genes with which they have a one-to-one relationship. Even here cattle twins have the same blood type more frequently than predicted from genetic theory. The proffered explanation is the transfer of blood-forming elements through a common circulation in the placenta (Owen, 1945).

2. A non-hereditary or acquired trait has little or no genetically determined variance. Customs and language are conventional examples.

3. Variation in a third group of traits is significantly affected by both genetic and environmental factors. Skin color, body size, and most characteristics which vary quantitatively over a wide range belong in this "interaction" category.

The use of the convenient terms "hereditary traits" and "acquired traits" should not lead to the erroneous conclusion that they are fundamentally different from "interaction traits." An organism develops from a deceptively simple-appearing cell containing complex molecules in specific patterns. To produce a blood cell antigen a gene requires a supply of nutrients, oxygen, and other essentials. The point is that genetic determination of antigens is bound up so intimately with development that it cannot be modified without abolishing the organism. The observable variation of cellular antigens is wholly genetic. On the other hand, if one were to compare the acquisition of language in a population of normal children and microcephalics, one would find evidence for the inheritance of cultural patterns. The mentally deficient child though exposed to usually adequate stimulation fails to acquire the behavior which fits him for ordinary social living. The greater the demands of his culture, the greater is the extent of his incapacity.

Genes and Behavior Traits. Psychologists often object to such phrases as "the inheritance of aggressiveness" or "the genetics of intelligence." It is not aggressiveness or intelligence which is inherited, say the critics, but some structure which in turn affects behavior through transactions with the environment (Kuo, 1929; Anastasi and Foley, 1948). The point is well made, but there is an inconsistency in the critic's mention of the inheritance of body size, skin color, or the shape of the nose. These characters, too, are not transmitted in the genes but arise from gene-environment transactions. "Inheritance of intelligence" implies no more than "inheritance of body size." Both terms signify acceptance of the evidence that genes do make a difference in the development of the named trait. The effects of lack of intellectual stimulation or malnutrition are not excluded.

A related criticism is that the evidence for heritability of behavior cannot be considered conclusive until the physiological basis of the effect has been demonstrated. Such a demonstration is certainly desirable, but it is doubtful whether a complete physiological explanation has been attained for any inherited physical trait of higher organisms. Progress in this direction poses another set of questions at a more sophisticated level. Failure to achieve a complete explanation for gene action has not prevented genetics from moving forward on the basis of statistical rather than mechanistic associations between genes and traits. In a parallel fashion psychology has made great progress in relating behavior to previous experience without much success in explaining learning in physiological terms (Lashley, 1950). Behavioral techniques may well prove to be the most sensitive (perhaps the only) method for detecting certain genetic differences, just as they are now the only way of determining whether a rat has learned a maze.

It is an interesting speculation that gene action and learning are fundamentally similar. The gene-controlled pattern of body form tends to remain constant throughout life in spite of the rapid overturn of the constituent atoms (Schoenheimer, 1942). In this constant resynthesis of protoplasm the modifications which have been impressed by learning are retained along with those determined by genes. We remember our childhoods with molecules which were not in our bodies when we experienced them. Learning may be something like mutation (Davis, 1954), and it can be viewed as the process of completing the differentiation of the nervous system in greater detail and more adaptively than can be accomplished through gene encoding alone (Katz and Halstead, 1950).

Problems in the Choice of Behavior Traits for Study. An infinite number of measurements may be made upon the body of an organism or upon his behavior. In a sense each of them may be considered as a character whose inheritance may be studied. Since the number of genes is finite, characters of this sort far outnumber genes. In practice the geneticist selects characters which are convenient and will provide maximum information concerning other characters. Such a correlated set of characters defines a trait. The choice is often simpler among physical characters than it is among behavioral characters. No theoretical issues are raised when one studies the inheritance of body length. The dimensions of temperament and personality, however, have not been standardized. Many psychologists have dealt with this question from a variety of viewpoints, and a book larger than this would be required to deal adequately with the subject. (For sample discussions see Anastasi, 1948, 1958b; Cattell, 1955; Murphy, 1947; Thurstone, 1947.) In our review of the literature we have, for practical reasons, followed the usage of each author. Traits which have been utilized in behavior genetics range from specific motor components of fish courtship to susceptibility to perceptual illusions and scores on Stanford-Binet tests. Surprisingly, genetic effects have been shown at both extremes of complexity. We shall return to this subject in Chapter 10, where we consider whether genetics can assist in defining behavioral traits which also make biological sense.

Subjects for Behavior Genetics. Success in biological research often depends upon proper selection of material. Genetic studies require a variable species, one which is prolific and easily maintained and with a small number of large-sized chromosomes so that hereditary factors can be manipulated and directly observed. The fruit flies, drosophilae, fit these specifications. Man fails on all counts except variability. Yet because of the particular interest in the study of man, human subjects have been much more commonly used in behavior genetics than drosophila.

An advantage of Drosophila, other insects, fish, and, to a lesser degree, birds is that the gene-behavior-trait relationship is more direct than is typically true of mammals. The concepts of intelligence and temperament are less applicable to species whose individuals are more stereotyped in behavior. Hence the behavioral characters selected for study in the "lower" phyla and orders are specific movements in response to specific stimuli. The advantage from the biological side is countered by the difficulty in generalizing to the kinds of individual differences which are characteristic of man. Man is a mammal, and there are many parallels between the development of behavior in subhuman mammals and in human infants before the beginning of speech. This probably explains the predilection of psychologists for mammals as subjects for behavior genetics. Biologists, less concerned with generalization to other species, have done most of the experiments with the "lower" species.

Among mammals the house mouse, *Mus musculus,* is now the favorite subject for genetics. Over two hundred named mutations are known, many distinctive inbred strains are available, and the chromosomes are partially identified. The behavior of mice has been fairly well studied, though not nearly so thoroughly as that of rats. Compared with their larger cousins, mice are less convenient for some psychological and physiological procedures. The formal genetics of rats is less well known than that of mice, but it is questionable whether knowledge of the mode of inheritance of coat color and developmental anomalies is as valuable for behavior genetics as information on the physiological correlates of the behavior of a species. On the whole, rats and mice each have advantages from a scientific point of view. For experiments in which either species would be satisfactory, mice may be favored for economic reasons.

Cats and dogs are man's oldest domestic animals. The worldwide distribution of these species and the existence of many specialized breeds provide a ready-made source of material for behavior genetics. These carnivores give an impression of greater individuality than rodents, but this impression may reflect our greater intimacy with them. Dogs have considerable use (Scott and Fuller, 1951) because of their highly developed social behavior. Cats have not been used in behavior genetics to our knowledge, although the extensive knowledge of feline neurophysiology should make them useful for certain problems. Scattered references will be found to behavior genetics research on other species of mammals, but these reports are incidental to other studies. Subhuman primates would seem to have advantages for research on the inheritance of intelligence, but the difficulties of laboratory rearing and the relatively low fecundity have discouraged attempts in this direction.

To what extent is it possible to formulate general principles from genetic experiments performed on diverse species? The problem is similar to that faced by Tolman (1932) in writing of "Purposive Behavior in Animals and Men" and Beach (1947) in his cross-species survey of sexual behavior. When a sufficiently large spectrum of species is observed, principles emerge which would not be evident in more limited studies. Fortunately the mechanisms of gene transmission are practically identical in all the organisms we shall consider. The primary physiological action of genes is also believed to be broadly similar in all species, though more complicated structures involve more steps between primary gene action and the completed character. There is no reason to expect that the specific gene systems controlling courtship behavior will be the same in rats and dogs, but the manner in which control is exerted is probably as similar as the effects of hormones upon the behavior in the two species. It is safe to conclude that the problems of generalizing from comparative genetic studies are of the same order as those encountered in synthesizing results of experiments in different species on the effects of early experience or brain lesions.

Some Methodological Problems. In this section we shall be concerned with some of the broader methodological problems of behavior genetics. In general, heredity as an independent variable can be incorporated into the design of a psychological experiment just as one introduces physiological or experiential factors. The dependent variable can be any form of behavior which interests the investigator. The simplest experiment is to take two groups of different heredity, treat them alike in all other respects, and administer a behavior test. The results are compared against the prediction from the null hypothesis, that the groups differ no more than two independent samples drawn from the same population. If the null hypothesis is not supported, evidence for heritability of the behavior variation has been obtained.

But though logically identical with other experimental procedures in psychology, behavior genetics has certain peculiarities. The differential treatments (distribution of genes) precede the existence of the subjects of the experiment. In fact genetic control may extend back many generations before the birth of the actual subjects of an experiment. The need for long periods of treatment (selective breeding) is inherent in this area. Another feature is the impossibility of manipulating genes directly. The distribution of genes to subjects is essentially random and is controlled by the experimenter only in a statistical sense. Since genes are not observed directly, their presence is deduced from their effects. At first thought the argument for their existence may seem circular. Traits are ascribed to genes whose presence is proved by the occurrence of the trait. Fortunately the gene theory rests upon a more ample foundation, which is described briefly in Chapter 2. The worker in behavior genetics must understand chromosome behavior as well as organismic behavior in order to design his experiments.

The heredity of an organism is fixed at the moment of fertilization. This imposes a limitation upon experimental design. One can present stimulus A before or after stimulus B and can train subjects before or after a cortical ablation, but genes cannot be changed in the middle of the life span. Thus there is no way of teasing apart the effects produced by the genic control of contemporary metabolism and the effects due to genic determination of growth and differentiation. The latter effects are inevitably confounded with conditions during development.

A special concern of behavior genetics is the avoidance of non-random association between environmental and hereditary factors. The fact that families share experiences as well as genes makes the human data in this area difficult to interpret. The problem also occurs in experimental behavior genetics, at least in birds and mammals, which give parental care. Uteri, compared with the external world, may provide protection against many stimuli, though recent experiments (Thompson, 1957) have reopened the question of effects of prenatal experience upon later behavior. Differences in postnatal family environment are of greater potential significance. Cross-fostering of the young of one strain to the dam of another permits evaluation of effects of different nutrition and type of maternal care. Experimental regulation of litter size can be used to control the nature of early experience, degree of competition, and the like. Statistical corrections can be applied to allow for the fact that members of a litter share experiences unique to that litter. These techniques have their parallels in human society, but they cannot be applied with the same rigor.

Concern for the environment in behavior genetics research goes beyond avoidance of heredity-environment correlations. Simply providing the same conditions for all subjects is not enough for good design. In the context of research a controlled environment is one in which stimuli are introduced in the same systematic fashion to all subjects. They must be not only uniform for all subjects but also favorable to the development of the trait being studied. An unsuitable rearing system may modify or even completely suppress the manifestations of a genetic difference (Howells, 1946; Freedman, 1958).

Perhaps the most important conclusion to be drawn is that research in behavior genetics cannot be isolated from research in the development of behavior, the area traditionally known as genetic psychology. Heredity-environment interactions are more than a statistical abstraction. They can be observed and analyzed in experiments in which genetic and experiential factors are varied simultaneously in controlled fashion.

Applications of Behavior Genetics. Behavior genetics has relationships with both parent sciences. Behavioral characters, because they are so environment-sensitive, are unsuitable for most research of interest to formal genetics. Some application has been made of behavioral tests to the detection of genetic differences not discernible from morphology (Reed, Williams, and Chadwick, 1942). Considerable effort has been expended upon mating behavior, particularly in Drosophila, because of the importance of sexual selection in evolutionary theory. Human geneticists have been concerned with the inheritance of mental deficiency and psychiatric disorders in order to provide genetic counseling. To a minor degree behavior genetics has found applications in applied animal breeding.

Undoubtedly, more research in this area has been motivated by interest in behavior than by interest in genetics. Even investigators who consider individual differences a nuisance use littermate controls, cotwin controls, and pure-bred stocks to reduce genetic sources of variability in their material. More significant for our purposes are attempts to utilize genetics as a research tool (Scott, 1949). Such uses go beyond the demonstration of heritability of a particular kind of behavior.

The repetition of a procedure with different strains is a means of extending or limiting generalizations based upon a single type of experimental animal. Comparisons between domesticated and wild rats, for example, have demonstrated important psycho-physiological differences within the same species (Richter, 1952, 1954). General laws in the behavioral sciences can be fully justified only when they are based upon observations of numerous species and strains.

The use of mutant stocks or of strains selected for special behavioral characteristics provides material for physiological psychology which cannot be duplicated by surgery, electrical stimulation, drugs, or other techniques. Inherited factors are perhaps more likely to contribute to our understanding of individual differences in intact organisms. Sample studies of this type include Fuller and Smith's (1953) study of the kinetics of sound-induced convulsions in a number of mouse strains and Fuller and Jacoby's (1955) investigation of control of eating in the obese mouse.

Finally, behavior genetics has a potential contribution to education, psychiatry, clinical psychology, and other professions which deal at first hand with a variety of human problems. Heritability of a deleterious deviation does not mean that it cannot be ameliorated. If heredity does play a role, recognition of the fact and understanding of the intermediate physiological mechanisms may be the most direct way to a satisfactory treatment. A behavioral disorder associated with a correctable metabolic defect would call for a rational rather than a symptomatic therapy.

Plan of the Book. In this chapter we have considered the special problems and potentialities of behavior genetics. Chapter 2 is inserted as a brief introduction for those who have not studied genetics or as a review for the reader who has been out of contact with the subject. In Chapters 3 and 4 the discussion of genetics is continued with special emphasis on methods and concepts useful in the study of behavior. The treatment is not extensive enough to serve as a handbook of genetic techniques, but it does provide a background for reading specialized papers. Chapters 5 through 9 are devoted to a review of the literature of experimental and human behavior genetics. Chapter 10 surveys general problems of behavior genetics, including the relationships between genes and characters and the importance of genetic factors to variations in behavior within and between populations.

2

Some principles
of genetics

Although the application of hereditary principles to the development of various varieties of domesticated plants and animals goes back into prehistory, a comprehensive theory of inheritance is the product of the twentieth century (Dunn, 1951). Present-day genetics represents the fusion of two lines of investigation, one dealing with the processes of cell division and fertilization, the other concerned with crossing variant types and analyzing the characteristics of the offspring by statistical methods.

The following pages contain an elementary account of selected topics in genetics for individuals without formal training in this area or for those who have lost contact with a science which is constantly adding to its factual and theoretical foundations. Readers who are acquainted with the science may omit this chapter and portions of Chapters 3 and 4 without disrupting the continuity of the discussion. Modern advances in such fields as physiological genetics, selection theory, and the genetics of quantitative characters have special significance for the student of the behavioral sciences. To a great extent these concepts have been under-represented in elementary biology courses. Perhaps the predilection of some investigators for simple genetic models to explain complex behavioral characters is due to unfamiliarity with more complex systems. And perhaps some anti-heredity bias stems from the realization that single-gene models are inadequate, as well as from a lack of acquaintance with other concepts.

Major areas of genetics which have only a peripheral relationship to behavior have been omitted in this brief summary. Obviously our choice is arbitrary, and those who are stimulated to seek a more complete account are advised to find it in one of several excellent general or specialized textbooks. (For example, Srb and Owen, 1953;

Sinnott, Dunn, and Dobzhansky, 1958; Waddington, 1950; Stern, 1949.)

ORGANIC PATTERNS AND LIFE CYCLES

The fertilized ova of different mammals appear much alike under the microscope and can be identified only by a trained microscopist. If it were possible to provide adequate nourishment and protection so that development would proceed on the microscope stage, these cells would be observed to divide, to increase in mass until a microscope could no longer be used, and to diverge in form until their identities as human, seal, horse, or rat would be apparent. The result of the developmental process identifies the source of each ovum, for it is a biological axiom that each species reproduces its own kind.

The regularity of development tempts the observer to compare it with the unfolding of a predetermined form as exemplified in the Chinese paper flowers which expand into intricate patterns when placed in water. But the analogy is incorrect. The process is not an unfolding, but the carrying out of a series of reactions which are encoded in the genes and perhaps in other cellular elements. The result is a structure which adheres to the characteristic pattern of its species but varies in detail from other members of the species. Both the constancy and the variability of the overall organization have their basis in the functions of genes.

Patterns are observable in living organisms at many levels from size factors expressed over the whole body down to the configuration of protein molecules. It is convenient to begin a consideration of genetics at the intermediate level of the cell. Every higher organism is an aggregate of cells, some of which are highly specialized in structure and function. The central, denser-appearing *nucleus* is more uniform in different tissues than the outer portion, which is known as *cytoplasm* (Figure 2-1). This cytoplasm may be stretched into a nerve fiber several feet long specialized for conducting electrical pulses or compressed into a cube in the thyroid gland where it is the site of hormone synthesis. Experiments on separation of nucleus and cytoplasm have shown that the nucleus is essential for the continued existence of the cell as an organized system. Apparently it controls the synthesis of molecules which are necessary for cytoplasm. The nucleus also plays a unique part in the process of cell division known as *mitosis*.

Chromosomes and Mitosis. At the time of cell division the nucleus undergoes complete reorganization, and in this period it is possible

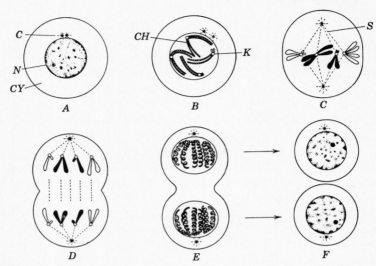

FIGURE 2-1. Diagram of cell division and mitosis. C = centriole; N = nucleus; CY = cytoplasm; CH = chromosome; K = kinetochore; S = spindle. (From *Principles of Human Genetics* by Curt Stern. San Francisco: W. H. Freeman and Co., 1949.)

to observe elongated bodies known as *chromosomes* (colored bodies) because of their capacity to absorb certain dyes. Each species has a characteristic number of chromosomes, for example, the mouse has 40; the rat, 42; dog, 78; corn, 20; *Drosophila melanogaster,* 8; potatoes, 48; and man, probably 46 (Tjio and Levan, 1956).

Careful examination reveals that in sexually reproducing species the chromosomes occur in pairs, and that there are slight differences between the chromosomes of males and females. For example, each body cell of a woman contains 23 pairs. Each nucleus in a man contains 22 pairs plus one mismatched doubleton known as the X- and Y-chromosomes. Two X-chromosomes are found in the body cells of women. The X- and Y-chromosomes are collectively known as the *sex chromosomes;* the remaining pairs are called *autosomes.* The complements of each sex may be summarized as:

Female: 44A + 2X = 46 chromosomes
Male: 44A + X + Y = 46 chromosomes

In the majority of animals sex determination is like that in man, though in birds and butterflies females are found to have the mismatched pair.

In ordinary cell division, as in the growth of an embryo or the replacement of worn-out skin, each chromosome duplicates itself as the cell divides so that each daughter cell comes to possess a complete set of 46 chromosomes. This process, known as *mitosis,* is illustrated in Figure·2-1. This figure shows the successive events of chromosome division and the formation of a new nucleus, starting with the resting stage (not truly an inactive nucleus, but only one which is not dividing). Not all the features of the diagram are seen in every cell, but the onset of mitosis is usually indicated by division of the *centriole* (Figure 2-1, *A*). The chromosomes first appear as elongated bodies with a specialized region, the *kinetochore,* which serves as an attachment point for *spindle fibers* (Figure 2-1, *B*). Later the chromosomes become more condensed, the centrioles move to opposite poles of the cell, and spindle fibers running from centrioles to kinetochores are seen. The nuclear membrane breaks down in this stage which is called *metaphase* (Figure 2-1, *C*). The remaining diagrams (*D, E, F*) illustrate the separation of each chromosome from its newly replicated partner, the re-establishment of the nuclear boundaries, and the eventual separation of the daughter cells.

The significant result of mitosis is the duplication of chromosomes to produce a series of pairs, followed by the separation of each pair. It is probably significant that the nuclear membrane breaks down during mitosis so that cytoplasmic constituents are available for the synthesis of new chromosome material. Also important is the fact that although each daughter cell receives the same chromosomes,* hence the same genetic factors, the two cells may eventually be markedly different. This simple fact demonstrates that development is not an unfolding of an inner pattern, but an active process of interaction between extracellular and intracellular forces.

Meiosis and Crossing Over. The cell divisions of the somatic cells of organisms are mitotic, but the production of germ cells involves a variation known as *meiosis.* In the course of meiosis two cell divisions occur with only one duplication of chromosomes, hence the chromosome number is exactly halved in sperm and ova as compared with somatic cells. The essentials of the process are simple, and they are diagrammed in the upper part of Figure 2-2. *Homologous chromosomes* (members of the same pair, one of maternal and another of paternal origin) approach each other and come to lie side by side (Figure 2-2, *A*). This pairing, known as *synapsis,* involves close contact

* Exceptions to the equality of chromosome numbers in somatic cells do occur, but their significance is difficult to evaluate. Certainly these differences have not been found to be related to cell function. (See Srb and Owen, 1953, pp. 108 ff.)

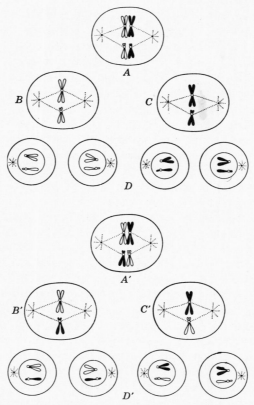

FIGURE 2-2. Simplified diagram of meiosis, including the two meiotic divisions. *A, A'.* The two alternative arrangements of the chromosome pairs on the first meiotic spindle. *B–D,* and *B'–D'.* The second meiotic divisions and the different types of reduced chromosome constitutions of the gametes. (From *Principles of Human Genetics* by Curt Stern. San Francisco: W. H. Freeman and Co., 1949.)

of the corresponding parts of each chromosome. Centrioles and spindle fibers are seen in meiosis as in mitosis. Before pairing, the chromosomes have reduplicated so that a four-strand structure is formed. In the first meiotic division each set of four is reduced to a group of two, and in the second meiotic division the pairs divide again so that the original four chromosomes are distributed one each to four germ cells.

The most important feature of meiosis is the reshuffling of chromosomes and the consequent appearance of combinations in the offspring which are unlike those in the parents. The redistribution is possible because of different arrangements of the chromosome pairs as they line up in the metaphase stage of the first meiotic division. Consider Figure 2-2 again, this time comparing the upper and lower portions. In a species with two pairs of chromosomes there are two alternative arrangements, A and A'. In this figure the chromosomes of maternal origin are shown in outline, those from the father as solid areas. Four types of daughter cells, B, B', C, and C', are produced in equal numbers, and four corresponding types of gametes are found (D, D'). It can readily be shown that the number of possible types of gametes is 2^n, where n is the number of pairs of chromosomes. When $n = 23$, the number of gametic types is 8,388,608.

Expressed in another fashion, each human parent has the potentiality of producing over 8 million distinct types of germ cells. The probability of any particular combination's occurring in a mating between two specified individuals is the product of 8,388,608 by itself. It is probable that no human beings except identical twins have ever been genetic duplicates. If complicating effects such as crossing over (see below) are considered, the possibilities of recombination become much greater. Stern (1949) has estimated that a single human pair have the potentiality of producing 20^{24} different types of children, a number far greater than the total number of human beings who have ever existed. Of course much of this genetic variability may have little importance for behavior, but on purely logical grounds uniqueness of heredity is as much a fact as uniqueness of experience.

Homologous chromosomes are not merely similar externally but are comparable part by part. Thus during the intimate contact of synapsis each section or *locus* within a chromosome of maternal origin is associated with the corresponding locus in a chromosome of paternal origin. In Figure 2-3 a single pair of chromosomes is depicted, the maternal by outline and the paternal by a solid bar. The chromosomes are different (heterozygous) at three loci; M, N, and O on one chromosome, M', N', and O' on the other. Synapsis is shown in (A) and duplication in (B). Crossing over between M and N is diagrammed in (C) and between N and O in (D). When the intertwining is followed by breakage and recombination of parts, the resultant chromosomes are a composite of maternal and paternal contributions (middle chromosomes of E). This process obviously increases the possibilities for recombinations of hereditary factors in meiosis. Were it not for crossing over, the chromosome rather than the gene would be the unit of heredity. Crossing over may be double, triple, or even

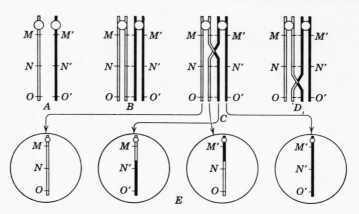

FIGURE 2-3. Crossing over. *A*. A pair of homologous chromosomes heterozygous for three pairs of loci *M*, *M'*; *N*, *N'*; and *O*, *O'*. *B*. Four-strand stage. *C*. Crossing over between two of the four strands in the region between *M*, *M'* and *N*, *N'*. *D*. Same in the region between *N*, *N'* and *O*, *O'*. *E*. The four types of reduced chromosome constitutions of the gametes resulting from crossing over in *C*. (From *Principles of Human Genetics* by Curt Stern. San Francisco: W. W. Freeman and Co., 1949.)

more complex, and this variation complicates calculations of cross-over frequencies. This problem will not ordinarily arise in behavior genetics, which is seldom concerned with the location of individual genetic entities such as *M*, *N*, and *O* in Figure 2-3.

Gametogenesis. The process of gamete formation, *gametogenesis,* is similar in male and female insofar as the nuclear processes in meiosis are concerned, but the cytoplasmic events are modified in relation to the different functions of sperm and ovum. The two processes are diagrammed side by side in Figure 2-4. In spermatogenesis the germinal cells which line the walls of tubules in the testis are known as *spermatogonia.* The cells in which synapsis occurs (*A* through *E*) are *primary spermatocytes,* the cells containing dyads (*F*, *G*) are secondary spermatocytes, and the final products of meiosis are four *spermatids* which metamorphose into *spermatozoa.* The head of a spermatozoon is composed almost entirely of chromosomes. Thus a male's contribution to the substance of his offspring is compressed into a few cubic micra (one micron = $\frac{1}{1000}$ millimeter).

In *oögenesis* the division of the cytoplasm at the two meiotic divisions is unequal (Figure 2-4, *E*, *F*, *G*). Practically all the cytoplasm is retained within one of the cells, the secondary oöcyte. The smaller cell, containing a full set of chromosomes (*F*, *G*), is known as a *polar*

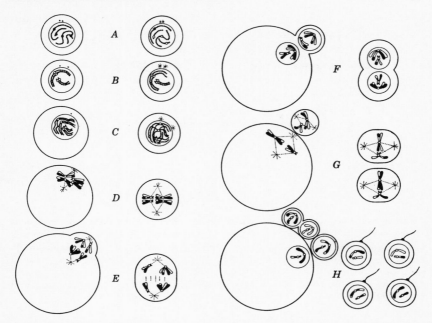

FIGURE 2-4. Diagram of meiosis and formation of gametes. Left, oogenesis; right, spermatogenesis. *A–C.* Chromosome pairing and crossing over. *D–E.* First meiotic division. *F.* Products of first division. *G.* Second meiotic division. *H.* Egg with polar bodies (left), sperm cells (right). (From *Principles of Human Genetics* by Curt Stern. San Francisco: W. H. Freeman and Co., 1949.)

body. It may divide again. A second polar body is produced at the second meiotic division (*H*). Both polar bodies normally degenerate, as their one function is to serve as a repository for excess nuclear material. Thus when the ovum is fertilized by a sperm the somatic number of chromosomes is reconstituted.

The ovum contains a considerable amount of cytoplasm and sometimes much stored food in addition. Thus the possibility exists that the maternal gamete may contribute more to the determination of biological characteristics than does the sperm. Possibly the broad patterns of development are encoded in the cytoplasm and variations on the main theme in the genes. It is impossible to prove the point one way or the other until cells are synthesized with nuclei of one species and cytoplasm of another. The weight of the evidence is that each parent contributes equally to genetic variation. In mammals maternal influences operate through the health of the mother during pregnancy, the quality of her milk, the adequacy of her care for her helpless young. These may be important sources of variation, but they are classified as environmental rather than genetic factors.

Sex Determination. It is apparent from the previous sections on chromosomes and gametogenesis that the formulae for human germ cells may be written as:

$$\text{Ovum:} \quad 22A + X$$
$$\text{Sperm:} \quad 22A + X; \text{ or } 22A + Y$$

Each type of sperm has an equal chance to fertilize an ovum and form a *zygote* with the somatic number of chromosomes. Thus:

$$(22A + X) + (22A + X) = 44A + 2X = \text{Female zygote}$$
$$(22A + Y) + (22A + X) = 44A + X + Y = \text{Male zygote}$$

This system should produce equal numbers of male and female off-spring, and this is approximately realized in nature. In man there is a slight, but statistically significant, excess of male births over female. The reasons for this are unknown (Stern, 1949, Chapter 20).

As stated above, the general principles of sex determination are similar throughout the animal kingdom. However, sex is no exception to the principle that phenotype does not always precisely follow genotype. Comprehensive discussions of the complexities of sex determination and differentiation may be found in Srb and Owen (1953), Danforth (1939), and Witschi (1939). Some of the variations, particularly the intersexes in moths discovered by Goldschmidt, have significance for behavior genetics.

Goldschmidt (1923) found that crosses between different geographical races of the gypsy moth, *Lymantria dispar,* produced large numbers of intersexual forms. In his most extreme crosses, he obtained only morphological males, since all genetic females were transformed.

In this species, as in other Lepidoptera, males are homogametic, ZZ, and females heterogametic, ZW. Goldschmidt hypothesized that the cytoplasm of the gypsy moth ovum was feminizing in its developmental tendency; one Z-chromosome could not overbalance this, hence ZW individuals were female. Two Z-chromosomes would push the balance to the other side and produce maleness. Within each geographical race the "valences" of cytoplasm and chromosomes were balanced, so that the mechanism yielded a normal sex ratio. In racial crosses a single "strong" Z would nearly or completely overbalance a "weak" cytoplasmic valence and produce an intersex or even a male who was actually a genetic female. This theory has enjoyed some popularity as a possible explanation of human homosexuality (see page 301).

A different effect of autosomal genes upon sex differentiation has been reported by Sturtevant (1945) in *D. melanogaster*. The gene *tra* transformed genetically female (XX) flies into morphologically normal, but sterile, males. Since the courtship behavior of the transformed "females" was typically masculine, we may conclude that behavior follows structure rather than chromosomes.

GENES: UNIT FACTORS IN INHERITANCE

Perhaps the greatest difference between modern genetic concepts and traditional folk ideas of heredity is that today we conceive of the transmission of individual particles of hereditary material from parents to offspring, whereas older ideas postulated a blending of the hereditary elements of the two sexes. The name gene is applied to a unit factor of heredity.

Some of the basic ideas of the gene theory are illustrated in a report on the varitint-waddler mouse by Cloudman and Bunker (1945). This rather exotically named mouse variety first appeared in a cross between a solid-colored black and a solid-colored brown strain which had bred true for generations. These more lightly pigmented and spotted mice also bred true. The change, therefore, was a *mutation,* a persistent alteration of one of the hereditary units. Cloudman and Bunker assigned the symbol *Va* to the mutant gene and the symbol *va* to its unmutated normal counterpart. *Va* and *va* are *alleles,* genes which differ in their physiological properties although they occupy the same locus on a chromosome. Since every mouse has two complete sets of chromosomes, its genetic formula with respect to the *Va* locus can be, *Va/Va, Va/va,* or *va/va.* Each of these formulae symbolizes a different *genotype. Genotype* in its most general sense is the complete assemblage of genes which an individual possesses. Genotypic formulae are never complete since it is impossible to identify all genes present, and it is rare in mammals to specify more than five or six loci.

Individuals with identical genes at corresponding loci are *homozygous* at this locus (for example, *va/va* and *Va/Va*). *Heterozygous* individuals have unlike genes at corresponding loci (for example, *Va/va*).

Each genotype in this series is identifiable from the physical characteristics or *phenotype* of its possessor. A *va/va* mouse may be of many colors and forms, depending upon the remainder of his genotype, but it is certain that he will not be a varitint-waddler. The typical waddler (Va/va) shows piebald spotting, erratic ducklike locomotion, circling, and head shaking. Mice homozygous for Va are practically all white, and are so hyperexcitable at 14 days of age that jarring the cages in which they live may induce violent convulsions. Most Va/Va animals are sterile, and the heterozygotes show reduced fertility.

An alternative way of writing genotypic formulae is to use the symbol + for the "wild-type" or "normal" allele present in the general population. Ordinary mice are $+/+$, varitint-waddlers, $Va/+$, and homozygous defectives Va/Va.

Testing Genetic Hypotheses. Genetic theory can be used to predict the outcome of breeding heterozygous waddlers to normal mice. If we assume, as is in fact true, that the gene is located on an autosome, it will make no difference whether the waddler parent is male or female. This assumption must be checked by comparing the results of reciprocal crosses in which the waddler gene is introduced through the paternal and maternal sides. The model for prediction is shown in Table 2-1.

TABLE 2-1

Prediction Model Based on the Single-Gene Hypothesis

(The ratio below is obtained if it is assumed that the varitint-waddler character is produced by a single gene. Cross is between normal and varitint-waddler mice.)

Genotype of V-W mouse = $Va/+$
This will produce equal numbers of gametes of the following types:

			Va	$+$
Genotype of Normal Mouse ($+/+$)	This can produce only one type of gamete.	$+$	$Va/+$	$+/+$

Types of Zygotes Formed

Predicted ratio of offspring (zygotes): $\frac{1}{2}\ Va/+ : \frac{1}{2}\ +/+$

If the normal mice resulting from this cross are mated *inter se,* all the offspring will be normal although each has a waddler grandparent. If waddlers are mated with waddlers, the gametes and resultant zygotes are shown in Table 2-2.

TABLE 2-2

Prediction Model Based on the Single-Gene Hypothesis

(The ratio below is obtained if it is assumed that the varitint-waddler character is produced by a single gene. Cross is between two varitint-waddler mice. Each parent will produce equal numbers of Va and $+$ gametes.)

Gametes of the First Parent

	Va	$+$
Gametes of the Second Parent Va	Va/Va	$Va/+$
$+$	$+/Va$	$+/+$

Types of Zygotes Formed

Predicted ratio of offspring (zygotes): ¼ Va/Va:½ $Va/+$:¼ $+/+$

These two procedures, (*A*) crossing heterozygotes to homozygotes and obtaining a 1:1 ratio in the offspring and (*B*) crossing heterozygote with heterozygote and obtaining a 1:2:1 ratio, are the basic devices of experimental genetics. More complicated designs are extensions of the same principles.

Cloudman and Bunker carried out these procedures with the following results (Table 2-3).

TABLE 2-3

Results of Breeding Experiments on the Varitint-Waddler Mouse (Cloudman and Bunker, 1945)

Type of Mating	Litters	Individuals		White Defective	Varitint Waddler	Wild Type
Waddler × Wild type	93	665	Pred.	0	332.5	332.5
			Obs.	0	325	340
Wild type* × Wild type*	7	52	Pred.	0	0	52
			Obs.	0	0	52
Waddler × Waddler	62	386	Pred.	96	192	96
			Obs.	18	236	132

Phenotypic Classes header spans White Defective, Varitint Waddler, Wild Type.

* These animals each had a waddler parent.

In two of the crosses agreement with prediction is good. The significance of the difference between the 325 $Va/+$ obtained and the 332.5 predicted can be evaluated by the chi-square test. A text on statistics should be consulted for a discussion of this procedure. The formula used in computing chi-square is

$$\chi^2 = \frac{\Sigma(O - P)^2}{P}$$

where O = the observed number in each class of offspring and P = the predicted number in each class. For the $Va/+$ by $+/+$ cross, the cal culation is as follows:

$$\chi^2 = \frac{(325 - 332.5)^2}{332.5} + \frac{(340 - 332.5)^2}{332.5} = .339$$

with a p value of more than .5. Obviously the data agree satisfactorily with the hypothesis.

The $Va/+ \times Va/+$ cross produces far too few homozygous white mice. Chi-square is calculated as follows:

$$\chi^2 = \frac{(18 - 96)^2}{96} + \frac{(236 - 192)^2}{192} + \frac{(132 - 96)^2}{96} = 86.85$$

$$p < .001$$

Since the discrepancy is too large to be attributed to random sampling, an explanation must be given, or the hypothesis of single gene inheritance must be rejected. It is known that the homozygous white mice are biologically inferior. Thus it is reasonable to assume that many Va/Va mice succumb before birth and never enter the statistics. From the number of $Va/+$ and $+/+$ individuals produced we would expect 123 homozygous whites ($1/3 \times (236 + 132)$). Presumably all but 18 of these failed to attain a stage of development permitting their classification. Numerous examples are known of genes with lethal or sporadically lethal effects which disrupt ratios calculated from simple assumptions. Statistical predictions must take biological realities into account.

The contrast between the particulate or Mendelian theory of heredity and a blending theory is illustrated by the data in the second row of Table 2-3. None of the 52 offspring of normal parents, but with defective grandparents, were themselves defective. Thus the progeny of a wild type by waddler mating are either defective and capable of transmitting the waddler gene, or they are normal with no such gene to pass on. None are intermediate-strength waddlers either in behavior or in genetic potentiality, as would be predicted if genetic determiners were blended. We will see later that the Mendelian mechanism operating on numerous independent genes can result in intermediate individuals, but the principles illustrated by the varitint-waddler trait still hold for the inheritance of each pair of genes.

Dominant and Recessive Genes. In the varitint-waddler mouse there is a correlation between the number of Va genes and their phenotypic expression. The disruption of normal function is more extreme in Va/Va animals than in $Va/+$ mice. This seems very rea-sonable and represents superficially a blending of genetic effects, though, as the breeding results show, not a blending of genetic substance. The phenomenon of dominance upsets the one-to-one correlation between phenotype and genotype. Consider another example from mouse genetics, this time a coat-color character. When mice from a pure-breeding black stock are bred to those from a pure-breeding brown stock, the offspring are all black. Breeding the first filial generation hybrids (F_1) *inter se* yields a second filial generation (F_2) comprised of approximately three-fourths black and one-fourth brown animals. In situations of this type black (B) is said to be *dominant* to brown (b), which is called *recessive*. The genetic situation is depicted in Table 2-4.

TABLE 2-4

Predicted Results of Crossing Black and Brown Mice: Black is Dominant

Parental Generation	Sex	Male or Female	Female or Male
	Phenotype	Black	Brown
	Genotype	B/B	b/b
	Gametes produced	B	b

Combination of these gametes produces an F_1 generation.

		Male or Female	Female or Male
	Phenotype	Black	Black
	Genotype	B/b	B/b
	Gametes produced	½ B : ½ b	½ B : ½ b

Combination of these gametes at random produces an F_2 generation.

	Phenotype	¾ Black	¼ Brown
	Genotype	¼ B/B : ½ B/b	¼ b/b

The 3:1 ratio is merely a variant of the 1:2:1 ratio previously described. It is characteristic of the F_2 generation whenever dominant inheritance is found. The distinction between dominance and non-

dominance is not always clear-cut or fundamental. It depends in part upon the state of knowledge of the effects of the gene, for if the heterozygote can be distinguished phenotypically dominance is not complete. The degree of dominance is very important whenever there is natural or artificial selection. Suppose that it was desired to eliminate the b gene from the F_2 population produced by crossing blacks with browns. Removing the animals with a brown phenotype would eliminate only one-half of the brown genes. Those in the heterozygotes would be detected only when brown offspring turned up in the next generation.

In general, the zygosity of an animal with a dominant phenotype can be determined only from its ancestry or its progeny. A black mouse coming from a long line of inbred ancestors who have bred true for black is probably homozygous; one whose father or mother was brown is certainly heterozygous. In any other circumstance the diagnosis must be uncertain. The progeny test is most efficiently made by breeding the animal whose genotype is in question to a homozygous recessive (b/b). The prediction for a mating of the type $B/b \times b/b$ is that one-half the offspring will show the dominant character, and the probability that all (of a series of n) progeny will be of this type is $1/2^n$. When $n = 7$, $p = .0078$, so that a series of seven offspring of the dominant type is a strong indication that the tested individual is in fact B/B, not the hypothesized B/b.

Because test matings are not possible with human beings, human geneticists are on the lookout for small effects of genes in a heterozygous state. In some cases it is possible to identify individuals carrying "recessive" genes which produce anomalies when homozygous (Neel, 1949) and to provide information to prospective parents who come from families with serious hereditary defects.

Multiple Alleles. If more than two alternative genes are known at a locus, the system is said to be *polyallelic*. A well-known example is the A, B, O red cell isoantigen system in man. If the symbols I^A, I^B, and I^O are used to represent the genes corresponding to each of these antigens, the possible genotypes are I^A/I^A, I^A/I^B, I^A/I^O, I^B/I^B, I^B/I^O, and I^O/I^O. A given individual can carry only two members of a polyallelic system, but there is no fixed limit on the number of different alleles in a population. In this example I^A and I^B are dominant over I^O, but not over each other. Thus four phenotypes, A, B, AB, and O, correspond to six genotypes. In the dominant white spotting series in the mouse, the mutant alleles produce effects upon hair pigment and hemoglobin formation (Russell, 1955). The order of strength of effect is different for each phenotypic character. The existence of multiple alleles greatly increases the possibility of genetic variation. With two alleles there are three possible genotypes; with three alleles, six genotypes; and with four alleles, ten genotypes.

P generation	AABB	×	aabb	
P gametes	AB		ab	
F_1 generation		AaBb		

F_1 gametes ⟶

F_1 gametes	AB	Ab	aB	ab
AB	① AABB	② AABb	③ AaBB	④ AaBb
Ab	⑤ AABb	⑥ AAbb	⑦ AaBb	⑧ Aabb
aB	⑨ AaBB	⑩ AaBb	⑪ aaBB	⑫ aaBb
ab	⑬ AaBb	⑭ Aabb	⑮ aaBb	⑯ aabb

F_2 generation

FIGURE 2-5. Combinations of two independently segregating genes in the F_2 of a hybrid between pure strains. Both male and female in the F_1 can produce four kinds of gametes; hence there are 16 combinations, though some of these are identical. Actually there are nine different genotypes in the ratio 1:1:1:1:2:2:2:2:4. The phenotypic ratios observed in the F_2 of a dihybrid cross vary according to the type of physiological interaction between the genes. (See Table 2-5.)

Two or More Independent Alleles. Transmission of genes which lie in separate chromosomes is independently determined during gametogenesis. This is best illustrated by a diagram such as Figure 2-5, the lower portion of which is known as a Punnett square. This example shows a dihybrid (two-locus) system, but polyhybrid systems require no additional concepts. The diagram represents the F_2 from a cross between two genotypes, AABB and aabb. Along the edges are the expected proportions of male and female gametes from the F_1. Each cell in the diagram corresponds to an expected one-sixteenth of the F_2 population and has been given a number which is used as a reference in Table 2-5. It is also possible to compute the expected genotypic proportions algebraically, as is generally more convenient when complex polyhybrid systems are considered.

TABLE 2-5

Some Phenotypic Possibilities in the F_2 of a Dihybrid Cross

Type of Gene Interaction and Specific Example	Phenotypic Expectation		Cells in Fig. 2-5
	Proportion	Phenotype	
1. Physiological independence, complete dominance at both loci.	9/16	Full black	1, 2, 3, 4, 5, 7, 9, 10, 13
Mice: Black pigment (B) dominant over brown (b)	3/16	Dilute black	6, 8, 14
Full color (D) dominant over dilute (d).	3/16	Full brown	11, 12, 15
	1/16	Dilute brown	16
2. Complementary physiological action, complete dominance at both loci.	9/16	Colored	1, 2, 3, 4, 5, 7, 9, 10, 13
Sweet peas: color depends upon simultaneous presence of two different dominant genes, C and P.	7/16	White	6, 8, 11, 12, 14, 15, 16
3. Complementary physiological action, dominance at both loci, but different epistatic effects for some combinations.	9/16	Agouti	1, 2, 3, 4, 5, 7, 9, 10, 13
	3/16	Black	6, 8, 14
Mice: C needed for any color; A produces agouti hair color, aa produces black hair.	4/16	Albino	11, 12, 15, 16
4. Additive gene action. Each allele represented by A or B produces one unit of effect on phenotype produced by $aabb$. Strength of trait measured on a 5+ scale.	1/16	+++++	1
	4/16	++++	2, 3, 5, 9
	6/16	+++	4, 6, 7, 10, 11, 13
	4/16	++	8, 12, 14, 15
	1/16	+	16

Note. The first-named gene in each example corresponds to the (A, a) combination in Fig. 2-5; the second gene to the (B, b) combination.

The phenotypic results of a dihybrid cross depend upon the physiological interaction between the non-allelic genes. Four of the many possible outcomes are set forth in Table 2-5. The first example represents independence of physiological effect as well as independence

of transmission. This is the Mendelian law of independent assortment. The second and third portions of the table illustrate complementary gene action, as genes at two loci are necessary for a certain
phenotype to appear. In the sweet pea (example 2) two phenotypes
are distinguishable, red and white; in the mouse (example 3) three
coat-color phenotypes are produced by a dihybrid system. Interactions
between non-allelic genes are known as *epistatic* effects; thus in the
example of the mouse, gene C is essential for manifestation of B and
b. The fourth example is an idealized model for quantitative inheritance, which we shall consider in more detail later. Here the phenotypic effect of A equals that of B; the effects are cumulative in a
strictly additive fashion. These examples by no means exhaust the
possibilities of genetic interaction, but they illustrate the variety of
phenotypic ratios which are known to result from the same type of
genotypic ratios.

LINKAGE

The mechanics of meiotic cell division impose certain limitations
upon independent assortment of genes. Homologous chromosomes
synapse and separate as units, so that all genes of a single chromosome
tend to segregate together. This is a tendency rather than an absolute
law because of the crossing-over phenomenon described earlier.

Sex-linkage. It is convenient to introduce linkage in general with
a discussion of sex-linkage. The transmission of genes included in the
X- or Y-chromosome is inextricably bound up with the sex-determining
properties of these chromosomes. The consequences of sex-linkage differ depending upon whether the gene in question is on the X- or
Y-chromosome, whether it is dominant or recessive, and whether crossing over from X to Y is ever possible. Sex-linkage is easy to detect,
and examples have been described from many species.

Y-linkage inheritance has been reported for the "porcupine men"
who lived in England during the eighteenth and nineteenth centuries.
There is, however, some question of the accuracy of the records on
which this famous pedigree is based (Stern, personal communication).
At any rate, Y-linked inheritance has no immediate application to
behavior genetics.

A gene located upon the X-chromosome of a mammal may be present in single or double dose in females, but only in a single dose in
males. (The reverse is true in butterflies and birds where the female
is heterogametic.) Such a gene may behave as a recessive in females
and as a dominant in males where the normal allele cannot be simul-

taneously present. One of the most thoroughly studied cases of this type is "red-green" color blindness. Actually this is not a single defect, but a composite of several distinct but related anomalies of color vision, whose individual attributes can be neglected in an elementary account.

Color blindness is transmitted in a crisscross fashion from fathers through daughters to grandsons. Non-affected males never pass the

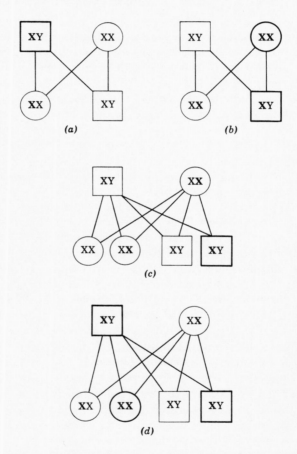

FIGURE 2-6. The transmission of red-green color blindness in man. The gene is carried on the X-chromosome and is expressed in females only when homozygous. X-chromosomes containing the gene are shown in heavy letters; afflicted individuals are shown in heavy outline. (*a*) Color-blind man × normal woman. (*b*) Normal man × color-blind woman. (*c*) Normal man × carrier. (*d*) Color-blind man × carrier.

gene on to children of either sex, but non-affected females who are carriers of the gene show their heterozygosity by bearing on the average 50% of color-blind sons. Likewise, one-half the daughters of such women prove to be carriers like their mothers. Color-blind women have color-blind fathers and often color-blind brothers. If a color-blind woman marries a normal-visioned man her sons are all color blind, while her daughters have normal vision like their father. All of these facts fall into place if we assume that the condition is brought about through the intermediacy of a gene c which is recessive. The diagrams of Figure 2-6 represent the probabilities of different types of offspring from individuals bearing the color-blindness gene.

Sex-linkage is probably not often significantly involved in behavior genetics, although it has been strongly implicated in the inheritance of broodiness in domestic fowl (page 180). Most behavioral traits depend upon the interaction of many genes, which are probably distributed over a number of chromosomes. The effect of genes located on the X-chromosome might be difficult to separate from the effects of a much larger number of genes located on autosomes. Nevertheless, appropriate tests for sex-linkage should be introduced into experimental designs whenever feasible.

This is an appropriate place to contrast sex-linked genes with *sex-limited* characters. All that sex-linkage implies is that the genes involved are located on the X- or the Y-chromosome. Sex-limited characters are restricted in manifestation to only one sex, although genes influencing the character may be carried in both sexes. It is well known that bulls transmit genetic factors which affect the milk production of their daughters, even though the bull has no active mammary glands. This does not mean that the genes concerned have no functions in males. The genes affect some process at the cellular level; in a sense their effect on milk production is fortuitous.

Autosomal Linkage. Two genes which occupy loci close together on a chromosome tend to go together in the process of gametogenesis. In the account below, A and B are a pair of such genes. A cross between an animal homozygous for A and B, and one homozygous for a and b is designated below. Bars are placed below the formulae to show that the genes are on the same chromosome.

Parents: $AB/AB \times ab/ab$

Gametes: $AB \qquad ab$

F_1 $\qquad AB/ab$

To measure linkage, a test cross is made between the F_1 and a double recessive stock. The F_1 produces four varieties of gametes in unequal numbers. In the computation in Table 2-6 it is assumed that crossing over between the A and B loci occurs in 20% of all meioses.

TABLE 2-6

Results of a Test Cross (F_1 × Double Recessive) When Crossover Frequency Is 20%

F_1 Gametes Type	Frequency	Test Gametes	Zygotes	Frequency
$\underline{AB}$	40%	$\underline{ab}$	$\underline{AB}/\underline{ab}$	40%
$\underline{ab}$	40%	$\underline{ab}$	$\underline{ab}/\underline{ab}$	40%
$\underline{Ab}$	10%	$\underline{ab}$	$\underline{Ab}/\underline{ab}$	10%
$\underline{aB}$	10%	$\underline{ab}$	$\underline{aB}/\underline{ab}$	10%

The offspring of the test cross include a preponderance of the parental combinations, and the sum of the recombinants is approximately equal to the percentage of crossing over. This ratio differs greatly from the 1:1:1:1 ratio which is expected under the assumption of independent assortment.

In the example given, the genes A and B are said to be *coupled* since they are associated in the same chromosome. Hence the phenotypic traits associated with each will tend to be correlated positively. A different sort of association between the phenotypes will result if the genes are in *repulsion* (in opposite homologous chromosomes) at the beginning of the observation: thus; $\underline{Ab}/\underline{Ab} \times \underline{aB}/\underline{aB}$. Carrying through the same operations as above we obtain from a test cross of the F_1: 40% $\underline{Ab}/\underline{ab}$, 40% $\underline{aB}/\underline{ab}$, 10% $\underline{AB}/\underline{ab}$, and 10% $\underline{ab}/\underline{ab}$. Now there is a negative correlation between the phenotypes associated with A and B. The association between characters related through a common chromosome is inconsistent in the population at large, though often significant in selected families.

Chromosome Maps. Linkage measurements have contributed greatly to the science of genetics. If it is assumed that close linkage indicates proximity on a chromosome, crossover frequencies can be used to construct chromosome maps. In Drosophila it has long been possible to confirm microscopically the validity of maps based upon this assumption, and thus strengthen faith in results with other species where such visual checking is technically more difficult. Chromosome mapping is a brilliant accomplishment, but its methods are not pertinent to behavior genetics except as the results substantiate the basic concept of the gene.

One result of linkage studies has been a formal definition of a gene as a factor in heredity which is not separable by crossing over. This is clearly an operational definition, and the classification of any particular gene can be changed by new facts. The question of whether certain blood cell antigens are determined by different alleles at a single locus or by closely linked genes with very low crossover frequency is indeed a matter of some dispute among geneticists. When one is working close to the primary effects of the gene there is some possibility of resolving such questions. With behavioral traits such refined analysis is not practicable, and the issues need not be raised.

PHYSIOLOGICAL GENETICS

Physiology and genetics come into contact at many points in the vast range of biological science. At one extreme is gene-centered research in which chemical and physical techniques are applied to events within the nucleus and even within chromosomes. Tools in these investigations are microspectroscopy and histochemistry, ultraviolet and electron microscopy, serology and biochemistry. The phenotypic traits selected for study are chemical differences which are close to the primary action of genes. Micro-organisms with a minimum of structural differentiation are the most suitable subjects.

This type of physiological genetics is not directly applicable to behavior research, but it does provide guidance in the search for a path between gene and behavioral character (Davis, 1954). Physiological genetics can, however, start with any heritable variation in an organism and trace its origin backward in development nearer and nearer to the gene. If the character chosen has behavioral significance, this aspect of behavior genetics merges imperceptibly with developmental or genetic psychology. In this section we shall consider genes as regulators of function at various levels of organization, with occasional reference to applications in behavior genetics.

Nature of the Gene. When the word "gene" was first employed as the name for a unit hereditary factor, it was very much a hypothetical construct. Since this time, in spite of intermittent criticism of the gene theory, the hypothetical construct has become increasingly concrete. Much of our information is still indirect, and the details of description may be revised, but the main elements of the picture are well established.

The size of genes appears to be somewhere between a sphere 6 milli-microns in diameter, and a cylinder 20 millimicrons in diameter and 100 millimicrons long. The larger estimate is probably too high, but even so it would be possible to lay 1,000 such bodies end to end in the thickness of a single sheet of book paper. One method of estimation is to count the number of detectable non-lethal mutations produced when germ cells are bombarded by ionizing radiation. Each hit on a gene is assumed to produce a mutation, but not all will be detectable. A similar method might be used to estimate the size of windows in a building. By throwing stones in a certain pattern and counting the number of windows broken, some estimate could be made of window size.

The chemical nature of individual genes is not, and may never be, accessible to standard methods of chemical analysis. However, chromosomes can be collected and analyzed *en masse*. Wherever taken, chromosomes are found to be nucleoproteins, a combination of proteins and nucleic acids. It has been known for years that proteins can exist in almost limitless variety. Each species has its own varieties of protein, and those of species considered to be closely related on the basis of structure are more alike than those of distantly related species. Recently nucleic acids have been found to be extremely variable in structure, and the specific functional properties of a gene may be attributes of nucleic acid chemistry (Beadle, 1955). Two major types are recognized, desoxyribosenucleic acid (DNA) and ribonucleic acid (RNA). DNA contains the sugar, desoxyribose, and seems to be found only in chromosomes. RNA contains ribose and is a constituent of both nucleus and cytoplasm. Viruses, which are self-duplicating particles like genes, are also composed of nucleic acids. Most animal viruses are of the DNA type, which seems to indicate that DNA is the essential component for self-duplication. However, some plant viruses contain RNA.

Gene Action and Metabolism. Wright (1954) distinguishes two types of primary processes controlled by genes in addition to self-duplication. Both involve the determination of macromolecular patterns, first of enzymes, and second, of antigens. His diagram of the relationship of physiological genetics to different levels of organization is shown in Figure 2-7. The sum of the genetic material is here referred to as the *genome*. The solid arrows represent the influence of the simpler levels of organization upon the more complex; the dotted lines indicate feedback. Note that the only one-way process is the genome to enzyme-antigen pair relationship. In discussing the relationship of genes to metabolism, we are already moving one step away from primary gene

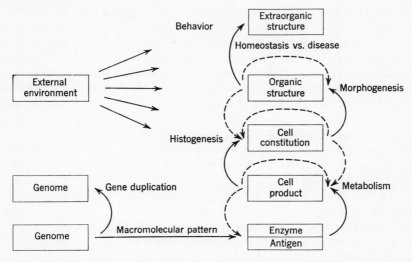

FIGURE 2-7. Diagram of relations of genome and external environment to observed characters at various levels of organization. (Wright, 1954.)

action into an area influenced by environmental factors and intraorganismic feedback.

The following discussion of genetics and metabolism is based largely upon Wagner and Mitchell (1955). References to original sources may be found in this work. As an example of the effect of specific gene substitutions upon metabolic patterns, we have chosen the variations in eye color of *D. melanogaster*. Ordinarily the eyes are reddish-brown owing to a combination of a red and brown pigment. Four non-allelic recessive genes are known which in the homozygous state produce a bright red eye. One can infer that these genes interfere with the production of brown pigment. The chemistry of the formation of the brown pigment has been rather thoroughly worked out. Starting with the amino-acid tryptophane, the series of reactions goes as follows:

$$\text{Tryptophane} \xrightarrow{1} \text{formylkynurenine} \xrightarrow{2} \text{kynurenine} \xrightarrow{3}$$
$$\text{hydroxykynurenine} \xrightarrow{4} \text{brown pigments}$$

If one of these reactions is blocked because of a mutation, the reactant will accumulate. Thus *D. melanogaster* homozygous for vermilion (*v*) accumulate tryptophane, those homozygous for cinnabar (*cn*) accumulate kynurenine, and flies homozygous for scarlet (*st*) or cardinal (*cd*) accumulate hydroxykynurenine.

Feeding formylkynurenine and kynurenine to *v/v* larvae permits the formation of brown pigment, but this is ineffective in *st/st* or *cd/cd* larvae. Transplanting eye primordia from a *v/v* larva to a wild-type larva allows the *v/v* eye to form brown pigment, for the surrounding tissues of the host larva provide the necessary substrate, and the *v/v* eye is perfectly competent to proceed with the synthesis once it is provided with the means of overcoming its particular metabolic deficiency.

Experiments of this type provide the geneticist with a key for pairing a mutation with a particular process, *v* with reaction 1, *cn* with reaction 3, and *cd* and *st* with reaction 4. Similar results upon organisms ranging from bacteria and poppies to man have provided a broad base for the generalization that genes operate by controlling the rate of specific chemical reactions.

Beadle (1945) proposed the theory that a given enzyme has its specificity set by one gene, and that in general each allelic type has a unique specificity. This may be briefly characterized as the "one gene–one enzyme" hypothesis. It has been critically reviewed by Horowitz and Leupold (1951) and Wagner and Mitchell (1955). Possibly the hypothesis can never be definitely proved or disproved. Even if it is correct, the interactions between products of various genes soon produce a complexity which is not readily explained in terms of primary gene action alone. In highly differentiated organisms, genes probably always affect many traits. For example, many mutant genes in Drosophila which are known by their morphological effects also affect frequency of wing vibration (Williams and Reed, 1944).

Although most mutant genes are still named for their morphological effects, the number known to influence specific metabolic processes is increasing. Garrod (1909) pioneered in the study of "inborn metabolic errors." Examples of biochemical effects of genes are presented by Beadle (1949) and by Haldane (1954). Phenylketonuria, a disease characterized by mental defect and a specific metabolic error, is of particular psychological interest (Jervis, 1954; Bickel, Boscott, and Gerrard, 1955). This syndrome is discussed more fully on page 312, and it is sufficient to say here that an understanding of the genetics and the biochemistry of the condition gives some hope of partial alleviation of the defect.

Currently there is considerable interest in the possibility that brain enzymes may play a critical role in mental dysfunction (Ashby, 1950; Gerard, 1955; Pope et al., 1952; Williams et al., 1949*a*). The hypothesis is certainly worth testing to the utmost, but alternative paths of gene action must be carefully explored at the same time (Kety, 1959).

The peculiarities of nitrogen excretion in the Dalmatian dog will serve to illustrate the point.

The Dalmatian breed excretes uric acid as the chief nitrogenous waste, while other dogs primarily excrete allantoin (Benedict, 1916). Trimble and Keeler (1938) summarized evidence that this "error" was associated with a single pair of recessive genes. The metabolism of uric acid is well known. An enzyme, uricase, in the liver converts it into allantoin. It seemed reasonable to explain the facts by a deficiency or absence of uricase in Dalmatians, but no such deficiency was found in actual enzyme assays. The problem was reinvestigated by Friedman and Byers (1948), who found that the difference was in the kidney of the Dalmatian, not in his enzymes. For some reason the kidney tubule cells of this breed do not reabsorb uric acid. It is removed from the body of the Dalmatian about as fast as it is produced in metabolism and is never exposed to the action of uricase. The point of this example is that genetic effects upon cell permeability might be as important to behavior as effects upon enzyme systems.

Pleiotropy. Although each gene may have a single biochemical function, its effects are not limited to a unit function at the structural, physiological or behavioral level. Descriptions of the effects of identified genes in mammals are at present better phrased in terms of specific tissues affected and specific stages of development than in terms of chemical reactions. When a tissue (cartilage, for example) enters into the development of many structures, all will be affected by a gene substitution affecting the tissue. The multiple effects are an example of pleiotropy, in this case, secondary pleiotropy, since all stem from one basic process.

Not all cases of pleiotropy have been traced back to a single common origin. The dominant white spotting series of genes in the house mouse (W and W^v) produce, in addition to their effects on pigment, anemia and impaired gonadal function (Russell, 1955). Careful embryological studies have traced the gene action backward in development without convergence on a common process. Russell, however, is not convinced that the genes at this locus show primary pleiotropism, and suggests that they may act upon the three biological systems through a single chemical reaction. Perhaps the contrast between primary and secondary pleiotropism is a little forced, since one can never prove that divergent but correlated phenomena are not related by some undiscovered unitary process lying between them and their genes. At any rate, the distinction is not important in behavior genetics. The significant fact is that in complex organisms the consequences of a gene substitution may be manifest in a number of apparently independent functions. Yet these deviations will be correlated because of dependence upon a common genetic mechanism.

Duplicate Phenotypes, Different Genotypes. The eye-color mutants of Drosophila discussed above illustrate the principle that organisms with the same phenotype may be different genotypically. A further illustration, a behavior mutation in mice, illustrates some of the complexities of such systems. Shaker mice have choreic head movements, and some tendency to run in circles. Gates (1934) proved that there were two distinct genetic forms, both inherited in a recessive fashion, which were phenotypically alike. Shaker-1 has normal alleles at the shaker-2 locus, and vice versa. The mating between the two is represented as follows:

$$\text{Parents:} \quad sh\text{-}1/sh\text{-}1,\ +/+\ \times\ +/+,\ sh\text{-}2/sh\text{-}2$$
Both are "shakers."

$$F_1: \qquad sh\text{-}1/+,\ +/sh\text{-}2$$
All are "non-shakers."

In the F_1 each mutant gene is counteracted by its normal allele obtained from the other side of the cross. The fact that the F_1 is normal while the parents are not indicates that the two shaker genes do not have the same function. It may be inferred that each locus is concerned with a different step in morphogenesis of the nervous system, and that blocking the process in either place produces the same result.

In human genetics it is not feasible to make test crosses to determine whether two similar phenotypes are also genotypically alike. Sometimes, however, genetic analysis of a series of pedigrees of clinically similar cases leads to the discovery that inheritance of a particular defect in one family follows a pattern of dominance, in another, recessivity, and in still another, recessive sex-linkage. This appears to be true of *retinitis pigmentosa,* a chronic progressive degenerative disease of the retina (Sorsby, 1953). This type of evidence proves genetic polymorphism, but does not indicate whether the several genes have the same or different physiological effects.

Phenocopies. Treatments by physical agents can produce effects upon phenotype comparable to those of a known mutant gene. Landauer (1945) injected insulin into developing hen's eggs and produced a large number of rumpless chicks phenotypically similar to the rumpless birds produced by a pair of autosomal recessive genes. Goldschmidt (1938) produced aberrant types of Drosophila by exposing developing larvae of wild-type stock to elevated temperature for various periods of time at particular stages of development. The resultant anomalies were often faithful replicas of recognized inherited mutant phenotypes. Rubella (German measles) in pregnant women leads to a high proportion of malformed children who may be indistinguishable from those bearing genetically induced deformities.

The production of phenocopies experimentally seems to have some promise as a means of elucidating the mode of action of mutant genes. There must be something in common between two agents which produce the same result, and, if the copy is very precise, the point of action may be the same. This approach is similar to the attack on the physiology of psychoses through the use of psychotomimetic drugs. The results may stimulate hypothesis formation, but it is difficult to obtain conclusive evidence in this fashion.

The Statistical Nature of Genotypic Control. A living organism is a dynamic system, whose range of adaptation is a function of its genotype as a whole. This concept is diagrammed in Figure 2-8. Genotype A is the modal or "normal" form which has essentially the same phenotype under a variety of environmental conditions. Genotype A'' is a variant which is always clearly distinguishable from the mode. Genotype A' is extremely variable, and cannot be perfectly separated from either A or A'' on the basis of phenotype alone. The A' individuals falling far to the left are variants; those on the right are

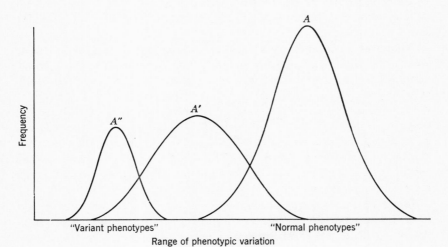

FIGURE 2-8. The statistical nature of genotypic control of phenotype is depicted in these three curves. Each represents the distribution of phenotypes in a related genotype. The range of variation in A' is much greater than in the "normal" A genotype or "variant" A'' genotype, and overlaps both. Hence, phenotype is not an absolute guide to genotype.

"normal overlaps." Genotypes control differentiation and development in a statistical sense. Sometimes the choice between alternative phenotypes is regulated with practically all-or-none precision. In other situations non-genetic factors are more critical. This amounts to saying that the heritability of a character is not necessarily one or zero, but may take any intermediate value.

The terms *penetrance* and *expressivity* are often used with respect to the action of genes. Penetrance is a measure of the probability that a genotype can be identified by its phenotypic effects. Penetrance values are provisional, since new effects may be discovered and individuals reclassified on the basis of obscure characters. The more general term, expressivity, refers to the intensity of the phenotypic manifestation. For example, one form of jaundice is inherited as a dominant autosomal character. All individuals with the gene show fragility of their red blood corpuscles, but the amount of red-cell breakdown in vivo and the severity of the resultant disease vary from apparently none to a severe fatal disorder (Snyder and David, 1953).

The "environment" of a gene includes the effects of the other genes present, although none of them may be identifiable as specific contributors to the trait concerned. This is well exemplified in an experiment reported by Runner (1954). The Fused (*Fu*) gene which produces structural anomalies in the tail and other parts of the skeleton of mice was placed on two different genetic backgrounds by repeatedly crossing fused individuals into an inbred line. The results are shown in Table 2-7. It is evident that the gene was more effective

TABLE 2-7

Effect of Genetic Background on Penetrance of Fused in Heterozygotes (Runner, 1954)

Strain:	Source of *Fu* gene	
	Mother	Father
BALB/c	72%	88%
C57BR/a	34%	65%

in modifying the BALB/c phenotype than the C57BR/a phenotype. Furthermore, a remarkable difference between the reciprocal crosses was found, particularly in the C57BR/a strain. The reciprocal cross difference could be explained as due to cytoplasmic factors present in the ova or by modifying genes in the Y-chromosome (Grüneberg, 1952). A more likely explanation is that the uterine environment of *Fu*/+

mothers is less favorable for the expression of the gene than that of
+/+ mothers.

Variations in expression of a gene are presumably caused by small
forces acting at random. By manipulating the environment systematically, it is possible to shift the modal phenotype. The incidence of
skeletal anomalies in the mouse can be shifted by such procedures as:
(1) producing temporary anoxia in the mother at the 7th day of
gestation; (2) transferring ova of one strain to the uterus of another;
(3) simply allowing the mothers to grow older (Runner, 1954). Effects
such as these are functions of genotype, but the anomalies themselves
are not inherited in the usual sense of the word. What has been inherited is a reactive system which responds in a characteristic way to
stress.

We shall refer again and again to the relationship between gene and
character in our survey of behavior genetics. There is a great gap
between enzymes controlling phosphorylation reactions and a brain
capable of solving differential equations. Yet genes are concerned with
both, and both are problems for behavior genetics in the broadest
sense.

Summary of Physiological Genetics. Perhaps the most important
genetic principles for the student of behavior are those concerned
with the nature of the genotype-phenotype relationship. The laws of
genetics relate to the transmission of genes and chromosomes from
parent to offspring. These laws have been quite precisely formulated,
and within the limits imposed by errors of sampling they can be used
to predict the outcome of breeding experiments.

The phenotype of an organism is the sum of its physical characteristics, body size, form, color, and chemistry. Although these traits
are always related to genotype, they are not perfectly correlated. A
particular genotype determines the way an organism will respond in
a particular environment, and, since there are infinite numbers of
environments, this is equivalent to saying that a single genotype might
be associated with an infinite number of phenotypes. The potentialities
for phenotypic variation increase with distance from the primary
chemical functions of genes. For practical purposes blood-group
phenotypes are a reliable guide to genotype, but body size and form are
less so.

Behavior is still more remotely related to primary gene action. In
fact the definition of phenotype as the physical make-up of an individual must be modified for behavior genetics. By extension one
may decide to include actions in the list of an organism's characteristics;
thus the number of pellets hoarded by a rat or the number of correct

test responses by a college freshman can be considered as essentially equivalent to physical measurements. The difficulty with this approach lies in the generally lower repeatability of behavior measures, since behavior is so greatly dependent upon past experience. Hence the phenotypic description of behavior is often the slope of a learning curve or the final level of performance attained after a period of practice. Selecting appropriate phenotypic measures is one of the most significant problems in behavior genetics. Whatever behavioral measure is used, and however much it is affected by heredity, it is never a genotypic character.

Although the method of family correlations is frequently used in behavior genetics, similarity of phenotypes is not a proof of heredity, nor is dissimilarity an argument against heredity. Evidence from phenotypes is used as a proof of heritability, but only when the appearance of a trait can be predicted by the Mendelian laws (and their extensions) and when the nature of the environment is adequately specified. When such conditions are met, there need be no more hesitation in using the techniques of genetics to study the heritability of behavior than in using them to study the inheritance of physical characters. There is logically no difference between manipulating genes to observe the effects upon behavior and manipulating experience to modify later behavior. In the next chapter we shall consider some genetic techniques which have been found useful in behavioral investigations. Before doing so, however, we shall discuss some of the principles governing the distribution of genes within populations.

POPULATION GENETICS

To draw inferences about genetic mechanisms from the distribution of a trait among members of families requires knowledge of the behavior of genes within populations. This in turn is a function of mating systems and selection, the area known as population genetics. We have illustrated the principles from human examples because of their particular pertinence to behavior genetics.

Panmixis and the Hardy-Weinberg Law. Population genetics deals with two sorts of questions: (1) What are the proportions of different genotypes in a population? (2) How are these proportions related from generation to generation? In experiments, the researcher controls the flow of genes by regulating the mating system and by selecting particular individuals for reproduction. Here we are concerned with situations in which the scientist must deduce what is happening when he can do nothing to control gene flow.

It is convenient to start with an analogy to describe a panmictic or random-mating system. Imagine a lake into which all the ova and all the sperm of a population are thrown, thoroughly mixed, and allowed to combine to form zygotes. If we consider any particular autosomal locus (A, A'), a gamete may contain either A or A' but not both. We now assume that the proportion of A is p, and the proportion of A' is q, that these proportions are equal in ova and sperm, and that $p + q = 1$. The probability of an A sperm uniting with an A ovum as well as the probabilities of all other combinations are summarized in Table 2-8. Since the two heterozygotes are genetically equivalent, the

TABLE 2-8

Frequency of Zygote Types in Panmixia

Sperm Type	Frequency	Ovum Type	Frequency	Zygote Type	Frequency
A	p	A	p	AA	p^2
A	p	A'	q	AA'	pq
A'	q	A	p	$A'A$	pq
A'	q	A'	q	$A'A'$	q^2

proportions of the three genotypes may be expressed as $p^2(AA) + 2pq(AA') + q^2(A'A')$. This is the familiar binomial expansion of $(p + q)^2$. When $p = q = 0.5$, as in the F_2 of two pure-breeding lines, these proportions are $.25(AA) + .50(AA') + .25(A'A')$. If $p = 0.9$, and $q = 0.1$, the proportions are $.81(AA) + .18(AA') + .01(A'A')$.

It is important to note that the attainment of these frequencies of combination bears no relationship to the source of the genes, provided they are thoroughly mixed before combining. The gametes could come from two pure stocks, one AA and the other $A'A'$, or they could come from a single population already in panmictic equilibrium. If complete random mating occurs, the amount of previous assortment of the genes is inconsequential. This fact, discovered independently by two geneticists, is known as the Hardy-Weinberg law.

Perhaps the fertilization of the ova of the starfish occurs in the random manner assumed in our model, for the gametes of this animal are shed into sea water where they combine. In higher animals mating occurs between individuals, and in some species monogamous sexual relations are the rule. This imposes certain restrictions upon the randomness of gene combination, but it can be shown that these are of no practical importance in human populations provided mate selection is random with respect to genotype (Dahlberg, 1947). Even the fact that marriages are generally contracted between individuals of approximately the same age does not affect the essential randomness of genetic combination, for genotypes do not change with age.

Deviations from Genetic Equilibrium. A population in panmixia will not alter its genotypic composition, except for random variations about a constant mean. There are five ways in which deviations from genetic equilibrium may occur.

(1) Selection. Some combinations of gametes may produce zygotes which are less likely to survive and contribute their genes to the gene pool from which a new generation of zygotes must be produced. If zygotes of the $A'A'$ type are non-viable (or non-fertile), successive gene pools will contain fewer and fewer A' genes, and their only chance for survival will be in combination with an A gene. This situation, which results in complete selection against the homozygous recessive, is exemplified in severe incapacitating syndromes such as juvenile amaurotic idiocy. Selection may be partial rather than complete. If any genotype fails on the average to contribute equal numbers of offspring to the next generation, its contribution to the gene pool will be reduced accordingly. Hemophiliacs, for example, are not sterile, but their physical vigor and life expectancy are so reduced that they leave fewer offspring than the average.

Selection, of course, acts on the phenotype, but its genetic consequences depend upon changes in gene frequency. Hence the relationship between phenotype and genotype is of fundamental importance. A dominant gene of high penetrance is exposed to selection in practically every individual who carries it, but a recessive gene is so exposed only when it is in homozygous combination. The effectiveness of selection for quantitative characters in a natural population depends upon the heritability of the character just as is true of experimental populations. The long-term genetic effects of differential birth rates correlated with I.Q. can be predicted only if we know the heritability of the I.Q. And heritability, as we shall show, is an attribute of a population and not of a trait.

Selection in the population-genetics sense should not be confused with individual survival, which is a necessary but not a sufficient condition for gene survival. Social factors such as attitudes towards birth control, prevalent age of marriage, the relative prestige value of children and expensive homes, all these become agents of selection when translated into behavior. Whether they will have any genotypic effect depends upon the relationship between genes and reproductive behavior.

(2) Mutation. Another way in which genes can be withdrawn from the pool is through mutation, say from A' to A''. Over long periods of time mutations are believed to play an important role in adaptive evolutionary change, and one reason for the continued survival of severe genetic disabilities in the face of strong negative selection is believed to be the occurrence of new mutations. The rate is so low, however, that it can ordinarily be neglected in calculations involving a few generations.

(3) Consanguineous Marriages. Since relatives are more likely to have genes in common than are unrelated persons, marriages between relatives cause deviations from random assortment of genes postulated under the Hardy-Weinberg law. Close inbreeding seldom occurs in man, and even marriages between first cousins are relatively uncommon. Consanguineous marriages are more likely in isolated populations where the choice of mates is restricted. In general, the breaking down of barriers to migration in the Western world has reduced the number of consanguineous marriages. (See Stern, 1949, Chapter 18, for a concise discussion.) The effects of consanguinity, particularly of a remote degree, are not very important when dealing with common genes, for a relative may have little-greater likelihood of carrying a particular gene than any person taken at random. The situation is different when one deals with rare recessive genes. About the only spouse who might have such a gene is one who acquired it from a common ancestor. Consanguineous marriage does not of itself influence gene frequency, but it may result in exposing more deleterious recessive genes to the action of selection.

(4) Genetic Drift. Perfect mixing of the gametes in the hypothetical gene pool of our model would be difficult to attain in practice. Ova or sperm from one source might tend to stay together, so that a small sample drawn from a particular region might not truly represent the whole population. If this non-representative sample were now used to seed a new pool, the gene frequencies of the old and new pools would be different and would remain different. Successive serial sampling might eventually result in other gene pools with very wide differences in gene frequency compared with the original source. Examples of this model in human affairs are small geographical or religious isolates which remain reproductively isolated. Many of the features which differentiate human racial groups probably arose by genetic drift when man generally lived in small communities.

(5) Assortative Mating. Whenever individuals with a given trait marry other individuals with the same character more often (or less often) than would be predicted by random association, assortative mating is said to occur. Assortative mating is determined from phenotypes, but it will obviously have genetic consequences if the traits concerned are heritable. Assortative mating with respect to physical type, height, skin color, and deafness has been demonstrated. It is also found with reference to psychological characters such as the I.Q. (Conrad and Jones, 1940).

All five factors which produce deviations from genetic equilibrium are continuously active in every human population. Only selection and mutation directly affect gene frequency. Consanguineous marriages, genetic drift, and assortative mating influence only the distribution of genes to individuals and do not of themselves change the proportions of genes in the population as a whole. Indirectly, they may facilitate selection and thus alter the rate of genetic change. These three factors are alike in producing greater homozygosity than would be found under panmixia, and thus their genetic consequences are similar. The social milieu in which each operates is different, and they may even operate antagonistically. Rules against marriage to relatives may counteract, for example, a general tendency to marry within one's social class and to select mates of similar physical type.

Estimating Gene Frequency in Populations. The Hardy-Weinberg law furnishes a basis for the estimation of gene frequency whenever the phenotype permits recognition of gene-carriers and conditions of random mating with respect to the trait can be reasonably assumed. The greatest success with these methods has been obtained with blood groups, since the phenotype is an accurate representation of the genotype, and marriages are seldom contracted with any knowledge of the blood groups of the prospective spouses. Only the simpler situations are considered here. The reader is referred to such texts as Hogben (1946), Neel and Schull (1954), and Li (1955) for derivations of formulae and for discussions of assumptions underlying the analysis of complex cases.

We shall consider a single pair of genes, A and a, in a specified population. The following terms will be used:

$$p = \text{proportion of gene } A$$
$$q = \text{proportion of gene } a$$
$$p + q = 1$$
$$N = \text{total number of individuals in the population}$$

$n_{AA}, n_{Aa}, n_{aa} = $ number of individuals of the three possible genotypes, indicated by the subscripts

Three different types of inheritance will be described.

(1) Two Alleles without Dominance. This means that all three genotypes can be identified by their phenotypes. According to the Hardy-Weinberg law the population at equilibrium will be distributed as follows: $n_{AA} = p^2N$; $n_{Aa} = 2pqN$; $n_{aa} = q^2N$. The best estimate of $p(p^*)$ is a simple count of each type of gene divided by the total number of genes, $2N$. Each homozygote (AA) has two genes, and must be counted twice; each heterozygote has one A gene and must be counted once. The final formulae are:

$$(2\text{-}1) \qquad\qquad p^* = \frac{2n_{AA} + n_{Aa}}{2N}$$

$$(2\text{-}2) \qquad\qquad q^* = \frac{n_{Aa} + 2n_{aa}}{2N}$$

$$(2\text{-}3) \qquad\qquad \sigma_p{}^2 = \frac{p(1 - p)}{2N}$$

The MN blood groups are an example of a system which fits the model. The genotype of an individual is determined by typing his blood with M and N antisera according to the following scheme:

Genotype	$M^m M^m$	$M^m M^n$	$M^n M^n$
Phenotype (Blood Group)	M	MN	N

Table 2-9 is a small portion of a larger table (Wiener, 1943) giving the percentage of each blood type found in three very distinct races. The expected phenotypic proportions calculated from the estimated

TABLE 2-9

**Frequencies of M-N Blood Types in Different Populations
(Wiener, 1943)**

Number of Individuals	Population		Percentages of Blood Types			Allele Freq.	
			M	N	MN	M^m	M^n
6129	Whites	Obs.	29.16	49.58	21.26	0.540	0.460
	U.S.	Exp.	29.16	49.68	21.16	—	—
569	Eskimos	Obs.	83.48	15.64	0.88	0.913	0.087
	E. Greenland	Exp.	83.35	15.89	0.76	—	—
730	Australian	Obs.	3.00	29.6	67.4	0.178	0.882
	aborigines	Exp.	3.17	29.26	67.57	—	—

gene frequencies are also given. Agreement of observed and expected values in Wiener's table is excellent. The high degree of correspondence indicates (a) that the hypothesis of allelism between M and N is correct, and (b) there is no deviation from random mating with respect to this particular trait. If the reader suspects that the argument is circular and that agreement must always be obtained, since estimates of M^m and M^n frequency based on observed data are used to calculate the "expected values," he may try to solve the equations for $\% \, M = 28$; $\% \, N = 35$; $\% \, MN = 47$. These sum to 100%, but do not fit the conditions for genetic equilibrium.

(2) Two Alleles, A Dominant over a. We can distinguish only the aa genotype, since the AA and Aa phenotypes are the same. The best estimate of the frequency of a is:

$$(2\text{-}4) \qquad q^* = \sqrt{n_{aa}/N}$$

$$(2\text{-}5) \qquad \sigma_q^2 = (1 - q^2)/4N$$

The frequency of the non-taster gene (t) which induces inability to taste phenyl-thio-carbazide (PTC) and related compounds may be cited as an example. The gene t is recessive to T, which permits tasting PTC. The proportion of non-tasters ranges from about 30% in north Europeans to about 4% in west Africans. These correspond to gene frequencies of .548 and .20 respectively. Estimates of gene frequency in different races have played a major part in modern anthropology.

(3) Sex-linked Alleles with Dominance. The derivation of the formulae for this case is moderately complex, since the phenotypic manifestation differs in the two sexes. The dominant trait is shown by genotypes AA, Aa, and AY; the recessive trait by aa and aY.

$$(2\text{-}6) \qquad q^* = \frac{n_{AY} = n_{AY}^2 + 4(2N_f + N_m)(2n_{aa} + n_{ay})}{2(2N_f + N_m)}$$

$$(2\text{-}7) \qquad p^* = 1 - q^*$$

A simple approximate solution can be obtained by using only the data from males. Counting the phenotypes is actually a gene count.

$$(2\text{-}8) \qquad q = n_{aY}/n_{AY} + n_{aY} = \frac{\text{No. males with recessive trait}}{\text{Total number of males}}$$

Red-green color blindness is a classical example of this type of inheritance. Waaler's data (1927) based upon a survey of Oslo school children is given in Table 2-10. We calculate $q^* = 0.0772$ using the data from both sexes and $q = 0.0801$ from the males alone.

TABLE 2-10

Color Blindness in 18,121 Oslo School Children
(After Waaler, 1927)

Vision	Male	Female	Both Sexes
Color blind	725	40	765
Normal	8324	9032	17,356
Sum	9049	9072	18,121

Gene frequency analysis is an important tool of population genetics. To some extent it permits reconstruction of the genetic history of populations. The extent to which cultural barriers serve to prevent intermarriage can be quantitatively estimated by comparing gene frequencies between cultural groups inhabiting the same geographical area (Glass and Li, 1953). Psychological factors can affect gene flow just as genes may affect behavior. Some of the traits studied by population geneticists pertain to the domain of sensory variability, an area which has long been studied by psychologists. Equivalence of all racial groups cannot safely be assumed, as is illustrated by the data on the distribution of the non-taster gene. The consistent finding that racial groups differ with respect to genes which can be reliably identified probably indicates that there are many more differences at loci which are not conveniently tagged. This means that racial groups differ statistically with respect to genetic systems influencing most functions, including behavior. The significance of such differences with respect to so-called race psychology is probably slight, though there is no way of really testing the matter. We shall return to the problem in the final chapter.

To some extent gene frequency analysis can be applied to conditions of psychiatric interest which have a known Mendelian basis. For example, a defect inherited as a recessive which occurs once in every 10,000 births must have a gene frequency of $\sqrt{.0001} = .01$. In other words, 1% of all individuals would carry the gene for this trait. Estimates of this type are useful in portraying the problem of genetic disease. Difficulty is often encountered in ascertaining the true frequency of the disorder in the general population. Comparing populations with different standards of recording vital statistics is particularly risky. Lumping together two or more disorders which are clinically alike but genetically different is another source of error.

3

Experimental methods in behavior genetics

This chapter is concerned with the details of certain genetical procedures adapted to animal experimentation. Although not an exhaustive account of methods, it describes the procedures most used in psychological genetics and suggests others of potential value which have not yet been widely tested in behavior studies. Our objective is not so much to provide a source for all possible procedures as to facilitate communication between psychologists and geneticists. In order to describe the rationale of some techniques used in the study of the inheritance of quantitative characters, it has been necessary to introduce additional theoretical material from time to time. Unfortunately, the need for conciseness has forced the introduction of some topics before they have been properly discussed in detail. Inbred strains, for example, are mentioned several times before the section on inbreeding. The index has been arranged to facilitate the location of definitions of genetic terms.

Methods have been divided into two classes: (1) those concerned with specific loci; (2) those dealing with the combined effects of genes at many loci. The latter will be referred to as polygenic systems. Whether one deals with single genes or many, two general approaches to psychological genetics are possible. The starting point may be individual variability in behavior, and experiments can be designed to determine whether or not the variations are heritable. If the answer is positive, further breeding experiments are carried out to determine whether the occurrence of the character fits a particular hypothesis of genetic transmission, expressed either in terms of Mendelian units or in the statistical form usual for quantitative characters under polygenic control. The second type of approach starts with two groups of animals known to be genetically unlike and looks for phenotypic behavioral differences between them. Here there is again a choice between working with differences at one or a few named loci and working with multiple differences such as occur between a set of distantly related inbred strains. Phenotypically and genotypically oriented research plans tend to converge on the same problems, and in practice they cannot be rigidly separated. The choice of approach depends upon the problem of interest and the availability of animal material.

WORKING WITH INDIVIDUAL GENES

Testing a Genetic Hypothesis. The type of problem considered here deals with the occurrence of two classes of individuals who are classified in terms of behavior as trait-bearers, D, or non-trait-bearers, R. More than two phenotypic classes may be recognized, but the essential requirement for the methods considered here is that the classes be sharply distinguishable from each other.

All of the principles can be illustrated by considering the possibilities associated with substitutions at a single locus in which the heterozygote Aa may or may not have a distinctive phenotype, H.

The general method for the study of unit characters is to start with strains breeding true for AA and aa, cross them, and count the classes of offspring in the F_2 and backcrosses. These figures are then compared with the proportions predicted on the basis of various genetic hypotheses. The chi-square test described on page 22 is commonly used to test the agreement of observed and predicted numbers. Deviations from expected numbers can result from incomplete penetrance or from differential viability of certain genotypes. Table 3-1 summarizes the expected phenotypic results on the basis of some common hypotheses. Each experiment starts with P_1, which breeds true for one phenotype, and P_2 which breeds true for another. The purpose of this table is not so much to provide a ready reference for simple Mendelian ratios, as to demonstrate that hypotheses about penetrance can take care of deviations from the simple ratios given in lines 1 and 2 of the table. If penetrance must be assumed to be below 70% in order to fit observed and calculated figures, a conservative geneticist may suspect the hypothesis. It should be remembered that agreement of the data with a particular hypothesis does not prove that it is correct. Agreement with a simple Mendelian ratio has been taken as evidence for monofactorial inheritance, when more extensive observations would have shown the insufficiency of the scheme (Wright, 1934).

The experiment of Fuller, Easler, and Smith (1950) on the inheritance of audiogenic-seizure susceptibility in the mouse illustrates this point. Seizure susceptibility had been attributed to a single dominant gene (Witt and Hall, 1949) on the basis of a statistically

TABLE 3-1

Predicted Phenotypic Ratios in Several Types of Hybrids on the Basis of Various Genetic Hypotheses

(All experiments start with strain P_1 breeding true for AA with a phenotype D, and strain P_2 breeding true for aa with phenotype R.)

| | Hybrid Generations and Genotypes | | |
Hypothesis	F_1 $1.00Aa$	F_2 $.25AA:.50Aa:25aa$	$F_1 \times P_2$ $.50Aa:.50aa$
1. Trait inherited as autosomal dominant	All D	$.75D:.25R$	$.50D:.50R$
2. Heterozygote has a distinctive phenotype, H	All H	$.25D:.50H:.25R$	$.50H:.50R$
3. Penetrance 100% in homozygote, 50% in heterozygote	$.50D$ $.50R$	$.50D:.50R$	$.25D:.75R$
4. Semilethal, 50% of homozygotes fail to develop	All D	$.71D:.29R$	$.50D:.50R$

adequate number of observations on the F_1, F_2, and backcrosses between a susceptible and non-susceptible strain. Critical evidence against this interpretation was secured by repeatedly backcrossing susceptible hybrids into the non-susceptible line for a series of generations. These individuals, on the dominant gene hypothesis, would always be Aa. Crossed with aa they would always produce one-half Aa (susceptible) and one-half aa (non-susceptible). Actually the proportion of susceptible animals fell in successive generations to 20%, 8%, 4%, and 2% as the "susceptibility genes" were diluted. The threshold model proposed to explain this result is described later in this chapter. There are reasons for believing that such models are inherently more plausible as explanations of behavioral variation than one- or two-factor systems. When the more simple hypotheses are proposed, it seems justifiable to require that they be confirmed either by anchoring them to a morphological trait which segregates clearly or by demonstrating that the trait follows a simple pattern of inheritance for a number of generations.

A major difficulty with the application of simple Mendelian hypotheses to behavioral data is the continuous nature of the phenotypic distributions. Animals do not readily fit into categories: wild versus not wild; strong sex drive versus weak sex drive. Unfortunately it is all too easy to find examples of artificial divisions into high, medium, and low categories of some trait, the boundaries being selected in such fashion as to produce the ratios demanded by the hypothesis being tested. Even if a bimodal distribution of test scores is obtained, this does not necessarily justify separation into two groups. Behavior is a dynamic attribute, and it is possible to produce an apparently dichotomous classification system by adopting a test technique which gives a pass-fail result. One of the authors (see Fuller and Scott, 1954) has studied differences in delayed response performance in several breeds of dogs. Some animals never reached criterion within the alloted number of training trials, but this should not be used as a basis of separation into two psychological types any more than one should distinguish only two sizes of dogs based upon their ability to squeeze through a narrow opening. It is conceivable that some dogs might have lacked a particular piece of neurological equipment which was essential for delayed response, but it is also certain that a better method of training or longer training would have changed the proportion of successful animals. The techniques used for measuring behavioral traits determine the nature of the traits which will be found. This is also true of physical characteristics, but the use of a ruler to measure height has more self-evident validity than the use of a particular type of apparatus and training method to test delayed-response performance.

Testing Individual Gene Effects upon Behavior. Theoretically every gene may contribute to some degree to behavioral variance. This hypothesis must be tested by placing known genes or combinations of known genes upon a uniform genetic background, for if results are to be attributed to a single gene, it is necessary to eliminate all other sources of genetic variation. Williams and Reed (1944) employed the following mating system to compare the effects of a series of sex-linked genes upon frequency of wing vibration in *Drosophila melanogaster*.

Generation 1. Mutant male × wild type female (from inbred stock).
Generation 2. Female heterozygote × male wild type (both from 1).
Generation 3. Male mutant from 2 × wild type female.
Generation 4. Female heterozygote × male wild type (both from 3).
Generation 5. 6, . . . , N were alternately of the two types of mating.

Backcrossing for 24 generations was considered to have eliminated all chromosomes of the original mutant stock except the X-chromosome bearing the mutant gene. It was also assumed that most of this chromosome had been exchanged with the X-chromosome from the inbred line by means of crossovers during transfer through the female heterozygotes. Crossing over does not occur in male Drosophila.

Merrell (1949) used the same method starting with a set of four mutant sex-linked genes. By selecting favorable crossovers he was able to isolate stocks which possessed all possible combinations of the four mutated genes and to test the effects of the combinations upon mating behavior. This type of procedure is particularly interesting, since it permits quantitative manipulation of the independent variable. The nature of the system is illustrated in Figure 3-1.

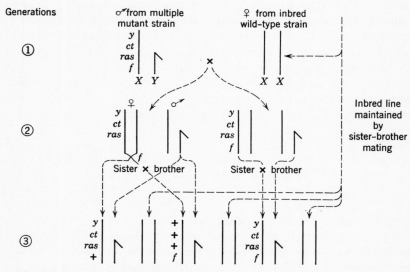

FIGURE 3-1. A method for obtaining various combinations of the sex-linked genes, *y*, *ct*, *ras* and *f* on a constant genetic background, by continuous backcrossing of the multiple mutant stock into an inbred strain, and isolation of the various crossover classes as they occur. On the left, for example, is shown a crossover which produces a *y ct ras* line, and an *f* line. (After Merrell, 1949.)

Scott (1943) compared in *D. melanogaster* the effects upon behavior of an autosomal recessive gene *bw* with that of its normal allele. He employed the following mating system.

Generation 1. $+/+ \times bw/bw$
Generation 2. $\female \ +/bw \times \male \ bw/bw$

Generation 3 and subsequent generations were repetitions of 2. The heterozygous females were used to give an opportunity for crossovers between *bw* and adjacent genes on the same chromosome. In this experiment the wild-type allele was introduced into the mutant stock, so that when the experiment was conducted males of two types were available, $+/bw$ with normal red-eyed phenotype and bw/bw which were brown-eyed. Scott made thirteen consecutive crosses, and concluded that the difference between the two phenotypes at the end of the experiment was due either to the bw gene or to a closely linked gene.

Drosophila is particularly well suited for experiments of this sort because of the large number of known genes and the ease of obtaining many generations in a short time. However the same techniques are applicable to mammals. It is not too difficult to introduce a dominant gene into an inbred stock which bears a recessive allele by repeatedly backcrossing trait bearers into the inbred line. If the gene is an autosomal recessive, progress is slower. After each cross into the inbred line, brother-sister matings must again be made to produce trait bearers (R) which can be crossed into the inbred line. The plan is as follows:

Generation 1:   Trait bearers (R) $\times$ Inbred line (D)
                         a/a $+/+$
Generation 2:   All D $+/a \times +/a$ (Brother-sister)
Generation 3: $\frac{1}{4}R$ (from 2) a/a $\times +/+$ (Inbred strain)

Subsequent generations repeat this alternation.

Sometimes the bearers of a homozygous recessive gene are sterile or almost so. In such cases the gene has to be transmitted through heterozygous $+/a$ individuals. It is still possible to put such a gene onto a standard background although the process is laborious.

Generation 1:   Known gene bearer $\times$ Inbred line
                         $+/a$ $+/+$
Generation 2:   (a) Offspring will be $\frac{1}{2} +/a$, $\frac{1}{2} +/+$. These must be test-mated to known $+/a$, in order to identify the $+/a$ genotype.
                (b) Tested heterozygote $\times$ Inbred line
                         $+/a$ $+/+$

Subsequent matings are repetitions of $2b$.

The number of generations of crossing into an inbred line which is necessary is a matter of judgment. Even after 50 crosses, genes with a crossover value of 2% would fail to be separated in 36.4% of all lines developed by this method. The degree of homogeneity of background needed before the effects of 2 alleles can be compared will vary from case to case. The obese gene (ob) in the mouse produces essentially the same phenotype on all backgrounds where it has been observed. It appears sufficient to carry this gene in a non-inbred stock and compare the behavior of *ob/ob* and *ob/+* littermates. The need for more elaborate procedures arises when an investigator tries to measure the behavioral effects of mutant genes whose conspicuous morphological effects have no obvious relationship to psychological traits. The alleged fiery temper of red-heads, for example, finds no explanation in terms of a common basis for pigment formation and development of emotional centers in the brain. Proving that such a hair-color gene has *no* effect upon behavior is very difficult, though it may be shown that its effect cannot be very large.

Some genes known from their morphological action have been reported to have non-specific effects upon behavior. Since many mutations reduce vigor in a rather general fashion, the particular effects reported may simply reflect the interest of the experimenter. It is probable that the behavioral influence of many genes is small, and that it can be isolated only when the control of the genetic environment of the gene is as precise as the physical control of the environment. For this reason the various species of Drosophila and the domestic mouse are the materials of choice for experiments which seek to measure the psychological effects of single genes.

WORKING WITH POLYGENIC SYSTEMS

Genetic models based upon the cumulative effects of genes at many loci are better adapted to handle the inheritance of quantitative characteristics. In one common type of experiment two pure-breeding races are chosen on the basis of a phenotypic difference in average size, weight or activity. The experimental breeding plan is similar to that described for testing hypotheses of Mendelian inheritance, but the various genetic groups (P_1, P_2, F_1, F_2, etc.) are described in terms of a mean-trait value, $\bar{x}$, and a variance σ_x^2, rather than in terms of the proportion of trait-bearers and non-trait bearers.

Another technique is to start with a phenotypically and genotypically diverse population and to breed selectively on the basis of a behavioral characteristic. If selection results in a change in the average value of a trait, proof of heritability is established, provided there has been proper control for environmental sources of error. Selection may also be used to reduce variability in experimental material or to increase the rate of production of a phenotype which occurs rarely under random mating. Whatever the objectives of a selection program, its effectiveness depends upon the extent to which phenotype is a reliable guide to genotype. Permanent changes in a population under a constant environment can be achieved only through changes in gene frequency.

Before discussing the testing of genetic hypotheses and techniques of selection, the basic principles of polygenic systems will be illustrated by means of a simple model. Much of the theory of these systems has been outlined by Wright (1921–1952) in a series of important papers. Lush (1945) and Lerner (1950, 1958) have adapted Wright's theories to problems of animal breeding, and we have drawn heavily on these sources in the following sections, adapting when necessary to the special needs of behavior genetics. Reference should also be made to Mather's monograph (1949) on biometrical genetics and a series of papers edited by Reeve and Waddington (1952). The reader should be warned that the English system of notation differs from the American so that comparisons must be made with care.

A Simplified Model of Quantitative Inheritance. The concepts of quantitative inheritance are conveniently discussed with reference to a cross between two strains homozygous for different alleles at two unlinked autosomal loci. The parental stocks and their F_1 hybrid are represented thus:

$$P_1 = AABB \ (4); \qquad P_2 = aabb \ (0); \qquad F_1 = AaBb \ (2)$$

where the letters symbolize genes and the figures in parentheses represent mean phenotypic values on an arbitrary scale. Each capital-letter gene is assumed to produce one unit of change in a plus direction from the zero-level phenotype produced by the small-letter genes. The zero assigned to P_2 is, of course, purely formal and merely represents a phenotypic base-line. If the gene effects are strictly additive and environmental sources of variation are absent, the measurement of the phenotype gives a direct estimate of the number of "plus" genes. In Table 3-2 we have set out the expected proportions of each genotype in the usual types of interstrain crosses and assigned phenotypic values to each, assuming additive gene effects and no environmental contribution to variance.

The parental and F_1 generations differ from each other, but within each group all members have identical genotypes and (under our ideal assumptions) identical phenotypes. In the F_2 and backcrosses, segregation and recombination produce genetic variability which is best measured by the variance, σ^2. This is defined as:

$$(3\text{-}1) \qquad \sigma^2 = 1/n \sum_1^n (x_i - \bar{x})^2$$

where x_i stands for a measurement on the ith individual in a sample of n, and $\bar{x}$ is the mean of the population. The genetic variances of the backcrosses and F_2 are shown in Tables 3-3 and 3-4. Only the computation for the backcross to P_1 is given, for the distribution of the backcross to P_2 is identical even though its mean value is different.

TABLE 3-2

Predicted Genotypes and Phenotypes of the F_2 and Backcrosses in a Two-Locus System with Additive Gene Effects

		Proportion of Total Group		
Genotype	Phenotype Score	F_2	Backcross to P_1	Backcross to P_2
$AABB$	4	$\frac{1}{16}$	$\frac{1}{4}$	0
$AABb$	3	$\frac{1}{8}$	$\frac{1}{4}$	0
$AaBB$	3	$\frac{1}{8}$	$\frac{1}{4}$	0
$AaBb$	2	$\frac{1}{4}$	$\frac{1}{4}$	$\frac{1}{4}$
$AAbb$	2	$\frac{1}{16}$	0	0
$aaBB$	2	$\frac{1}{16}$	0	0
$Aabb$	1	$\frac{1}{8}$	0	$\frac{1}{4}$
$aaBb$	1	$\frac{1}{8}$	0	$\frac{1}{4}$
$aabb$	0	$\frac{1}{16}$	0	$\frac{1}{4}$
Mean Phenotype Score		2	3	1

TABLE 3-3

Computation of Genetic Variance in a Backcross Generation ($F_1 \times P_1$)

Score	Frequency F	Deviation $(x - \bar{x})$	$(x - \bar{x})^2$	$F(x - \bar{x})^2$
4	.25	+1	1	.25
3	.50	0	0	.00
2	.25	−1	1	.25
Sum	1.00	0		.50
		Variance = .50		

Although these computations have been made for a two-locus system, the relationships found for the additive genetic variance are generally true for a larger number of genes. If all variation in a trait is caused by genes acting additively, these computations apply to both phenotypic and genotypic variance.

TABLE 3-4

Computation of Genetic Variance in an F_2 Generation

Score	Frequency, F	Deviation $(x - \bar{x})$	$(x - \bar{x})^2$	$F(x - \bar{x})^2$
4	.0625	$+2$	4	.25
3	.250	$+1$	1	.25
2	.375	0	0	.00
1	.250	-1	1	.25
0	.0625	-2	4	.25
Sum	1.00			1.00
		Variance $= 1.00$		

Effects of Dominance and Epistasis. Deviations from additivity may occur because of interactions between genes at the same locus (dominance) or at different loci (epistasis). To illustrate the effect of dominance on our hypothetical model, we will make one change in the assumptions. The phenotypic effect of Aa will be considered equal to AA, though aa will still have the value of zero. In Table 3-5, the dominance and additive models are compared in columns 3 and

TABLE 3-5

The Effect of Dominance and Epistasis in the F_2 of a Cross between Two Pure Strains (Hypothetical Data)

Geno-type	Proportion of Total Group	Phenotype Score Additive Hypothesis $A = B = 1,$ $a = b = 0$	Dominance Hypothesis $Aa = AA = 2,$ $aa = 0, B = 1,$ $b = 0$	Epistatic Hypothesis $A = 1, a = b = 0,$ $AB = 2, aB = 0$
$AABB$	$\frac{1}{16}$	4	4	4
$AABb$	$\frac{1}{8}$	3	3	3
$AaBB$	$\frac{1}{8}$	3	4	3
$AaBb$	$\frac{1}{4}$	2	3	2
$AAbb$	$\frac{1}{16}$	2	2	2
$aaBB$	$\frac{1}{16}$	2	2	0
$Aabb$	$\frac{1}{8}$	1	2	1
$aaBb$	$\frac{1}{8}$	1	1	0
$aabb$	$\frac{1}{16}$	0	0	0

4. From this table following the procedures previously described, the phenotypic mean, $\bar{x}$, is computed to be 2.5 and the variance, 1.25. If B is also dominant over b, $\bar{x} = 3.0$ and $\sigma^2 = 1.50$. The effect of dominance is to produce non-symmetrical distributions, to shift the mean from the midparental value towards the mean of the parent with dominant genes, and to increase variance. In polygenic systems it is possible only to measure average dominance, or potence, without reference to specific pairs of alleles. In general the importance of dominance deviations depends upon the relative frequency of the alleles, the degree of dominance, and the cumulative effect of deviations at different loci. Wright (1952, page 15) has discussed the subject in some detail.

Epistatic interactions can be illustrated by a similar model. We shall assume that B now has a plus effect only in the presence of A. The results of this assumption are shown in column 5 of Table 3-5. Again computing as in Tables 3-3 and 3-4, we find a mean of 1.75 and variance of 1.56. Quantitatively the effects of epistatic deviations from additivity are similar to those produced by dominance, and distinguishing them requires complicated breeding experiments as yet beyond the scope of behavior genetics. Theory testing, in this instance, requires more precise measurement than is available to the psychologist.

Nevertheless, both phenomena are significant to the investigator pursuing a selection program. Phenotypic gains based upon selection from dominance and epistatic effects are not permanent if the mating system permits breaking up the specific combinations of genes responsible for the gains. Favorable combinations may become fixed within families, however, and these will persist if outbreeding is avoided. But in the ordinary procedure of selecting breeding stock on the basis of performance and breeding like to like, gains based on epistasis are unstable. The discriminatory power of the selector is reduced when he cannot distinguish between genes which produce a plus effect under any conditions and those whose plus effect is dependent upon the presence of other genes.

The principle can be illustrated from the material just considered. In our epistatic model $AAbb$ and $AaBb$ have the same phenotype score, 2.0. In Table 3-6 are set forth the results of breeding the two genotypes *inter se*. The progeny of $AAbb$ maintain their position whereas those from the $AaBb$ lose ground. Because only gains based on additive gene action can be readily maintained in selection, it follows that the differences between selected strains, provided inbreeding is minimal, will tend to be additive in nature.

Polygenic Systems in General. It is important to bear in mind that

TABLE 3-6

Comparison of Heritability of Characters Dependent upon Additive and Epistatic Gene Effects

Gene Effects	Genotypes of Parents	Parental Phenotype	Genotypes of Offspring	Phenotypes of Offspring	Mean Phenotype
Additive only	$AAbb \times AAbb$	2	All $AAbb$	2	2.00
Additive plus	$AaBb \times AaBa$	2	$\frac{1}{16}AABB$	4	
epistatic			$\frac{1}{8}AABb$	3	
			$\frac{1}{8}AaBB$	3	
			$\frac{1}{4}AaBb$	2	
			$\frac{1}{16}AAbb$	2	
			$\frac{1}{16}aaBB$	0	
			$\frac{1}{8}Aabb$	1	
			$\frac{1}{8}aaBb$	0	
			$\frac{1}{16}aabb$	0	1.75

the transmission of polygenes follows the ordinary rules of Mendelian genetics. The methods of quantitative genetics are statistical, but the statistics are derived from the laws of segregation and recombination, dominance, epistasis, sex and autosomal linkage, just as in classical genetics. The failure to isolate the effects of individual polygenes stems from the fact that there are many of them affecting each character; hence each has a small individual contribution to variance. In a statistical sense at least, one plus allele can substitute in some measure for any other plus allele. This apparent physiological equivalence is probably spurious. Each gene may influence a different metabolic pathway in a network arrangement, but if the critical point is the number of open paths rather than their chemical nature, the phenotypic effect would be simply a function of gene number. No major physiological discontinuity is evident between major genes and polygenes, and many major genes have been shown to have quantitative effects in addition to their obvious qualitative action. Not all polygenes are expected to have identical effects upon variance of a trait, and just where the line should be drawn between major and minor effects is somewhat arbitrary. When marked discontinuities are found in the expression of a trait, an explanation should be sought in terms of major segregating units. But even though much of the variance can be explained by a single gene, some may be better accounted for by polygenic modifiers.

It is helpful in applying polygenic theory to the inheritance of a trait to employ units which maximize the additive genetic effect. Often this requires some type of scale transformation, since the cumulative effects of added genes, though perfectly orderly, may be a multiplicative or exponential rather than an addition function. It is also important that the variance attributed to environment be expressed so that it is independent of genotype. To illustrate, one homogeneous strain of rats might average 100 revolutions per day in an activity cage with a standard deviation of 10 and variance of 100. Another strain might average 1000 revolutions per day, with standard deviation of 100 and variance of 10,000. In terms of variability relative to the mean, the second strain is no less homogeneous than the first, yet the variance is enormously greater. Transformation of activity scores to logarithms of revolutions will give the strains means of 2.0 and 3.0 and equal variances of 1.0.

Scale transformations are familiar to experimental psychologists who employ them to equalize variances as just described, to convert skewed distributions to normal form, and to enable the relationship between an independent and dependent variable to be expressed in linear form. Their uses are exactly the same in behavior genetics. Conversions to adjust for wide phenotypic differences are commonly needed, and the type of transformation needed gives a rough idea of the quantitative nature of the gene-character relationship. Care must be used in normalizing a distribution by means of a scale transformation, since non-normality is one way of recognizing genetic effects. When skewness or kurtosis can be shown to be not dependent upon genotypic differences, normalization is justifiable. If, for example, skewness is found in the distribution of test scores from a highly inbred, genetically homogeneous line, it is probably due to some feature of the test, and a formula for normalization derived from these data can be applied with caution to other populations.

Wright (1952) describes four criteria for scaling and gives examples of their application. The best scale is one on which the effects of both genetic and environmental factors are as additive as possible. This desideratum may be sought by various methods. (1) A scale may be derived on which the variances of the pure-breeding (homozygous, if possible) strains and their F_1 are as uniform as possible. The assumption is that a scale which works well with environmental effects (the only ones operative if the strains are truly homozygous) will also serve well for genetically produced variance. (2) A second type of transformation uses Laplace's principle that a variable compounded from the effects of many small factors acting independently should be normally distributed irrespective of the frequency distribution of each individual component. This involves transforming a scale of measurement in such a way that the relative rank of each individual is maintained while the new distribution follows the normal curve. (3) Scales may be developed which permit two major factors to operate additively. (4) Scales may be based upon the relationships of the means of the parental and F_1 groups and so calculated that the means of the backcrosses and F_2 fit the following scheme:

$$\bar{X}_{b_1} = \bar{X}_{p_1} - \bar{X}_{f_1}/2; \qquad \bar{X}_{b_2} = \bar{X}_{p_2} + \bar{X}_{f_1}/2$$
$$\bar{X}_{f_2} = (\text{midparent}) + \bar{X}_{f_1}/2$$

where $\bar{X}_{p_1}$ = mean of parent generation, strain 1
$\bar{X}_{f_1}$ = mean of F_1 hybrid ($P_1 \times P_2$)
$\bar{X}_{b_1}$ = mean of backcross ($F_1 \times P_1$)
$\bar{X}_{p_2}$ = mean of parent generation, strain 2
$\bar{X}_{b_2}$ = mean of ($F_1 \times P_2$)
$\bar{X}_{f_2}$ = mean of ($F_1 \times F_1$)

There is no simple rule which can be followed, and the various criteria may conflict with each other. Procedures (1) and (2) have been used in various investigations in behavior genetics (Tryon, 1940a; Fuller, Easler, and Smith, 1950; Fuller and Scott, 1954; Thompson and Fuller, 1957). Each situation must be evaluated separately and a solution found which is genetically and psychologically defensible. The important thing is that experimenters be aware of the problem, for faulty scaling can lead to erroneous conclusions.

Polygenic systems may include few or many loci, and the properties of the system may vary somewhat as the number increases. It is possible to generalize from the dihybrid model used for purposes of exposition (page 55) to a system of n loci with a plus and a zero allele at each. There are $2n + 1$ genotypes possible in terms of the number of plus genes present. The proportions of each genotype are given by the successive terms of the binomial expansion $(p + q)^{2n}$, where all plus alleles have the same frequency, p, and $q = 1 - p$. This distribution converges on the normal frequency distribution as n becomes large (Figure 3-2). The effect of dominance is to produce marked skewness at low values of n, but the distortion from normal is small when n is 8 or more (right-hand side of Figure 3-2). If the gene frequencies are unlike, the variability is somewhat reduced; if the effects are unequal, variability is increased.

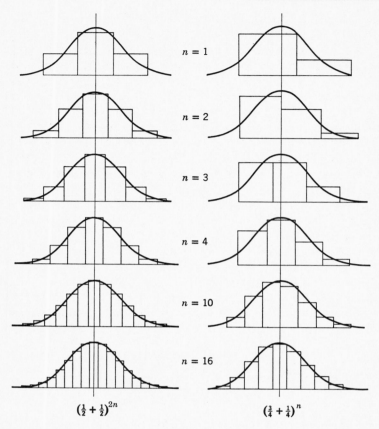

FIGURE 3-2. Binomial distributions for n pairs of genes with equal effects and superimposed normal curves with equal means, equal area, and equal variance. Left: no dominance. Right: complete dominance in the same direction in all pairs of genes. (After Lush, 1945.)

HERITABILITY

Basic Theorems. Heritability is briefly defined as the proportion of trait variance in a specified population which is determined by genotypic variation in that population. The idealized model of quantitative inheritance considered thus far included the unrealistic assumption that all variation was due to genotype; in other words, heritability was unity or 100%. Introducing environmental variance would create no difficulties if it were certain that environmental and genetic effects combine additively, for the technique of variance analysis is well adapted to situations in which total variance is equal to the sum of the component variances. The assumption of additivity is not easily justified when a large array of genotypes is exposed to a correspondingly great variety of environments. But one need not throw away a useful technique because it does not answer every problem, and the additive model may be useful as a first approximation. For purposes of exposition, we will consider heritability in a hypothetical experiment on strain differences conducted in a specified controlled environment. We shall credit the experimenter with sufficient psychological competence to have developed a reliable test and to have chosen an environment suitable for the development of the trait of interest.

In the experimental situation, microenvironmental effects are assumed to occur randomly within and between strains. Microenvironmental effects are in a sense "error," for they arise from the failure of the experimenter to control all factors perfectly. If two organisms of the same genotype have exactly the same life history, they should respond identically when subjected to identical test procedures. We know, in fact, that exact duplication of conditions for each subject is impossible, although the extent to which it can be approached is greatly affected by the skill and resources of the experimenter.

The additive theorem for the relationship between genetic and environmental factors can be formally stated:

$$(3\text{-}2) \qquad P_i = G_i + E_i + f(G_i, E_i)$$

The expected value of the phenotype of individual i is P_i, which is equal to the sum of an average value for its genotype in all environments (G_i), plus a term associated with the effect of a particular environment on all genotypes (E_i), plus an interaction term to take care of the possibility that a particular combination of G and E will effect P in a way not predictable from their average effects. We shall apply this theorem to a limited set of environments, represented by uncontrolled variation from a generally constant set of conditions. In terms of variances the total phenotypic variance, σ_p^2, is the sum of the variance due to genotype, plus that due to microenvironmental fluctuations, plus a term to take care of possible correlations between G and E, plus a term to account for non-linear interactions.

$$(3\text{-}3) \qquad \sigma_p^2 = \sigma_g^2 + \sigma_e^2 + r_{ge}\sigma_g\sigma_e + f(GE)$$

The third term on the right-hand side can usually be reduced to a negligible value in animal behavior experiments. Non-linear interactions between G and E can never be ruled out completely since we have postulated that microenvironmental variations are uncontrolled and inaccessible to observation. Intuitively one expects that departures from linearity over the range of microvariation permitted in a well-conducted experiment will be small. Though this is not susceptible of rigorous proof, it seems justifiable in such cases to include the third and fourth terms of equation 3-3 under σ_e^2 without risk of serious error.

We can then write a simplified version of the variance equation.

$$(3\text{-}4) \qquad\qquad \sigma_p^2 = \sigma_g^2 + \sigma_e^2$$

Heritability, symbolized by h^2, is the ratio

$$(3\text{-}5) \qquad\qquad h^2 = \sigma_g^2/\sigma_p^2 = \sigma_g^2/(\sigma_g^2 + \sigma_e^2)$$

It is also convenient to express the total variance as unity made up of two components, one heritable, the other not.

$$(3\text{-}6) \qquad\qquad h^2 + e^2 = 1$$

The heritability of a trait is of primary importance in behavior genetics, since it provides a measure of the expected rate of gain from selection. We may write $\Delta P = \Delta G/h^2$, from which we can see that the amount of change in phenotype for a given gene substitution is dependent upon the value of h^2. Even small amounts of genetic variability in a population provide a basis for successful selection if heritability is high; conversely genetic variability *per se* does not insure success when heritability is low. Another way of viewing heritability is as a measure of the accuracy with which a genotype can be identified by its own performance or those of its relatives. For example, when $h^2 = 0$, the phenotype offers no clue to the genetic composition of an individual. For the practical breeder or the psychologist trying to develop a strain characterized by particular behavioral qualities, heritability determinations provide a guide to the most efficient method of selection.

It is obvious that changing either σ_g^2 or σ_e^2 will change the value of h^2. Heritability is not an attribute of a trait with a fixed value which more and more refined methods will define with greater and greater precision, but a characteristic of a population with respect to a particular trait. Some of the ways in which h^2 can be lowered are: (1) inbreeding a single line which fixes the genotype and reduces σ_g^2 within the line; (2) selection which may involve discarding some genes and thus reducing σ_g^2 (this effect is most marked when we deal with dominant genes with large effects—it is of less significance when polygenic systems are involved); (3) relaxing environmental controls and increasing σ_e^2; (4) changing from an "expressive" to a "suppressive" environment. Suppose, for example, that early experience in the manipulation of objects is essential for inducing hoarding behavior. Genetic differences in this form of behavior will not be detected in animals reared without such experience.

Heritability can be increased by: (1) outcrossing, which brings in new genes; (2) inbreeding several lines within a population (the genetic variance within strains is reduced, but that of the population as a whole is increased); (3) mutations which bring in new genes; (4) selection for threshold characters which are originally rare (this is a special effect discussed in a later section); (5) tightening environmental controls and reducing σ_e^2; and (6) changing from a suppressive to an expressive environment. A parameter subject to so many influences is likely to vary considerably. Nevertheless, it is probable that under natural selection h^2 varies only within limits and a sort of genetic homeostasis exists within populations (Lerner, 1954).

Measuring Heritability. Various methods have been employed for the measurement of heritability. One is to compare the variance within isogenic lines (highly inbred lines are often considered to be approximately isogenic) with the variance in a random-bred population maintained under similar conditions. Since variance in the isogenic line is entirely environmental, the excess in the random-bred population is attributed to genetic sources.

A simple approximation for heritability is obtained by dividing the gain in selection in one generation by the applied selection differential. The principle is illustrated in Figure 3-3. The selection differential is the difference between the mean of the individuals taken as parents and the mean of the population from which they are drawn.

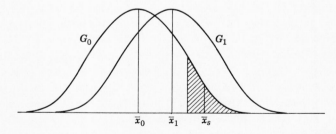

FIGURE 3-3. The results of selection for a heritable trait. Symbols are $\overline{x}_0$, mean of original population (G_0); $\overline{x}_s$, mean of selected group (shaded portion of G_0); $\overline{x}_1$, mean of offspring of selected group, G_1. The ratio of the selection differential $(\overline{x}_s - \overline{x}_0)$ to the gain $(\overline{x}_1 - \overline{x}_0)$ is an estimate of heritability.

The gain is the increase in the mean from generation 1 to generation 2. A control population bred from a random selection of generation 1 should be maintained for comparison. An apparent gain might be due to better environmental conditions for generation 2, or failure to gain might be caused by some adverse condition. Often a low line is selected at the same time, and the average of heritability in both directions is taken as h^2.

Perhaps the most generally useful method of estimating heritability is based upon correlations between relatives. The genetic correlation, that is, the average proportion of genes which relatives have in common over and above the communality of two individuals taken at random, can be calculated from the principles of segregation and recombination (page 80). The ratio of the observed correlation between individuals to their known genetic correlation provides a straightforward estimate of heritability. A detailed description of the various procedures which have been used, together with formal derivations, is beyond the scope of this treatment, but it is important to recognize the relationship between genetic methods and the experimental designs employed in various areas of behavioral science. This parallelism is emphasized in the following section.

Psychological and Genetic Experimental Design. A familiar design in psychological experiments is to test several groups of k subjects under n different treatments. The analysis of variance for the experiment is then conducted as follows (Table 3-7):

TABLE 3-7

Analysis of Variance of a Psychological or Genetic Experiment

Source of Variation	D.F.	M.S.	Mean Square Components
Between treatments	$n - 1$	M_b	$\sigma_w^2 + k\sigma_b^2$
Within treatments	$n(k - 1)$	M_w	σ_w^2
	$\sigma_b^2 = (M_b - M_w)/k$		

In the familiar F-test the ratio M_b/M_w is used to estimate the significance of the differences between the means of groups. Essentially the F-ratio measures the relative importance of the variance introduced by differences between group means (σ_b^2) to the variance of individuals within groups (σ_w^2). Another way of expressing the relative importance of σ_b^2 is the ratio of $\sigma_b^2/(\sigma_b^2 + \sigma_w^2)$, which is known as the intraclass correlation coefficient, r_i. This denotes the proportion of the variance due to differences in treatment in a sample drawn from the population without regard to subgroup boundaries. In the extreme case of no intragroup variation, $r_i = 1.0$; if the subgroup means are identical, $r_i = 0.0$.

In a genetic experiment genes are the treatments, and individuals who receive the same genes, that is, families, are the treatment groups. We cannot manipulate genes directly, but must work with them indirectly by controlling matings. This is subject to considerable error, for an individual receives only one-half his genetic endowment from each parent, and the particular half which he receives is not under experimental control. The average genetic correlation between either parent and his offspring is .5, which is interpreted as signifying that one-half their genes are the same. The genetic correlation between ordinary siblings is also .5. On the average each member of a pair of siblings shares one-fourth of the paternal genes and one-fourth of the maternal genes with the other member of the pair, for a total correlation of .5. Thus, the facts of biology limit our ability to control the genetic endowment of animals by providing them with common parents. Ordinarily the best that can be done is to control .5 of the genetic variance. Higher degrees of control can be obtained if the parents themselves are related, or better, inbred. Common ancestry in the parental lines increases the probability that the offspring will inherit the same genes. Identical twins formed by the separation of cells in an early zygotic stage share all genes and have a genetic correlation of 1.0. Well-established inbred lines may be nearly as homogeneous as identical-twin pairs.

Consider now a group of n families of k full siblings each, who have been measured on a scale of behavior. The assumption is made that the environment is uniform for all families. The analysis of variance is essentially the same as for the environmental treatment considered above, but we can append a genetic interpretation of the variance components (Table 3-8).

The within-families variance includes the environmental component, σ_e^2, plus the half of the genetic component which is non-pre-

TABLE 3-8

Genetic Interpretation of Analysis of Variance

Source of Variation	D.F.	M.S.	Variance Components	Genetic Interpretation
Between families	$n - 1$	M_b	$\sigma_w^2 + k\sigma_b^2$	$\sigma_b^2 = \sigma_g^2/2$
Within families	$n(k - 1)$	M_w	σ_w^2	$\sigma_w^2 = \sigma_g^2/2 + \sigma_e^2$

dictable. The between-families component is interpreted as being caused by the one-half of the genotype which siblings have in common because of having the same parentage. Substituting we have $\sigma_g^2 = 2$ σ_b^2 and $\sigma_e^2 = \sigma_w^2 - \sigma_b^2$ and the estimate of heritability is,

$$(3\text{-}7) \qquad h^2 = \sigma_g^2/(\sigma_g^2 + \sigma_e^2) = 2\sigma_b^2/(\sigma_w^2 + \sigma_b^2) = 2r_i$$

The same equation could be used to calculate heritability from parent-offspring correlations, although the fact that the generations must inevitably develop at different times, thus vitiating the assumption of uniform conditions for all subjects, greatly reduces the reliability of the method.

One weakness of the sibship correlation method is that non-genetic factors common to families are confounded with the common portion of their genotype and may produce an exaggerated estimate of h^2. Factors operating *in utero* or during the period of parental care are possible sources of confusion. As a rule these can be held to a minimum in laboratory experiments. The use of halfsib families which have a common sire but different mothers provides a method of detecting such effects. Half-sibs have on the average only one-fourth of their genotype in common, so that $h^2 = 4r_{ihs}$, where the subscript *hs* indicates that the correlation is between half-sibs. Lerner (1950) gives designs for heritability determinations when each sire is bred to several females. These have been applied in modified form to experimental behavior genetics by Broadhurst (1960) and have been shown to have great potential value.

SELECTION

Systems of Mating. A selection program is an attempt to change the phenotypic average of a population by changing gene frequencies through preventing some animals from reproducing. The process depends upon regulation of the mating system in relation to some criterion established by the investigator. Logically there are only three main systems of mating although variations and combinations of these exist in infinite variety. (1) In random mating or panmixia every sperm has an equal opportunity of fertilizing every ovum. Such a condition actually could be achieved only by mixing both types of gametes in some suspending fluid and allowing them to combine as chance brought them together. In a large laboratory colony approximate panmixia can be attained by mating animals according to a series of random numbers. (2) Genotypic-assortative mating involves pairing males with females on the basis of relationship. Mating individuals more closely related than the average is known as inbreeding; mating individuals less closely related than the average is known as outbreeding. (3) Phenotypic-assortative mating may be positive (like mated to like) or negative (unlikes mated). In pure phenotypic-assortative mating no attention is paid to degree of relationships in setting up matings.

All of these mating systems can be maintained with or without selection based upon phenotypic traits. None of them by itself has any effect upon the gene frequency of the total population unless combined with selection. Even selection has no effect upon the genotypic composition of a population unless it is directed. If animals are culled by drawing lots, the average genotype will remain the same except for accidents of random sampling. A selection experiment involves directed culling and the adoption of a system of mating. In the early stages of such an experiment, positive phenotypic-assortative mating is generally employed, and this may be continued indefinitely. Benefits from this process are likely to be greater in large colonies. In small populations, selection means using only a few individuals as parents. Unless precautions are taken to avoid inbreeding, genetic variability may be rapidly reduced with a corresponding reduction in the efficacy of selection. In behavior genetics, selection based solely on phenotype is seldom practiced. Usually more than one line is required, for example, a high-scoring and a low-scoring line or two high lines, and selection occurs only within lines. Such a system involves both genotypic and phenotypic-assortative mating. The same principle holds when multiple lines are selected; progress depends upon maintenance of genetic variation within the selected populations. This is more difficult in a multiple-line program, for some inbreeding is inevitable. The mating system itself does not directly produce changes in gene frequency; it affects progress (1) through making certain genes more accessible to selection by bringing about combinations in which they are expressed in the phenotype, and (2) by increasing or decreasing the amount of genetic variability which is essential for continued progress.

Effects of Selection. The objective of most selection programs in behavior genetics is the production of a phenotype which is adapted to certain experimental procedures. The goal is a "timid" or "bold" animal, a "maze-bright" or a "maze-dull" subject. Although economic considerations do not rank as high with scientists as with cattle and poultry breeders, they still like to achieve their purposes with maximum efficiency. It is clear from the discussion thus far that high heritability is essential for progress in selection, for it enables accurate identification of the genotype from observations on the phenotype. Selection is facilitated by any of the events which increase heritability as listed on page 64 and affected deleteriously by any factor which reduces heritability.

The principles of selection can be illustrated by considering a single locus at which A is dominant over a, p = frequency of A, and q = frequency of a. In a randomly mating population the frequencies of the three genotypes will be, p^2AA, $2pq$ Aa, and q^2aa. Suppose that we wish to eliminate by selection the trait associated with the dominant gene A. This can be done in one generation by breeding exclusively from the aa genotype which is identifiable because of the absence of the dominant trait. The only problem may be that if p is large, there may be insufficient aa's to provide enough parents. Several generations may be required to build up the number of homozygous recessives to the point that all Aa and AA individuals can be discarded.

If the objective is to eliminate a trait inherited as a recessive, all aa individuals will be rejected as breeders. However, the a genes in the heterozygote are protected from selection, and matings between such animals will continue to produce trait-bearers. The effectiveness of selection is related to gene frequency. When $p = q = .5$, the elimination of all aa individuals is equivalent to removing one-half the total a genes. For example, there will be 100 A and 100 a genes in a sample of 100 individuals. The number in a homozygous condition and thus accessible to selection will be: $q^2 \times 100 \times 2 = 50$, or the proportion of recessives (q^2) multiplied by the number of individuals (100) multiplied by the number of a genes per individual (2). The number in the heterozygotes protected from selection will be $2pq \times 100 \times 1 = 50$. When $p = .9$ and $q = .1$ the situation is different. In the same 100 individuals the number of a genes in homozygous combinations is $q^2 \times 100 \times 2 = 2$. The number in heterozygous combination is $2pq \times 100 \times 1 = 18$. Only one-tenth of the total a genes are accessible to selection. As the frequency of a recessive gene is reduced still more, the power of selection to change its frequency is likewise reduced. Eventually, continued selection pressure results in an equilibrium between the rate of gene elimination and the rate of mutation of other alleles to the undesired form. Mutation rates are so low (perhaps in the order of 10^{-5} to 10^{-7} per locus per generation) that they are unimportant in experimental behavior genetics. However, mutational changes must be considered when dealing with large populations over a period of years.

Selection in favor of a dominant allele is logically equivalent to selection against its recessive counterpart. Progress is rapid when the dominant allele is relatively rare, but eliminating all the recessives is slow. Examples can be found in domestic breeds where non-standard colors appear sporadically in spite of continued negative selection.

Selection for the heterozygote is a special case, for the Aa genotype cannot be fixed. Breeding $Aa \times Aa$ will yield one-fourth AA, one-half Aa, and one-fourth aa, in the familiar Mendelian ratio. When both alleles are of equal frequency, the production of heterozygotes is maximal, and random mating or selection of heterozygotes will produce the same proportions of offspring. To be sure, one generation of all Aa could be reared by crossing only $AA \times aa$, but there would be only Aa left to breed from to produce the next generation. If a is originally rare, selection for the heterozygote will be quite effective for a time in increasing its frequency, for most of the a genes will be in heterozygous combination.

The most favorable situation for selection is one in which each of the possible genotypes is identifiable from its phenotype. Selection can then isolate pure-breeding AA and aa strains in one generation. The intermediate Aa genotype cannot be fixed, but it can be identified, discarded, or used to produce a variable population.

Selection in Polygenic Systems. The psychologist selecting for a quantitative behavioral trait deals with simultaneous effects of genes at many loci. Under the simplest set of assumptions the outcome of such selection can be predicted from the principles already described. Consider a system of n pairs of genes, each plus allele producing one unit of effect equal to every other plus allele and the trait being 100% heritable. Figure 3-4 represents such an idealized experiment starting

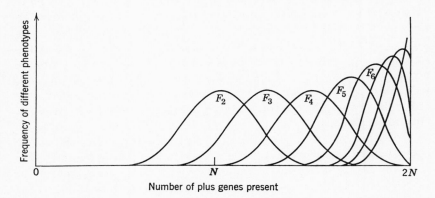

FIGURE 3-4. The distribution of successive generations under intense selection toward an extreme, with few mistakes from dominance or from environmental causes and with no epistasis. (After Lush, 1945.)

from a population in which the frequency of each plus allele is 0.5. It is interesting to note that this approximates the results of actual experiments such as those of Tryon (1940a). As n increases, the effect of selection upon the frequency of each individual gene is less, for the selector does not know whether he is choosing $+^a$, $+^b$, $+^c$, or some other plus allele. The rate of change of the population mean does not depend upon n, but is proportional to n times the average effect at each locus. However, genotypes will become fixed more slowly and progress will continue over more generations when n is large. Actually there may have been no individuals in the original population who possessed the maximum number of plus genes. These appear after the number of plus genes is increased in the general population. Only in this statistical sense does selection create new types. It does not add genetic material, but it frequently leads to combinations which would be highly improbable under a system of random mating and undirected culling.

Selection Experiments in Behavior Genetics. The investigator in behavior genetics who employs selection has two variables under his control, selection intensity and the nature of the mating system. The need for retaining an adequate number of breeders to maintain the experimental population places a limit upon intensity. If a series of generations of 50 animals (25 ♂ ♂ and 25 ♀ ♀) are required and a female can be expected to produce 10 young, the five highest scoring females of each generation must be set aside for one high line. Since some high-scoring animals should be retained as part of a random-bred control line and since some insurance must be provided against losses, it is usually necessary to broaden the criterion to the upper 30 or 35% of females. If more than one high line is selected, and this is strongly recommended, the intensity of selection must be further reduced. High fecundity facilitates a selection program since it permits more intensive culling. By using polygamous matings, the intensity of selection on the male side can be made more intense, and the entire process accelerated.

Selection can be based upon individual performance, upon average family performance, or upon some combination of these. Selection on the basis of progeny performance is often practiced in farm animals, but has had little application in behavior genetics. When h^2 is high, the phenotype of an individual is an accurate guide to his genotype, and individual selection is effective. When h^2 is low, selection of whole families on the basis of sibling averages will give faster results. A consequence of family selection is increased inbreeding, for more and more of the parents will eventually be closely related even though brother-sister matings are avoided. As a population becomes more inbred, family selection becomes relatively more effective than individual selection, and in an isogenic line, selection within the line is totally useless. Lerner (1950) has published diagrams comparing the efficiency of individual and family selection for various degrees of inbreeding, family size, and heritability. If the most rapid possible progress is of primary interest, all of these factors must be considered.

There are several ways in which a group of selected strains can be developed. Two or more heterogeneous populations may be subjected to selection in the same or opposite directions. After a period of selection these strains may be alike phenotypically, but they will be unlike genotypically since selection started with a different gene pool. Another procedure is to assign individuals from a single foundation stock randomly to separate groups and conduct a number of selection programs. Comparisons between these lines with respect to characteristics correlated with the selection criterion are particularly interesting. Still another method is to select on an individual basis from the population as a whole and establish family lines when heritability seems to be reduced. Practical experience with selection has shown that progress often ceases while genotypic variation is still present. In fact, selection alone without inbreeding has been demonstrated to have relatively little effect upon variability even though the mean value for a trait is greatly shifted. The choice of design depends upon the objective of the experiment and the material available.

Heritability has an effect upon the optimum intensity of selection. When it is high, progress is more rapid with more intense culling. If heritability is low, it is theoretically possible that intense culling may impede progress, for many of the selected individuals will owe their position to environmental rather than genetic factors. This is particularly likely if there are non-linear, genotype-environment interactions. Suppose that the genotype giving the lowest average-trait value is also the most environment-sensitive (most variable). Superior phenotypes in this case might come from a genotype which is poorest on the average, and intense selection might eliminate the less variable genotypes which actually yield higher average-quality phenotypes. These considerations may not be important in selection for behavioral traits, but experimenters should be aware of such possibilities.

It is important to avoid inbreeding, particularly during the early stages of selection in order to preserve as much genotypic variability as possible. If for practical reasons only a small colony can be maintained, inbreeding can be minimized by the mating systems shown in Figure 3-5. The foundation stock animals should be unrelated. In-

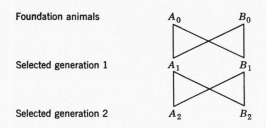

I. Two-Pair System

Foundation animals A_0 B_0

Selected generation 1 A_1 B_1

Selected generation 2 A_2 B_2

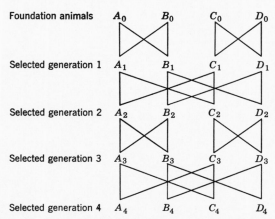

II. Four-Pair System

Foundation animals A_0 B_0 C_0 D_0

Selected generation 1 A_1 B_1 C_1 D_1

Selected generation 2 A_2 B_2 C_2 D_2

Selected generation 3 A_3 B_3 C_3 D_3

Selected generation 4 A_4 B_4 C_4 D_4

FIGURE 3-5. Mating systems to retard inbreeding in selection experiments. A_0, B_0, C_0, D_0 represent *pairs* of unrelated animals. A_1 is a pair whose father came from A_0 and mother from B_0. Other symbols have similar meaning. *Part* I. Two pairs are retained in each generation and males from one are mated to females from the other. *Part* II. Four pairs are retained in each generation and alternate generations mated in a similar pattern.

breeding increases at the rate of .0625 per generation under this system with two pairs (Figure 3-5, part I), and at half the rate with four pairs (part II).

An ingenious method for mass screening and selection has been developed by Hirsch and Tryon (1956). Essentially the technique consists of a standard procedure for permitting observations of a large number of subjects at one time while permitting separation of subgroup classes based on total cumulative score on a series of tests. The scheme can be illustrated by an apparatus designed by Hirsch to separate Drosophila on the basis of their geotactic response (Figure

3-6). The number of steps of selection can be extended without limit, though in the diagram it is restricted to three. In this particular device, separation is achieved automatically by the design of the apparatus, but the same plan of screening can be used for any selection based upon a two-point scoring system. Methods for computing the reliability of the measurements are given in the original paper. Mass screening procedures are particularly important in working with Drosophila, as the small size of individuals makes them difficult to handle. Furthermore, one of the advantages of such a species is the production of large numbers of offspring. This advantage is negated unless procedures are available for measuring individual differences reliably and rapidly. Possibly modifications of this technique will be suitable for mammalian work.

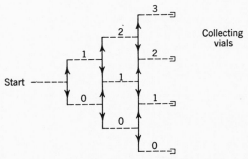

FIGURE 3-6. The diagram represents a set of pathways in a vertically oriented sheet of plastic. Arrowheads represent devices for the discouragement of retracing. Drosophila start at the left and move to the right. For each upward turning at a choice point each individual receives a score of one; for each downward turn, a score of zero. The pathways lead together in such a manner that individuals having the same cumulative scores are grouped together at the end of each trial.

Natural and Artificial Selection. Selection may be defined as the non-random differential reproduction of genotypes (Lerner, 1958), regardless of the nature of the responsible factors. Artificial selection in the laboratory or on the breeding farm is directed towards particular ends. Natural selection is unplanned, and its occurrence is only detectable after the event when genotypes have been observed to change. Mathematically, the same equations hold for each; but there are important differences between the two as biological processes, and the extrapolation from laboratory experiments to natural populations must be made with care. Since the purpose of a selection experiment may be to find principles of wide application, it is fitting to discuss here some of the differences between the two kinds of selection.

One important distinction is that of rate. Natural selection in rapidly evolving species changes the magnitude of metric characters by 1 to 2% per million years (Haldane, 1949). The rates of change of behavioral characters in such experiments as those of Tryon (1940a), Hall (1938), and Frings and Frings (1953) are fantastically greater. Part of this is certainly due to the greater intensity of artificial selection in which rejected animals are culled and leave no offspring, while a particularly desirable sire may have hundreds of offspring. In nature, selection may operate through a fertility differential of a fraction of one percent. Given time enough, genes with even small selective advantages can spread through a whole species and modify its genotype. The popular phrase "survival of the fittest" does no more than define the fittest as those who produce the most offspring. In this sense of maximizing fitness in its special technical meaning, natural selection does have a vague kind of directness, but the phenotypic basis of the advantage may be obscure.

A number of consequences follow from these characteristics. Natural selection does not act upon a single attribute of the organism, but upon the whole. Genotypes, not genes, are the real units which are selected. The result is that the genotypic structure of a population tends to be rather delicately balanced in a combination which produces the greatest average fitness. The process has been called *co-adaptation*. Another feature of natural selection is that the fitness value of particular genes and gene combinations is not uniform from generation to generation. The fluctuating intensity of various selective forces leads to retention of considerable genetic variability rather than fixation of one best genotype. The stable maintenance of a number of alleles within a population is called *polymorphism*. Another cause of polymorphism is the greater fitness of heterozygotes compared with either homozygote. At equilibrium the alternate alleles (A and A') exist in proportions dependent upon the selective disadvantages of each. A well-known example is sickle cell anemia commonly found in Africa. The homozygote S/S suffers from severe anemia; hence S is subject to negative selection (Allison, 1955). On the other hand, the homozygote s/s is more susceptible to malaria; hence s is subject to negative selection. As a result the heterozygotes S/s have some advantage, and both genes are maintained in the population. Such a system is said to be in balanced polymorphism. It has been suggested that the persistence of some inherited mental disorders in the face of negative selection is attributable to a similar mechanism (Penrose, 1950; Allen, 1957).

Natural selection is as old as life and does not cease during the course of artificial selection. The difficulties which some investigators have encountered in maintaining the fertility of lines selected for extreme forms of behavior may have been due to the disruption of co-adapted genetic systems. It is common to find that too rapid selection for extreme phenotypes does reduce fitness, and that progress in modifying the phenotype in the desired direction ceases while there is still abundant genetic variation within the population.

Correlated Characters. Selecting for one phenotypic trait often brings about changes in other characters not entering into the selection criterion. Castle (1941), MacArthur (1949), and Lewis and Warwick (1953) have described behavioral changes associated with selection for physical characters. Many psychologists have selected for one behavioral character and found accompanying changes of quite a different sort. In interpreting these results, consideration must be given to the genetic significance of phenotypic correlations (Thompson, 1957). Four sources of correlation may be recognized. (See also Chapter 10.)

1. The correlated traits may derive from a common functional dependence upon a particular gene (gene communality). In other words, the gene has pleiotropic effects. The relationship may be lineal:

$$\text{Gene} \rightarrow \text{Selected trait} \rightarrow \text{Correlated trait}$$

or collateral:

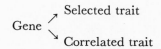

In the lineal relationship any environmental factor which suppresses the selected trait will also affect the correlated trait. This is not necessarily true when the relationship is collateral.

2. Genetic linkage (chromosomal communality) results in phenotypic correlations within families. Indeed, phenotypic correlations are the means by which linkages are detected. In large random-breeding populations, chromosomes of type AB, Ab, aB, and ab occur in numbers proportional to the products of the gene frequencies, and no correlation is found. In more limited populations, as in most behavior genetics experiments, the possibility of linkage must always be considered.

3. Phenotypic correlations may be generated whenever the mating system is non-random. Such correlated characters may be said to have

"gametic communality." The mechanisms which bring this about are as varied as the processes of assortative mating and selection. Many examples are found in domestic animals in which a particular color is selected as a sort of identification tag for the breed, along with a variety of functionally unrelated traits. In human populations, a correlation will be built up between two heritable traits if individuals high in one tend to choose mates high in the other without regard to standing on the first trait (Price, 1936; Bartlett, 1937). This phenomenon, cross-homogamy, probably characterizes some human societies.

Under special conditions phenotypic correlations arise from certain physiological properties of genetic systems. Most populations are genetically variable; hence attempts to change the population mean by selection are usually successful. But it is a mistake to consider the original population as really unselected or to believe that selection can actually deal with one criterion only. More vigorous and adaptable individuals leave on the average more progeny, and their genes increase in proportion. Over the generations, combinations of genes have been built up which produce the maximum average fitness of the species. This does not lead to genetic uniformity, for natural conditions are so variable that the fitness value of a particular genotype fluctuates from generation to generation. The great bulk of the population is intermediate genotypically and phenotypically with respect to the possible range of variation. The most common genotypes are balanced for maximum average fitness, while the extreme genotypes are a safety factor in the event of environmental changes. If selection for an extreme phenotype upsets the genic balance, a correlation may be generated between the selected character and such attributes as low fertility (Lerner, 1958, Chapter 6). Examples cited to illustrate disturbed genic balance usually refer to selection for traits of economic or esthetic significance to the breeder. Reduced fertility has sometimes been observed in stocks selected for behavioral characters, and this may represent a similar phenomenon.

4. A common response of two traits to environmental variation is the final source of phenotypic intercorrelations. A vitamin deficiency would affect both sensory functions and general activity; good home environments favor both physical growth and intelligence. If environmental factors were always recognized, these correlations would not be confused with genetic correlations. Actual experiments must be carefully scrutinized to insure against misinterpretations.

The stability of the various types of genetic correlations varies. Gene communalities are generally very stable in a constant environment under any mating system. Chromosomal communalities are unstable to an extent dependent upon crossover frequency. In a small-scale experiment lasting only a few generations, it may be impossible to distinguish these two forms of communality. Gametic communalities are disrupted by a single generation of random mating, and are thus readily identifiable in laboratory situations. Since human beings do not mate randomly with respect to behavioral traits, gametic communalities in this interesting species are less easily recognized.

The study of environmental communalities is, of course, the main task of all behavioral science except behavior genetics. For this one area it is desirable to minimize environmental variability while maximizing genetic variability. This procedure reduces the significance of environmental communalities. Phenotypic correlations which persist in a constant environment are probably genetic. Conversely, correlations in a highly inbred strain are safely inferred to be of environmental origin.

Phenotypic correlations are often used to analyze the organization of behavior. Animals selected for timidity, maze learning, activity, and the like are given various physiological and psychological tests. Positive correlations with the selected trait have been assumed to indicate a functional relationship dependent upon gene communality or pleiotropy. It should be obvious from the above discussion that correlations within small selected populations may be caused by any one type of communality or by any combination of them. To use correlations to prove a functional relationship based on common genes, one must study randomly bred populations raised under uniform conditions or demonstrate the particular association of characters in a number of independently selected lines.

INBRED STRAINS

The technique of strain comparison is widely used in behavior genetics. Sometimes the subjects come from strains selected with respect to the same trait as is used in the comparison study. More frequently the strains have been selected for quite different traits, often non-behavioral, or have not been selected at all. Inbred strains are maintained, not by selection, but by adherence to a particular mating system. Comparisons between non-inbred strains are useful in behavior genetics. Wild rats are strikingly different from laboratory albinos; pure breeds of dogs show reliable differences on almost all tests given. Nevertheless, the genetic homogeneity achieved by inbreeding provides a research tool for which there is no substitute. In the following section we shall consider some characteristics of inbred strains with special reference to behavioral studies.

Inbreeding and Its Consequences. Inbreeding is the mating of animals more closely related than the average, and its quantitative expression is in relative terms which have reference only to a specified foundation stock in genetic equilibrium. All of the individuals of a species are related to some extent, but usually only the closer degrees of relationship have significance for the problem of inbreeding. The measurement of relationship (r_g) between individuals has already been derived for parent-offspring and sibling pairs (page 67). In general r_g is computed by counting the number of Mendelian segregations (n) which have intervened in each line of descent connecting two individuals through a common ancestor. In the absence of previous inbreeding, the coefficient of relationship or genetic correlation with respect to this common ancestor is $(1/2)^n$. Figure 3-7 illustrates the

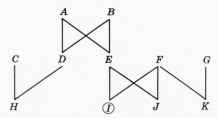

FIGURE 3-7. Diagram of some common relationships. Each line represents a Mendelian segregation. The relationship, genetic correlation or r_g, of I to other individuals in the pedigree is computed by counting the number of segregations between them (n) and substituting in the formula $r_g = (0.5)^n$. If more than one path exists, the r_g values must be added.

Relationship IE or $IF = .50$
Relationship $IK = (.50)^2 = .25$
Relationship $IH = (.50)^4 + (.50)^4 = .125$

Relationship $IJ = (.50)^2 + (.50)^2 = .50$
Relationship IA or $IB = (.50)^2 = .25$
Relationship $ID = (.50)^3 + (.50)^3 = .25$

calculations for simple situations such as parent-offspring (I, E), sibling (I, J), half-sibling (I, K), uncle-nephew (I, D), and first cousin (I, H) relationships. If individuals are connected by more than one line, it is necessary to add the coefficients for both paths. Other systems of describing degrees of relationship include the canonical, common-law, and civil-law arrangements. These have been used in investigations of human inbreeding, but they are primarily legal and religious, and they are not expressed in quantitative terms with genetic meaning. The coefficient of relationship is actually the most probable proportion of genes which are derived from common ancestors. We may also call this the genetic correlation coefficient.

Sex-linkage has the effect of increasing relationship between mother and son, and father and daughter as compared with the reciprocal relationship (see Hogben, 1932a). Computations are more complex if an individual appears in both the lineal and the collateral lines, although no new principles are involved (Lush, 1945).

Since inbreeding is a relative concept, its intensity varies over a wide range. Brother-sister and parent-offspring matings represent the most intense form possible with animals incapable of self-fertilization. Breeding to other families within a strain represents outbreeding with relation to the family group, but inbreeding with respect to the species as a whole. The primary effect of inbreeding is to increase the probability that offspring will inherit the same genes from both parents. Thus it leads to decreased heterozygosis and the fixation of genotypes. The rate of fixation is a function of inbreeding intensity, and Wright's (1923) coefficient of inbreeding is designed to express the expected decrease of heterozygosis in relation to the original foundation stock. There is no way of expressing the amount of heterozygosis of a random-bred stock in terms of the number of loci involved, but knowledge of the origin and phenotypic variability of a group may enable the experimenter to judge it as relatively great or small. When parents themselves are not inbred, the inbreeding coefficient of their offspring is one-half the degree of the relationship between the parents. Thus the offspring of the first generation of brother-sister matings, where no inbreeding has been previously practiced, are 0.25 inbred. When one of the common ancestors is inbred, the inbreeding coefficient F of animal i is:

$$F_i = 1/2 \cdot \frac{(1 + F_a)}{2^n}$$

where F_a = inbreeding coefficient of the ancestor

n = number of segregations in path between parents of animal i through a common ancestor

If there are several such paths, F is computed separately for each, and the results are summed. Examples of the calculations are given in Figure 3-8.

In a small laboratory colony inbreeding cannot be avoided since the choice of mates is limited and eventually all animals become related to each other. The rate of inbreeding increase per generation in a closed population mated at random is:

$$\tfrac{1}{8}M + \tfrac{1}{8}F$$

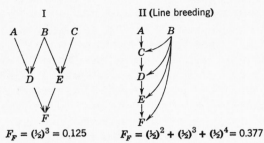

$$F_F = (\tfrac{1}{2})^3 = 0.125 \qquad F_F = (\tfrac{1}{2})^2 + (\tfrac{1}{2})^3 + (\tfrac{1}{2})^4 = 0.377$$

FIGURE 3-8. Computation of inbreeding coefficients, F_i. This is obtained by counting the number of segregations linking the parents through a common ancestor, n, and finding the value of $(\tfrac{1}{2})^{n+1}$. In I, there is one path *DBE*. In II, there are three paths, *EB, EDB, EDCB*. The values for the three paths must be added as they represent independent routes by which genes from *B* might have been transmitted to *E*.

where *M* and *F* are the number of "effective" breeding males and females respectively. With a systematic mating scheme, taking equal numbers of offspring from each mating and pairing them with the least related available mates, inbreeding can be reduced to approximately half the value given by the above formula. Russell's (1941) discussion of the effects of various mating systems upon homozygosity is useful to experimenters (Figure 3-9).

Inbred Lines in Behavior Genetics. Long-continued intense inbreeding leads to the production of very homozygous stocks. Whether such

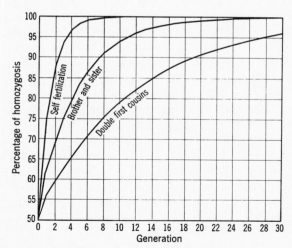

FIGURE 3-9. The percentage of homozygosis in successive generations under three different systems of inbreeding. (From Russell, 1941.)

strains ever attain a completely isogenic state is unknown. As a rule inbreeding is accompanied by a decrease in vigor and reproductive capacity, although some strains are fertile and active after. fifty or more generations of brother-sister matings. Possibly the necessity of selecting for viability results in the maintenance of some heterozygosity, but it must be relatively small and can usually be neglected. The investigator who employs these strains, however, must not assume that removing genotypic variance necessarily eliminates phenotypic variance. There is some evidence that homozygous individuals are less well buffered against minor environmental agents and inbred animals may be no more uniform in response than random-bred subjects (McLaren and Michie, 1956). The use of F_1 hybrids between inbred strains retains the advantages of genetic uniformity while adding the advantages of superior developmental and physiological homeostasis. Most of the evidence to support this view is derived from physiological and morphological studies (Lerner, 1954). There are some complications in applying the concept of developmental homeostasis to behavioral characters (Mordkoff and Fuller, 1959). Increased behavioral variability may actually facilitate physiological homeostasis. An organism must develop in only one out of a variety of possible patterns; it can behave successively in a multitude of ways. The phenomenon of thresholds, treated in a later section, also complicates matters. The hybrid between two inbred strains may actually be more variable than either parent if the hybrid genotype happens to fall in a critical range for determination of a trait. Thus almost all C57BL mice are resistant to audiogenic seizures, and almost all DBA/2 mice are susceptible. Their F_1 hybrid is intermediate, hence much more variable from individual to individual. In spite of these reservations, F_1 hybrids are highly recommended for general experimental purposes.

Once made homozygous, inbred lines retain their genetic characters for long periods of time in the absence of outcrossing. Over many generations mutations will occur, and the characteristics of the strain will change. Experience in biological sciences suggests that the drift will be small and unimportant over one investigator's lifetime. However examples are known of mutational changes which drastically altered the acceptability of transplanted tumors in an inbred mouse strain (Borges and Kvedar, 1952). This mutation would have been undetected had the mice not been challenged with a tumor. At least one investigator has described a similar cryptic mutation which altered the behavior of mice separated for thirty generations (Denenberg, 1959).

Certainly the prudent investigator in behavior genetics should take steps to prevent subline differentiation which is inevitable when stocks are separated over a period of generations. Comparisons with other workers will be facilitated if breeding stock is regularly replaced from a mammalian genetics center. Workers employing the same source will have genetically identical subjects. On a small scale a controlled mating system may be used to prevent diversification within a single colony. Figure 3-10 illustrates a suitable plan, which can be adapted to colonies of various sizes.

Inbred lines are almost essential for experiments on the inheritance of quantitative behavioral characters. The principles of such investigations are the concern of the following section. However the value of inbred lines in reducing experimental error variance in general is

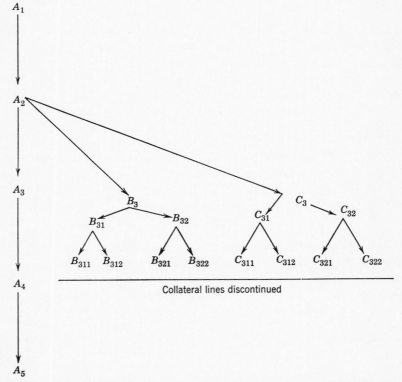

FIGURE 3-10. A mating system for routine maintenance of an inbred line. A_1, A_2, B_2, etc., are brother-sister pairs. The strain is maintained by a single direct line. $A_1 \rightarrow A_4$. At A_2 collateral pairs are taken, bred for two generations to produce experimental subjects, and then discontinued. The process is repeated as needed.

controversial, and their advantages, if any, may not be worth the added cost. Employing a number of inbred strains for comparative studies can be readily justified. Each strain may be considered, with some reservations, as an individual who can be duplicated over and over again. Members of the same strain are practically as alike genetically as monozygotic twins. Comparing a number of strains under a variety of treatments provides a striking demonstration of heredity-environment interaction.

Cross-breeding and Quantitative Characters. Crossing lines developed by selection, inbreeding, or some combination of the two procedures is a standard procedure of genetics. By suitable analytical techniques the inheritance of quantitative characters affected by many genes can be described in terms of additive effects, dominance, and epistasis. Estimates of the number of loci contributing to interstrain variation may also be sought. A concise summary of the mathematical methods and their underlying assumptions has been made by Wright (1952). More elaborate treatments will be found in Mather (1949) and Kempthorne (1957).

An example of biometrical analysis of a behavioral trait has been given by Thompson and Fuller (1957). (See also Chapter 8.) Crosses were made between an active strain of mouse (C57BR) and an inactive strain (A). Scores were assigned on the basis of the number of units entered in a Hebb-Williams (1946) type maze. Results are set forth in Table 3-9. Inspection of the raw-score means showed that these were arranged in an orderly fashion with respect to the contributions of the parental strains to the genotypes. The raw scores were,

TABLE 3-9

Inheritance of Exploratory Activity in C57BR × A Hybrids

Strain or Cross	Raw Scores		Transformed Scores	
	Mean	Variance	Mean	Variance
C57BR	532	22274	22.9	9.74
$F_1 \times$ BR	396	22259	18.9	30.15
F_1	303	10420	17.0	12.23
F_2	288	23613	16.1	29.60
$F_1 \times$ A	148	11816	11.0	27.58
A	11	80	1.0*	16.48*

* A special adjustment was made in the transformed scores to allow for a large number of zero scores.

however, unsuitable for variance analysis, since variances of the three genetically homogeneous groups, C57BR, A, and F_1 were positively correlated with the means. The variances in these groups must be of environmental origin. Hence a transformation of the scores was sought which would equalize the variances in the three groups. The square root of the raw scores was judged to be reasonably satisfactory. This appears to overcompensate for the A strain, but the large number of zero scores in this group makes any transformation unsuitable. The square root scores clearly show increased variance in the genetically heterogeneous groups. Agreement with the theoretical model is not perfect, for the F_2 variance should exceed that of the backcrosses. However, the data leave no doubt that genes affecting activity are segregating. The interpretation of such a table follows the lines laid down by Wright (1952) (Table 3-10). Because of the failure of the

TABLE 3-10

Variance Analysis of a Cross between Two Pure-Bred Lines (Wright, 1952)

Population	Symbol	Mean — Theoretical Value	Symbol	Variance — Theoretical Value
P_1	$\bar{P}_1$		σ_{P1}^2	σ_E^2
P_2	$\bar{P}_2$		σ_{P2}^2	σ_E^2
$P = \frac{1}{2}(P_1 + P_2)$	$\bar{P}_M$	$\frac{1}{2}(\bar{P}_1 + \bar{P}_2)$	σ_{PM}^2	$\frac{1}{2}\sigma_E^2$
$F_1(P_1 \times P_2)$	$\bar{F}_1$		σ_{F1}^2	σ_E^2
$F_2(F_1 \times F_1)$	$\bar{F}_2$	$\frac{1}{2}(\bar{P}_M + \bar{F}_1)$	σ_{F2}^2	$\sigma_D^2 + \sigma_G^2 + \sigma_E^2$
$B_1(P_1 \times F_1)$	$\bar{B}_1$	$\frac{1}{2}(\bar{P}_1 + \bar{F}_1)$	σ_{B1}^2	$\frac{1}{2}\sigma_G^2 + \sigma_D^2 + \sigma_E^2 + \Sigma GD$
$B_2(P_2 \times F_1)$	$\bar{B}_2$	$\frac{1}{2}(\bar{P}_2 + \bar{F}_1)$	σ_{B2}^2	$\frac{1}{2}\sigma_G^2 + \sigma_D^2 + \sigma_E^2 - \Sigma GD$

Assumptions: Non-additive interactions removed by means of an appropriate scale. The variances σ_G^2 (additive) and σ_D^2 (dominance) refer to F_2 even when used for backcrosses. ΣGD = non-linear dominance-genetic interaction.

σ_E^2 estimated from parents and F_1.

$\sigma_G^2 = \sigma_{F2}^2 - (\sigma_{B1}^2 + \sigma_{B2}^2)$ or $\sigma_{F2}^2 - \sigma_{F1}^2$.

$\sigma_D^2 = \sigma_{F2}^2 - \sigma_G^2 - \sigma_E^2$.

Number of factors $= \dfrac{R^2}{8\sigma_G^2}$, where R = range between means of P_1 and P_2.

$h^2 = \dfrac{\sigma_G^2}{\sigma_G^2 + \sigma_E^2}$

backcross data to follow the model, the results with the F_1 and F_2 alone have been used to illustrate the calculations of heritability (h^2) and number of factors (n):

(1) $$h^2 = \frac{29.60 - 12.23}{29.60} = .59$$

(2) $$n = \frac{(22.9 - 1.0)^2}{8 \times 17.37} = 3.5$$

No estimate can be made for $\sigma_D{}^2$.

The value of variance component analysis to behavior genetics remains to be tested. Basic assumptions of the methods have been challenged (Woolf, 1952) on the grounds that they take insufficient account of environmental variation. (But read also Mather's [1952] reply to this paper.) We shall develop later the concept of a gene-character relationship which emphasizes the non-congruence of the genetic and behavioral elements. In this model the additive genetic variance is a special rather than a general case. However, several sets of data on activity (other examples are cited on page 267) are reasonably well accounted for under the assumptions used, though the discrepancies should not be overlooked. At the present stage much more experimentation is needed.

Another way of viewing cross-breeding is quite independent of formal genetic analysis and interpretation. The method may be considered as a means of quantitatively varying the intensity of a treatment. If we have been able to concentrate $2n$ plus-alleles in one line, and the corresponding $2n$ neutral-alleles in another, we can regard the phenotype of their F_1 hybrid as the product of n plus-genes. The two backcrosses represent the effects of $1.5n$ and $0.5n$ plus-genes. This is equivalent to studying the effects of an independent variable at five levels of intensity in a classical psychological experiment. The analogy is not perfect for the backcross generations are not homogeneous and the groups differ in heterozygosity as well as in gene dosage, but this is inevitable with genetic techniques. This approach is similar to the use of single genes as "treatments," but the kinds of variation obtained represent ranges within a series of "normal" phenotypes, rather than pathological deviants.

SPECIAL TOPICS

In the remainder of this chapter we shall consider a number of topics which are often important in behavior genetics research. These relate to special problems of threshold characters, to the effects of continued training on genetic differentiation of behavior traits, and to the use of split-litters in general psychological experimentation.

Thresholds and Polygenic Systems. Sometimes the nature of measurement in science produces dichotomous classifications when the underlying phenomenon of genetic interest is a continuous variable. For example, the differential resistance of two strains of mice to a toxic drug could be measured by comparing the percentage of mice killed at several dose levels. Actually there is little difference in physiological efficiency between an animal which just survives and one which dies after a long period of illness. Nevertheless, for quantitative measurement we prefer the objectivity of the life-death dichotomy to subjective appraisal of the degree of illness produced in the survivors or estimation of the rate of dying in those who succumb.

Dichotomous classifications also occur in behavior genetics. An investigator may be interested in hereditary differences in an ability which can be tested only in trained subjects. A proportion of individuals may fail to meet the criterion of training which is necessary before a quantitative test can be given. Experimental psychologists in similar situations discard the rats which do not run the maze, the dogs which do not learn delayed response. The behavior geneticist must use all the subjects in every genetic subgroup, provided they are physically normal, if he is to secure a true estimate of the attributes of the population. Thus a pass-fail classification may be employed, even when it is obvious that the attribute of the animal which is being measured is distributed continuously.

It is generally better for genetic analysis to change tests which give pass-fail results so that all subjects receive a quantitative score, but this is not always practicable. Sometimes, too, the reliability of observation is improved by using a dichotomous classification. Many mice and rats exposed to high-pitched sounds of moderate intensity go into seizures which can culminate in convulsions. Some animals show minimal response to sound, others appear to be on the verge of a convulsion without actually having one; those which convulse may recover soon, suffer from prolonged postconvulsive ataxia, or even die. Grading the severity of various responses on a linear scale would be extremely difficult, but observers can agree perfectly on the occurrence or non-occurrence of a convulsion, and populations can be characterized in terms of convulsion risk. Fortunately, the polygenic models described in this chapter can be applied to the inheritance of such threshold characters as are considered to be dependent upon underlying physiological factors which vary quantitatively.

An excellent explanation of the threshold hypothesis is found in

Wright's (1934) study of polydactyly in guinea pigs. Fuller, Easler, and Smith (1950) applied Wright's concepts to the differences in audiogenic seizure susceptibility found in various inbred strains of mice. Although the genotype in each strain is fixed so that it can be considered the same in all individuals, susceptibility to convulsions is predictable only in a statistical sense. The various strains do not "breed true" for susceptibility. When tested under standard conditions about 99% of DBA/2, 80% of DBA/1, 35% of A, and 0.5% of C57BL were classified as convulsers. There is nothing absolute about these percentages. Changing the age of testing, the nature of the sound stimulus, or the method of handling can shift the values up or down. Under controlled conditions, however, each genotype is characterized by a constant percentage of individuals who surpass the threshold for convulsions.

The threshold hypothesis can be expressed in a somewhat more formal fashion. We shall denote the unknown physiological basis for susceptibility by the symbol, X, and assume that X varies continuously over a wide range of values. When $X < X_t$ a non-convulser phenotype is produced; when $X > X_t$ a convulser phenotype results. The value of X for a particular individual, i, of genotype g' is:

$$(3\text{-}8) \qquad\qquad {}_iX = X_{g'} + {}_iX_e$$

where $X_{g'}$ = the average value of X for all individuals of genotype g'

$\quad {}_iX_e$ = the sum of all the environmental effects upon X in i

These may be positive or negative, and the mean value within strain g' is zero.

The requirement for a resistant phenotype may be completely expressed as

$$X_{g'} + {}_iX_e < X_t$$

and for a susceptible phenotype as

$$X_{g'} + {}_iX_e > X_t$$

When the value of X_g is close to a threshold, fluctuations in ${}_iX_e$ are extremely important in determining whether ${}_iX$ will be above or below the threshold. When the genotypic mean is far from a threshold, environmental factors have less influence upon the observed phenotype.

Quantitative estimates of X_g are possible provided certain assumptions are made. We assume that the ${}_iX_e$'s within a genotype are normally distributed with a mean of zero and standard deviation of 1.0. Furthermore, we shall consider that genetic and environmental effects upon X are additive over the limited range of X which is near a threshold. Referring back to equation 3-8, we can predict that when the $_iX_e$'s are normally distributed, 68.2% of the X's will lie between $X_{g'} + 1$ and $X_{g'} - 1$. Similarly, 95.4% will be in the range of $X_{g'} \pm 2.0$ and 4.6% will be beyond this range. If $X_{g'}$ is located 2.0 units below the threshold, X_t, it is apparent that one-half of the 4.6% will be over the threshold and show a different phenotype. In practice this reasoning is reversed, and the values of X_g are computed from the observed percentages of the two phenotypes by means of the inverse probability transformation (Wright, 1920, 1952).

Some of the features of polygenic-threshold systems are illustrated in Figure 3-11 (Fuller, Easler, and Smith, 1950). Animals resistant to

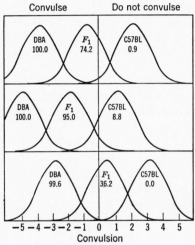

FIGURE 3-11. Changes in convulsive risk on first trial (figures under curves) associated with conditions shifting physiological susceptibility by one standard deviation. The abscissa is a scale of physiological susceptibility. Each genotype is assumed to vary normally about some point on this scale. The convulsive risk is dependent upon the proportion of the curve to the left of an arbitrary threshold.

audiogenic convulsions in a standard test are considered to be above the threshold. The three curves in each section of the figure represent the distribution of X in a highly susceptible strain, DBA, a resistant strain, C57BL, and their F_1 hybrid. These curves have been drawn so that the hybrid is exactly intermediate to the parent strains if additive genetic effects are assumed. The top set of curves represents the results in the main experiment. The effects of changing the testing conditions so that the threshold is raised by one unit are shown in the middle section of Figure 3-11. Reducing the threshold by one unit produces the results shown in the bottom section of the figure. A significant feature of the system is that a given amount of change on the X scale has quite different effects on the phenotypic ratios of genotypes lying near or far from X_t. Changes in the proportion of convulsions in DBA's are insignificant, but they are large in the hybrids. In general, threshold characters are most sensitive both to environmental and genetic effects when they are near threshold, i.e., their frequency is near 50%. This produces a complication in selecting for or against such characters, since their heritability decreases as the selected populations move away from a midpoint (Dempster and Lerner, 1950).

One further point should be emphasized. Crosses between strains which are high and low with respect to a behavioral trait may yield ratios in the F_1, F_2, and backcrosses which closely approximate Mendelian ratios for a single factor showing dominance (Witt and Hall, 1949). This similarity may lead to the adoption of a hypothesis of single-factor determination. However, these results are much like those which will be obtained in a polygenic threshold system if one strain is more distant from the threshold than the other. The predictions are not exactly the same, but the precision of measurement is usually not sufficient to decide between the two hypotheses in a small-scale experiment. One property of the polygenic threshold system is that the backcrosses tend to be somewhat closer to the parental types than to the F_1, so that an appearance of dominance in opposite directions may be found. Repeated backcrossing to the strain which appears to carry the recessive factors is one method of arriving at a decision between the polygenic and single-gene hypotheses and should always be employed before one or the other is adopted.

Effects of Practice on Genetic Differences. The genotype of an animal remains constant throughout life, but his behavioral phenotype changes. Responses and traits evolve during the lifetime of an individual, particularly in those species on the higher branches of the phylogenetic tree. Does the relative importance of genotype in producing individual differences also change during development? Reasons can be found for predicting either an increase or a decrease of heritability in a situation in which all subjects receive the same treatment. When one specific response is reinforced, other responses will be extinguished, and all subjects will converge upon a common pattern. With respect to the total potential repertory of behavior, any effects of heredity must be reduced, though there still remains the possibility of variation in the rate and intensity of the reinforced response. If the convergence hypothesis is true, heritability will be higher in the early stages of response acquisition than in later stages.

On the other side of the argument, one might predict that subjects free to exploit their environment in a variety of fashions will by chance light upon quite different modes of adaptation. These divergent responses with repetition will become canalized and fixed in different individuals. Thus interindividual (or interstrain) variation will increase, whereas intraindividual variation decreases. The divergence hypothesis predicts greater heritability after traits are well "shaped up."

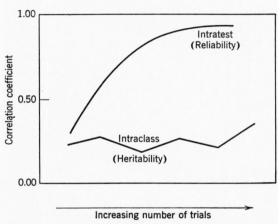

FIGURE 3-12. A comparison of the effects of repeated trails on the reliability and heritability of test scores. Based on data collected by the authors from a variety of tests.

Some empirical evidence upon this point has been obtained by one of the writers in a series of experiments comparing behavior in five dog breeds. (The intraclass correlation coefficient was used as an indicator of heritability.) The measure of intraindividual consistency was the product-moment correlation between scores on successive repetitions of the same test. The results of all experiments were similar (Figure 3-12). Between-test correlations rose on repeated trials. Intraclass correlations fluctuated randomly. McNemar (1933) and Brody (1937) obtained similar results from their studies of motor skills in twins.

These results indicate that under a variety of conditions, factors tending to produce changes in environmental variance are balanced by equal changes in genetic variance. Neither the divergence nor the convergence hypothesis is supported by the evidence. Both convergence and divergence of means of different breeds were found, but the relative importance of genetic variation was roughly constant. Genetic differences in response are found at every stage of learning, and there is no one best time to detect the effects of heredity. The psychological nature of the factors at work, however, undoubtedly changes with the perfection of the response.

The Split-Litter Technique. The majority of behavioral experiments are concerned with genetics only to the extent that heredity should be controlled like other variables which may contribute to the error variance. Two general approaches are possible: (1) genetic variance may be factored out statistically by means of the split-litter technique; (2) genetic variance may be reduced experimentally by inbreeding. Clearly the purpose of most psychologists is not the reduction of genotypic variance *per se*. If this were so there could be no argument regarding the superiority of inbred strains. Instead, the objective of a good experimental design is to minimize extraneous variance from both genetic and environmental sources. Both techniques of genetic control are inextricably interlocked with the effects of environmental factors.

In the split-litter technique individuals from a litter are randomly assigned to two or more treatment groups. This division insures balanced representation of families in the groups and permits extraction of a between-litters component of variance, presumably reducing the error variance and permitting greater efficiency of experimentation. Several theoretical discussions of the use of the split-litter technique in psychology have appeared (Scott, 1949; Ross, Ginsburg, and Denenberg, 1957). Empirical data from pharmacological research indicate that the efficiency of bioassays can be increased by a factor of two or more by the use of this technique (Mandl, 1955).

The effect of the split-litter technique depends upon the relative values of the between- and within-families environmental and hereditary variances. Three sources of animal material may be compared: (1) a colony maintained by random mating; (2) several more or less distinct lines within a colony; (3) a single inbred strain. In the first case the relative values of $_w\sigma_e^2$ and $_b\sigma_e^2$ depend upon the technique of rearing and the effects of prenatal and other maternal factors. If factors common to littermates are important, the split-litter technique will be of value whatever the genetic situation. In a random-breeding population the genetic variance within litters, $_w\sigma_g^2$, tends to approach the variance between litters, $_b\sigma_g^2$, with the limitation that the hereditary mechanism makes it impossible for any single pair of parents to be a representative sample of a population. The frequency of a given gene may assume *any* value between one and zero in a population, but only the values zero, one-half, and one in an individual. If a character is largely dependent upon a single locus, this limitation means that $_w\sigma_g^2$ will generally be less than $_b\sigma_g^2$, and the split-litter technique will improve efficiency. If a character is determined by many genes, the split-litter technique is less important as a means of controlling genetic variance.

When a population is subdivided into a number of parallel partially inbred lines, $_b\sigma_g^2$ is large in comparison with $_w\sigma_g^2$, and the split-litter method will have maximal efficiency. In the third type of mating system, genetic variance between families in an inbred strain approaches the vanishing point, so that the split-litter method becomes purely a method of controlling for litter-specific environmental factors.

Under special circumstances within-litter variability may exceed that between litters. For example, consider a number of litter pairs raised together and tested for social dominance. If each dominant subject receives a score of 1.0 and each subordinate a score of zero, the means of all litters will be one-half. All the variance will be within litter pairs. This peculiar result is dependent upon the relative scale used for measuring dominance, but it is conceivable that the effect of being dominant would generalize to other testing areas where measurement against an absolute standard is possible.

In general it is suggested that the split-litter technique is usually worth the trouble. An example may be cited from an experiment by Ashman (1957) performed in our laboratory. The subjects were mice from two closely related inbred strains, each maintained with heterozygosis at a single locus. Littermate pairs for one strain were either d/d (dilute) or $+/d$; for the other strain, pairs were se/se (short-ear) or $+/se$. A number of behavior measures were taken without detecting any significant differences between strains or between phenotypes. However, between-litter differences were highly significant. In this instance, no serious error would have been involved by neglecting obvious physical characters or even strain of origin, but precision would have been lost if litter pairs were not matched.

4

Methods of human behavior genetics

The distinction between human and animal behavior genetics is more than a matter of the species studied or the techniques which are feasible in the two fields. The primary objectives of the workers in the two areas are different. Animal experimenters use genetics as a device to study the nature of the variables which determine behavior. In gathering such information, traits and subjects are selected for study because of experimental convenience, not because wheel running, maze learning, and audiogenic seizures in rodents are socially or economically important.

In contrast, workers in human behavior genetics have concentrated on problems of social significance and accumulated a great body of observations on intelligence (particularly mental defect), psychoses, and other psychiatric problems. The desire to put the newly discovered science of genetics at the service of human welfare led some early twentieth-century scientists to make excessive claims for the importance of heredity in the origin of social maladjustment. The anti-heredity movement was equally one-sided in the opposite direction. Though the battle between hereditarians and environmentalists no longer rages conspicuously, the concern with applied problems still persists among most human geneticists who deal with psychological characters.

It is easy to understand why this is so. If one's major interest is a quantitative science of human heredity, psychological traits are inappropriate characters to use in this endeavor. If one is devoted to finding general laws relating genotype to behavior, human subjects are much less manipulable than are animals. Research in human behavior genetics, then, has been concentrated on such problems as:

(1) The mode of inheritance of mental dysfunction or other traits regarded as unit characters.

(2) The determination of the heritability of quantitative traits such as intelligence and personality.

(3) The mode of interaction of nature and nurture in development.

The discussion of methods in this chapter is built around these three problems. First to be considered are methods for discovering the mode of inheritance of unit characters when controlled matings are not possible. For the most part, traits inherited in this way are not "psychological" in the narrow sense. They involve a heritable organic lesion which has effects upon behavior. However a number of population surveys of mental deficiency and psychosis rely heavily upon this type of genetic analysis.

The inheritance of quantitative traits in man has been studied largely by means of correlations between relatives or by analysis of variance. Twin comparisons have played a major role in this area, so much so that one psychologist (Smith, 1949) complained of difficulty in finding naive subjects to use on his tests. The importance of the twin method has dictated a special section in this chapter.

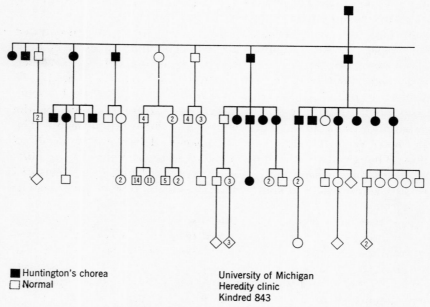

■ Huntington's chorea
□ Normal

University of Michigan
Heredity clinic
Kindred 843

FIGURE 4-1. A pedigree of Huntington's chorea. A single dominant autosomal gene is responsible for the onset at about age thirty to forty of degeneration of various areas of the brain. (From Neel and Schull, 1954.)

TESTING GENETIC HYPOTHESES IN MAN

Family Studies. The most direct method of determining the mode of inheritance of a trait is to examine a pedigree of a family which shows the trait and to attempt to fit it to a hypothesis of dominant or recessive, sex-linked or autosomal inheritance. A pedigree of Huntington's chorea is given in Figure 4-1. This progressive dementia has been traced through many generations (up to 12). Almost always the afflicted person has an afflicted parent, though there are rare cases in which an individual designated as a carrier by the occurrence of the disease in his children has survived to an old age without manifesting the disease. The facts indicate an autosomal dominant with almost complete penetrance. Huntington's chorea is a rather unusual case of a genetic syndrome which ordinarily is manifested clinically in middle age after the period of most active reproduction. Thus selection against the gene for the disease is impeded.

The pedigree of epilepsy in Figure 4-2 suggests an autosomal recessive mode of inheritance. The parents of the two afflicted children are themselves normal but have the same great-great-grandparents. A greater than average occurrence of a condition in the offspring of consanguineous marriages is a strong indication of recessive inheritance.

A single pedigree study, particularly if only a few individuals of

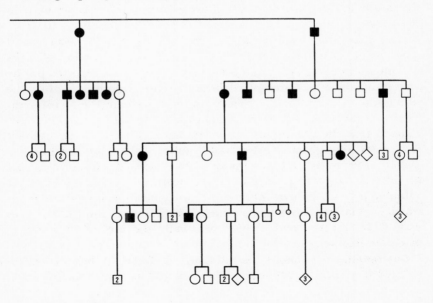

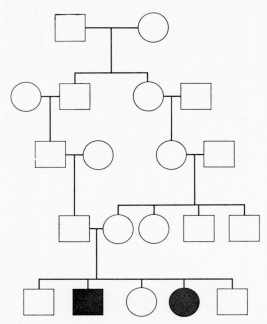

FIGURE 4-2. A pedigree of epilepsy in which the disease occurred in two of five children from a consanguineous marriage. This suggests a recessive mode of inheritance. (Alström, 1950.)

the family are diagnosed, is not of great value. Many biases exist in the collection of data, for a series of cases in one family is likely to attract attention, while isolated cases go unrecorded. Second-hand accounts of the presence (and even more so, of the absence) of traits are often unreliable. Neel and Schull (1954, page 227) reported on the appearance of a pedigree of diabetes mellitus before and after the siblings of the *propositus* (person through whom the family was located) were given sugar-tolerance tests. Before the tests the propositus claimed that she was the only diabetic among eleven living siblings. After tests were given to all available subjects the score stood at five diabetic, four tested and found normal, two untested. Non-professional psychiatric diagnoses are also untrustworthy. Certainly the most valuable data on human inheritance has come from investigations in which a qualified investigator and his assistants examined all cases with their relatives, and verified personally the presence or absence of a trait according to a uniform criterion.

Determining the Inheritance of Common Traits. When one is interested in testing a genetic hypothesis pertaining to a common trait, a random sample of the population may be selected and the occurrence of the trait within families compared with the values predicted under the hypothesis. It is reasonably simple to do this in a population in genetic equilibrium. We shall describe Snyder's (1932) study of the inheritance of the ability to taste PTC. Preliminary results suggested the hypothesis that non-tasting corresponded to the genotype tt and tasting to the genotypes Tt or TT. The problem was how to test a Mendelian hypothesis when the genotypes of the taster parents were unknown. The solution is based upon application of the Hardy-Weinberg law. We shall use the symbolism already adopted:

$$p = \text{frequency of } T$$
$$q = (1 - p)_{-} = \text{frequency of } t$$

At equilibrium the proportions of each genotype are:

$$p^2TT; \quad 2pqTt; \quad q^2tt$$

The results of marriages between tasters and non-tasters may be summarized as follows:

Type of Marriage	Frequency	Offspring	
		Tasters	Non-tasters
$TT \times tt$	$2p^2q^2$	$2p^2q^2$	0
$Tt \times tt$	$4pq^3$	$2pq^3$	$2pq^3$

Marriages between tasters and tasters may be of three types:

Type of Marriage	Frequency	Offspring	
$TT \times TT$	p^4	p^4	
$TT \times Tt$	$4p^3q$	$4pq^3$	
$Tt \times Tt$	$4p^2q^2$	$3p^2q^2$	p^2q^2

Summarizing we find that the proportion of non-taster offspring from taster by non-taster marriages is simply:

$$(4\text{-}1) \qquad q/(1 + q)$$

and from taster by taster marriages:

$$(4\text{-}2) \qquad q/(1 + q)^2$$

The results of the survey are summarized in Table 4-1.

The fact that five children from non-taster by non-taster marriages did not fit the prediction may be explained by illegitimacy, incomplete gene penetrance, or faulty classification on the test. A few individuals have taste sensitivities intermediate to the taster, non-taster groups.

TABLE 4-1

Numbers of Tasters and Non-tasters Classified
According to Parentage
(Snyder, 1932)

Marriages	Offspring		
		Tasters	Non-tasters
Tasters × Tasters	No. obs.	929	130
(425)	% obs.	87.7 ± 0.7	12.3 ± 0.7
	% cal.	87.6 ± 0.1	12.4 ± 0.1
Tasters × Non-tasters	No. obs.	483	278
(289)	% obs.	63.4 ± 1.2	36.6 ± 1.2
	% cal.	64.6 ± 1.2	35.4 ± 1.2
Non-tasters × Non-tasters	No. obs.	5	218
(86)	% obs.	2.1	97.9
	% cal.	0.0	100.0
Total 800		1417	626

Counting both parents and offspring, 2556 tasters and 1087 non-tasters are listed in Table 4-1. Thus the fraction of tasters, q^2, is .298, and $q = .545$. From this value the expected proportions of offspring from each type of marriage were calculated, and the observed results are seen to be in excellent agreement with the theory.

Extension to Environmentally Modified Traits. The power of population-genetics methods is well demonstrated by their success in explaining the distribution of blood types and confirming the recessive nature of taste blindness. These methods can be extended to more complex genetic situations than those considered above. When there are three alleles at a locus, the formulations become involved. Another complication is fundamentally more serious. Environmental forces may modify the expression of one of the phenotypes. Social pressures often act to favor conformity to one mode of behavior, usually the more common of two alternative patterns. Trankell (1955) has treated the inheritance of handedness from this point of view. He hypothesizes that left-handedness is the phenotype corresponding to the genotype aa, and right-handedness to genotypes AA or Aa. The combination of training towards right-handedness and exposure to a world whose structures and tools have been built for right-handed people prevents a certain number of aa individuals from expressing their genotype.

The *aa* genotype is permissive; it is necessary but not sufficient for left-handedness.

Trankell modified the familiar Hardy-Weinberg equation for the frequency of various phenotypes as related to gene frequency by postulating that the proportion (k) of trait bearers is less than the total proportion (q^2) of homozygous recessives, *aa*. The resultant balance sheet of a population in genetic equilibrium looks like this:

Recorded Phenotype	Genotype	Proportion
Trait absent, e.g., right-handed	AA	p^2
	Aa	$2pq$
	aa	$q^2 - k$
Trait present	aa	k

The symbolism has been changed to be consistent with other sections of this book.

Multiplying the frequencies of each genotype with every other genotype, adding, simplifying, and summarizing, leads to the following predictions with respect to the proportion of *aa* offspring in the progeny of various types of marriages:

Type of Marriage	Proportion of Recessive Homozygotes in Progeny
I. Trait bearer × trait bearer	1.0
II. Trait bearer × non-trait bearer	$(q - k)/(1 - k)$
III. Non-trait bearer × non-trait bearer	$(q - k)^2/(1 - k)^2$

Let N_1, N_2, N_3 = the total number of children from each type of marriage

X_1, X_2, X_3 = the number of children with the trait recorded in each type of family

b = the proportion of trait bearers in the total filial population; i.e., b corresponds to k in the parental population

Then $b/q^2 = X/q^2 \cdot N = X/N_{aa}$ = the proportion of recessive homozygotes in the filial generation recorded as trait carriers under the prevalent conditions of penetrance. Multiplying this proportion by the expected number of recessive homozygotes from each type of marriage yields an estimate of the number of trait bearers from each family type.

Family Type	Predictive Equation
I. LH $\times$ LH	$X_1 = b/q^2 \cdot N_1$
II. LH $\times$ RH	$X_2 = b/q^2 \cdot (q - k)/(1 - k) \cdot N_2$
III. RH $\times$ RH	$X_3 = b/q^2 \cdot (q - k)^2/(1 - k)^2 \cdot N_3$

The values of k and b can be determined for randomly selected families, and those of N and X for each type of marriage separately. The result is three separate estimations of q.

Applying this method to three published accounts of the familial occurrence of handedness and comparing observed and predicted values by chi-square showed substantial agreement between them. The summary is set forth in Table 4-2.

TABLE 4-2

Familial Occurrence of Handedness in Three Studies as Related to Trankell's Incomplete-Penetrance Hypothesis

Source of Data		Ramaley 1913	Chamberlain 1928	Rife 1940
Parental Generation				
	N	610	4354	1374
Left-Handed		49	155	72
	k	.0803	.0356	.0524
Filial Generation				
	N	1130	7714	2178
Left-Handed		177	367	191
	b	.1566	.0476	.0877
Type I Marriages				
LH $\times$ LH	N_1	7	25	11
	X_1	6	7	6
	q_1	.427	.412	.401
Type II Marriages				
LH $\times$ RH	N_2	170	464	174
	X_2	55	53	34
	q_2	.427	.393	.414
Type III Marriages				
RH $\times$ RH	N_3	953	7225	1993
	X_3	116	307	151
	q_3	.425	.401	.439
Best estimate of q		.427	.402	.410

Trankell has extended his theoretical treatment to the case of a dominant which is always expressed when homozygous, but incompletely expressed when heterozygous. He suggests that this model be applied to Hallgren's (1950) data on congenital *dyslexia* (word-blindness). It is too early to evaluate the final usefulness of the "calculus of penetrance" in psychological genetics. Essentially, the theory is related to the threshold concept discussed in Chapter 3 and alternative treatments in terms of multifactorial systems are also possible. In human material it may be impossible to secure crucial observations in favor of one or the other viewpoint.

The Rare Recessive. The methods described thus far are suitable for relatively common genes. When a trait is rare in a population, a general survey of all families is impracticable since most of them will throw no light upon the mode of inheritance. Genetic hypotheses must then be tested by locating trait bearers (known as propositi, probands, index cases) and studying their families. If the trait is dependent upon homozygosity of a rare recessive gene, most of the trait bearers will come from normal parents. According to our usual symbolism, this means that the mating involved is $Aa \times Aa$, and the expected proportion of trait bearers (aa) is one-fourth. However, there will be many families of this genetic composition who will not have an aa child and will not be located for the analysis, although their children should be counted in order to secure a correct genetic ratio. This is particularly true when families are small, but even with a five-child family there is a 23% probability that no aa offspring will be born.

Several methods for overcoming this difficulty have been used in behavior genetics, particularly in testing the heritability of various types of mental deficiency or psychosis. Naturally, the methods of selection of cases, the adequacy of diagnosis of both the propositus and his relatives, and the completeness of the family data are important. The tendency to remember cases which "run in families" and forget the isolated case must be counteracted by procedures of ascertainment which equalize the probability of finding all cases. This may be difficult in practice.

Weinberg's Propositus Method. The propositus is rejected. The family is then counted as many times as it contains persons with the trait under investigation. The value of p (probability that a child of heterozygous parents will be a trait bearer) is given by the formula:

$$(4\text{-}3) \qquad p = \Sigma[x(x - 1)]/\Sigma[x(s - 1)]$$

where $x =$ number of affected persons (including proband) in the family and $s =$ total number of children in families with affected offspring.

Dahlberg illustrates the rationale of this procedure by the following example. Consider 16 marriages of 2 heterozygotes, each producing 2 children. The expectancy of a double recessive for each marriage is 0.25; thus 8 affected children will be produced on the average. However, the most likely distribution by families is: 1 with 2 affected; 6 with 1 affected and 1 normal; and 9 with none affected, hence not available for genetic analysis. The proportion in the 7 families which are available is 8/14 (57.1%).

Data tabulated according to Weinberg's method are presented in Table 4-3.

TABLE 4-3

Weinberg's Propositus Method for Correcting Observed Incidence for Comparison with Expectancy for a Mendelian Recessive Character

Number of Families	Affected Children	Product	Product	Total Children	Product	Product
F	x	$x(x-1)$	$Fx(x-1)$	s	$x(s-1)$	$Fx(s-1)$
1	2	2	2	2	2	2
6	1	0	0	2	1	6
Sums			2			8

Corrected estimate = 2/8 = 0.25, the expected Mendelian ratio.

Dahlberg's Later-Sib Method. In this method the propositus and all earlier sibs are rejected. Once the heterozygous pairs have been located, the proportion of affected offspring gives the Mendelian ratio directly.

Hogben's a Priori and Haldane's a Posteriori Methods. The *a priori* method (Hogben, 1932b) tests the data against an assumed value of the Mendelian ratio, .25, for marriages between two non-trait bearers and .50 for marriages between a trait bearer and a non-trait bearer. The *a posteriori* method (Haldane, 1932) estimates the most likely value for the ratio, making no preliminary assumptions. Although logically different, the mathematical results are the same. We shall describe the somewhat simpler *a priori* method.

If we consider the marriage of two heterozygotes, the probability of an affected child is p, and of an unaffected child q, where $q = 1 - p$. For a simple recessive, $p = \frac{1}{4}$; $q = \frac{3}{4}$. For sibships of various sizes (s), the probabilities of obtaining 1, 2, 3 . . . s affected children are given by the successive terms of the binomial $(p + q)^s$ or $(\frac{1}{4} + \frac{3}{4})^s$ for the simple recessive case. The probability of obtaining no affected children is therefore $1 - q^s$, since q^s (last term of the expansion) is the probability of obtaining all non-affected children. The corrected expected proportion of affected children is $p/(1 - q^s)$. For a two-child sibship with at least one affected child, this equals 0.5714. The expected number of affected children in such sibships is therefore $2 \times 0.5714 = 1.1428$. This procedure corrects for the undetected two-child families of heterozygotes which happen to contain no affected children. The expected total number of affected children $E(a_s)$ in s-sized families is s times the corrected probability, or $E(a_s) = sp/(1 - q^s)$, and for all families:

$$(4\text{-}4) \qquad E(a) = \sum_{s=1}^{s=n} \frac{sp}{1 - q^s} f_s$$

where f_s is the frequency of s-sized families. This formula may be applied to the seven families with affected children which we used as an example in describing Weinberg's method. In this example, $s = 2$, $p = \frac{1}{4}$, $q = \frac{3}{4}$, and $f_s = 7$. Then:

$$\text{Expected no.} = \frac{2 \times \frac{1}{4}}{1 - \frac{9}{16}} \times 7 = 8$$

In an unselected sample of Aa by Aa marriages one would expect only 3.5 affected children from 14 offspring. Hogben's method (and Haldane's) corrects for the missing children in undetected families.

The test of the hypothesis is the comparison of the difference between observed and calculated values in terms of the standard deviation (σ) of the latter. The value of σ is obtained by extracting the square root of the summed variances for each value of s.

$$(4\text{-}5) \qquad \sigma_s{}^2 = \frac{spq}{1 - q^2} - \frac{s^2 p^2 q^2}{(1 - q^2)^2}$$

Tables of $E(a_s)$ and $\sigma_s{}^2$ for common values of p and s are given below.

Correcting Morbidity Rates for Age. A special problem in human genetics concerns the assessment of the true incidence rate of disorders which commence late in life. Suppose one were to count the number of cases of diagnosed schizophrenia in the younger and older siblings of a group of index-case schizophrenics. Almost inevitably one would find a higher case rate in the older siblings who had been exposed for a longer period to the risk of contracting the disease. Without correcting for this factor, no genetic or environmental interpretation is permissible. In any large-scale observation some subjects will die, others disappear from observation, and still others remain in the susceptible age range at the end of the investigation. A thorough

TABLE 4-4

Expected Number of Affected Offspring and Variance for Varying Sizes of Family as Determined by a *Priori* Method, where p is Probability of Affected Offspring
(Hogben, 1932)

Family Size	$p = .5$	σ_s^2	$p = .25$	σ_s^2
2	1.333	0.222	1.1428	0.122
3	1.715	0.490	1.2973	0.263
4	2.134	0.782	1.4628	0.420
5	2.581	1.082	1.6389	0.592
6	3.047	1.379	1.8248	0.776
7	3.527	1.667	2.0196	0.970
8	4.015	1.945	2.2225	1.172

discussion of several techniques for correcting morbidity figures is given by Strömgren (1950) and by Larsson and Sjögren (1954). Only Weinberg's short method will be discussed here. The calculation involves a number of approximations, but, if properly applied, the results are fairly satisfactory.

In Weinberg's method each observation is weighted according to the age at which the individual disappeared from observation. If the age of risk is considered to extend from t_1 years to t_2 years, individuals less than t_1 are weighted zero; those between t_1 and t_2, .5; and those over t_2, 1.0. The corrected morbidity risk q is then:

$$(4\text{-}6) \qquad\qquad q = \frac{f_t}{w_t \cdot n_t}$$

where f_t = frequency in each age class; w_t = weighting factor; and n_t = number of individuals in each age class. In Table 4-5 are computations for a disease with a risk period between 15 and 45 years. It is assumed that individuals 46 years and older who are disease-free will remain so. In this hypothetical example, the corrected risk is exactly twice the observed incidence. Corrections of this type are particularly important when dealing with the inheritance of epilepsy and the psychoses.

INHERITANCE OF QUANTITATIVE TRAITS

The Correlation Method. Members of a family often resemble each other in height, weight, intelligence-test scores, and performance on

TABLE 4-5

Hypothetical Computation of Morbidity Risk by Weinberg's Short Method

Age Class	Cases Observed	Population Size	Weight Factor	Corrected Population Size
	f_t	n_t	w_t	$n_t \times w_t$
0–15	0	1000	0	0
15–45	3	2000	0.5	1000
46+	8	1000	1.0	1000
Sum	11	4000		2000

Corrected morbidity rate $= 11 \div 2000 = .0055$.

objective psychological tests of great variety. In the previous chapter we have considered the nature of the genetic correlation between individuals and have shown how the average correlations between family members can be computed from the principles of genetics. The correlation between parent and offspring is .5, between siblings, .5, between half-siblings, .25, and so on. Extensive tables of genetic correlations may be found in Hogben (1933a) and Charles (1933). Correlations of similar magnitude have been reported for phenotypic traits such as height, weight, and I.Q. In other words, genetic factors could account for the total variance in the important traits just listed. This view was indeed put forward (Fisher, 1918) in the early days of nature-nurture studies.

The flaw in the argument is that families usually share the same environment as well as the same genes. One who knew nothing about genetic mechanisms might conclude that all variance of intelligence was caused by differences in nutrition, in parental vocabulary, or in the availability of books within the family. In animal experiments we can eliminate correlation between genotype and environment by suitable experimental design. In human families we must either guess at the value of heredity-environment correlations or attempt to measure them by comparisons between biological families living together and families with foster children. In its simple form, the correlational technique gives a quantitative value for the degree of resemblance within families, but it is inconclusive with respect to genetic interpretation (Hogben, 1933a). Investigators have turned to studies of twins and to complex analyses of variance (Cattell, 1953, 1957) in an effort to eliminate or statistically estimate the environment-heredity correlations which are the source of confusion.

Twin Methods. Twins may be monozygotic (MZ), derived from the splitting of a single fertilized ovum; or dizygotic (DZ), derived from the fertilization and development of independently formed ova. Triplets and other multiple births may be monozygotic, multizygotic, or combinations of these types. About one of every 70 births in American Negroes and Scandinavians is a twin birth (Neel and Schull, 1954; Strandskov and Edelen, 1946). In Japan the proportion is 1:145. A tendency towards dizygotic twinning appears to be heritable, but this is not true of monozygotic twinning. Monozygotic cotwins share identical sets of genes and are commonly called "identical twins." Actually this is not strictly true, since few traits are determined solely by heredity, and the differences between "identical" twins may become considerable. Dizygotic twins are no more alike genetically than ordinary sibs, and are commonly called fraternal twins. Since DZ twins share a common prenatal environment and usually grow up together, one might expect them to be more alike than siblings born at different times.

Important points regarding twin studies concern the method used to locate the twin pairs and the need for a homogeneous sample of adequate size. All pairs should be drawn from the same population as defined by age, culture, and geographical location. For example, comparisons between MZ pairs of one age and DZ pairs of another are spurious, since age may have important effects on the trait measured. It is best to select a sample from the total registry of twin births and to drop cases only because of unavailability or because of an accident to one member of a pair. Persons who identify themselves as twins in adult life are likely to be those who have maintained close contacts with their cotwins. MZ pairs are more readily recognized by teachers and associates than DZ pairs, and a sample selected by searching a population directly generally contains a relative excess of MZ twins. The twin method is particularly risky when it is used to study the role of heredity in relatively rare conditions. Only a small proportion of twins will be trait bearers, and there is generally a bias towards locating and reporting concordant twins. Sometimes, however, a single case of discordance in MZ twins is reported as an argument against the hereditary determination of a trait. The explanation may, of course, be incomplete penetrance in one twin of a gene which is a necessary but not a sufficient cause of the condition observed.

Twin methods of estimating the importance of heredity in producing individual differences generally depend upon the comparison of trait variance in MZ and DZ pairs. Accurate diagnosis of zygosity is of critical importance. (All unlike-sexed pairs are dizygotic, but such pairs are generally not used in psychological genetics because the sex difference introduces a complication in comparisons with necessarily like-sexed MZ pairs.) In the earliest literature the distinction between twin types was not recognized. When the two types were first separated, diagnosis was based upon degree of resemblance in a large number of physical traits. The method is accurate in the hands of experienced observers, though it is apparent that misclassifications can occur when the traits used as criteria of similarity are subject to environmental influences. Recently, zygosity estimation based upon serological tests has been widely employed. If the parents and siblings of a twin pair are typed with respect to a number of red-blood-cell antigens, the probability that the twins, if they were in fact dizygotic, might have the same blood type can be statistically evaluated. If they are of unlike blood type, dizygosity is proven even though physical resemblance may be strong. Whenever feasible, serological checks on zygosity should be a part of any psychological study of twins. Sometimes evidence regarding zygosity may be obtained from birth records. MZ twins often develop within one set of fetal membranes (chorion) and are classed as monochorionic. DZ twins are always dichorionic. However, a large proportion of MZ pairs (43% in one series; von Verschuer, 1939) develop in separate membranes, so that dichorionic twins cannot be classed as dizygotic without other investigation.

By the definitions we have adopted, all differences between MZ pairs have an environmental origin, while differences between DZ pairs arise from both environmental and genetic sources. In its simplest form the reasoning involved in comparisons of the two twin types is: if DZ pairs are more unlike than MZ pairs the excess is a function of the effect of heredity. This may be symbolically expressed as:

$$D_{dz} = E + H; \qquad D_{mz} = E$$
$$D_{dz} - D_{mz} = H$$

where E, H = differences in environment and heredity respectively
  D_{dz} = difference in score between dizygotic cotwins
  D_{mz} = difference in score between monozygotic cotwins

Methods of treating twin data cover a wide range of statistical procedures, some naive and others highly sophisticated. If the objective of a study is merely to show that heredity has something to do with individual differences, the mathematical form of the function employed to compare twin types is relatively unimportant. Provided one works with an unbiased sample and has a reliable test, one need only show that D_{dz} is significantly larger than D_{mz} to make the case. If the objective is to estimate the relative importance of nature and nurture, more assumptions are required, and the mathematical form of expression becomes important.

We shall examine first the assumptions involved in the simpler problem of determining whether heredity has anything to do with psychological differences between twins (and between people in general). In doing so we shall postulate unbiased sampling of the total twin population, accurate distinction between MZ and DZ pairs, and substantial equivalence of twins and the general population with respect to the trait studied. The last postulate restricts us to traits which are not greatly affected by their being in a twin. All of these requirements can be objectively verified.

A number of sources of "error" have been assumed to diminish D_{mz} as compared with D_{dz}, and thus lead to an overestimation of the importance of heredity (Östlyngen, 1949). MZ pairs tend to be together more and to select similar surroundings and common friends to a greater extent than DZ cotwins. MZ pairs are treated more alike, and may even be confused, by parents and associates. MZ cotwins model their behavior upon each other to a greater extent than DZ cotwins. When comparisons involve ratings by judges, the obvious physical similarity of MZ twins may induce underestimation of psychological differences (halo effect). Likewise the expectation of psychological differences associated with physical differences may lead to overestimation of D_{dz}.

Other possible sources of "error" might enlarge D_{mz} relative to D_{dz}, and result in underestimation of the importance of heredity (Östlyngen, 1949; Price, 1950). The prenatal conditions of monochorionic twins, particularly mutual circulation, may be unfavorable for one cotwin, and result in environmental variation which is unique for MZ pairs. MZ twins have more reversed asymmetries than DZ twins, as is shown by the large proportion of discordance of handedness in MZ pairs. Older MZ twins have been observed to adopt complementary roles in their outside contacts, one serving as spokesman while the other is quiet (von Bracken, 1936). Sometimes rebellion against identification with an identical cotwin leads to adoption of a different role. When judges are rating behavior, the great resemblance between MZ cotwins can lead to picking out minor differences as important (contrast effect). Finally, errors of measurement are more serious when the true difference is small. For example, even if the true D_{mz} were zero, a test with a low reliability would often yield different scores for MZ cotwins. On the other hand, the same unreliable test might serve adequately to distinguish DZ cotwins who were very different from one another.

It is probable that some of the effects listed are unimportant; at any rate the two lists tend to balance each other. Little control is possible over the primary prenatal and natal biases which are part of the process of being a twin. Likewise, it is impossible to keep genetically different DZ cotwins in as close step developmentally as is possible with a pair of MZ twins. The different genotypes of DZ pairs must interact differently with environment, and their responses lead to further differentiation accumulated upon a genotypic base. If monozygotic twins are placed in objectively different environments, it is conceivable that they will select similar parts for attention and effectively reduce the psychological consequences of environmental variability. The important thing is not to stop development in order to obtain pure measures of genetic effects, but to identify the factors which produce differentiation in development. Statistical analysis of twin data can give clues to the nature of these factors, but all hypotheses must be verified by observation and experiment.

Observations on identical twins reared apart represent an attempt to evaluate the plasticity of psychological expression of a single genotype. The differences between twins reared in different families and twins reared together represent the differentiating effects of environment.

Such cases are rare, and when they are found, the two homes in which the cotwins were reared often turn out to be similar in socioeconomic status. However, a series of 20 pairs of separated MZ twins reported by Newman, Freeman, and Holzinger (1937) were less alike than identical twins reared together. Effects of separation were greater upon psychological than physical characteristics.

Instead of using "nature's experiments" on the separation of MZ twins, some psychologists and biologists have used the method of cotwin controls for specific experimental procedures (Gesell, 1942). This method deserves wider use, as it is the equivalent of the use of genetically controlled animals in experimental psychological genetics. A population of MZ twins is selected as subjects, and differential treatment is given to one member of each group. Usually the subjects are young children, and treatments are methods of teaching new skills. However, adult twins show remarkable similarity in sensory and response capacities (Glass, 1954), so that the value of the method is not restricted to children.

Twin Methods, Statistical Aspects. A great variety of mathematical functions have been employed to analyze data from MZ and DZ twins with a view to quantifying the effects of nature and nurture. The attempt is legitimate and, provided the answers obtained are not interpreted as universal laws, laudable. Many of the formulations have no foundation in psychometric theory but provide rough and ready ratios which can be compared for different traits studied. Gottschaldt (1939) used the following expression, which may be interpreted as the ratio of the effects of hereditary and environmental differentiating factors together to environmental factors alone.

(4-7) $$mD_{dz}/mD_{mz} = (E + H + [HE])/(E)$$

where mD_{dz} = mean difference between cotwins in a sample of DZ pairs

mD_{mz} = mean difference between cotwins in a sample of MZ pairs

(E), (H), etc. = functions of environment, functions of heredity

When twins can be classified as trait bearers or non-trait bearers, the percentages of concordance (agreement between members of a pair) in MZ and DZ pairs may be used to give a measure of heritability.

(4-8) $$\text{Heritability} = \frac{C_{mz} - C_{dz}}{100 - C_{dz}}$$

C_{mz} and C_{dz} = percentage of MZ and DZ pairs classified alike with respect to a trait.

Analysis of variance leading to the calculation of an intraclass correlation coefficient is generally employed when the twin data consist of quantitative measurements which cannot be expressed as concordance or discordance (Newman, Freeman, and Holzinger, 1937; Neel and Schull, 1954). The intraclass correlation is defined as:

(4-9) $$r_i = \frac{\Sigma(x_i - a)(y_i - a)}{ns^2} = \frac{\Sigma x_i y_i - (na^2)}{ns^2}$$

where a = mean of all measurements
x_i, y_i = measurements on the ith pair of twins
n = number of pairs
s^2 = variance of total sample about a

It is interpreted as the proportion of the total variance which arises from the fact that the twin pairs differ from each other. The correlation will be 1.0 if cotwins always receive the same score, and 0.0 if cotwins are no more likely to receive the same score than two individuals selected at random. The relationship of r_i to variance may be seen in the following equations:

$$(4\text{-}10) \qquad 1 - r_{mz} = \frac{ns^2 - \Sigma xy + na^2}{ns^2} = \Sigma \frac{(x-y)^2}{2n} \times \frac{1}{s^2}$$

Mean square   Reciprocal
deviation between of total
twin pairs   variance

$$1 - r_{mz} = \sigma_{mz}^2 / \sigma^2$$
$$1 - r_{dz} = \sigma_{dz}^2 / \sigma^2$$

σ^2, σ_{mz}^2, and σ_{dz}^2, symbolize the population variance, the within-pair variance of MZ pairs, and the within-pair variance of DZ pairs. Holzinger's well-known heritability coefficient, H', is:

$$(4\text{-}11) \qquad H' = \frac{r_{mz} - r_{dz}}{1 - r_{dz}} = \frac{\sigma_{dz}^2 - \sigma_{mz}^2}{\sigma_{dz}^2}$$

This coefficient of heritability is not the same as that which we symbolized as h^2 in the previous chapter. Holzinger's ratio gives the proportion of variance produced by genetic differences *within families*. Methods based upon comparison of MZ and DZ intrapair differences underestimate the effects of heredity in the general population by a factor of two. DZ twins have an average genetic correlation of .5, or slightly more if only like-sexed pairs are considered. A more general test of heritability would be to compare intrapair differences of MZ twins with that of unrelated children raised together as twins. To find h^2 one would substitute σ_{ut}^2 for σ_{dz}^2, where σ_{ut}^2 symbolizes the variance of unrelated children raised as twins. Such pairs must, however, be extremely rare.

In Holzinger's formula several assumptions are made. (1) Environmental and genetic variances are additive; (2) MZ and DZ twins have equivalent means and between-pair variances on the trait studied; (3) MZ and DZ pairs are treated nearly enough alike so that environmental differences between cotwins are equal for both types. The first assumption has proven useful in other areas where analysis of variance is employed. Although additivity often cannot be rigorously proved, it provides a starting point from which more refined methods can be derived. The second assumption can be checked readily on the sample chosen. The third has already been discussed, and its validity is a matter of opinion. Perhaps the best judgment is that part of the greater similarity between MZ cotwins comes from the fact that they are treated more alike by parents and associates, but this factor is not great enough to account for the almost universal finding that MZ intrapair differences are significantly less than DZ differences on traits ranging from the number of dermal ridges to Rorshach responses.

Holzinger also devised a ratio to measure the effect of environmental factors. He utilized the intraclass correlations of MZ twins raised together (*mzt*) and apart (*mza*) to compute E'.

$$(4\text{-}12) \qquad E' = \frac{r_{mzt} - r_{mza}}{1 - r_{mza}} = \frac{\sigma^2_{mza} - \sigma^2_{mzt}}{\sigma^2_{mza}}$$

The usefulness of this formula is reduced because of the scarcity of MZ pairs reared apart, though there is evidence that such cases may be more common than has been believed (Shields, 1958; Juel-Nielsen and Mogensen, 1957).

The Multiple-Variance Model. A more general method for determining environmental and hereditary contributions to variance has been developed by Cattell (1953). Research employing these techniques (Cattell et al., 1955, 1957) has also involved another methodological innovation, the use of factor scores rather than test scores to characterize individuals. Although the latter procedure has important psychological implications, the multiple-variance method could be used with test scores instead of factor scores. Therefore, discussion in this chapter will be limited to the methods of genetic analysis.

The total variance of a trait in a particular society may be expressed as σ^2_{so}. This is made up of the sum of genetic and environmental variances plus a correlation term.

$$(4\text{-}13) \qquad \sigma^2_{so} = \sigma^2_g + \sigma^2_e + 2r_{ge}\sigma_g\sigma_e$$

For practical purposes the important hereditary and environmental variances are those within families, σ^2_{wg} and σ^2_{we}, and those between families σ^2_{bg} and σ^2_{be}. The complete expression for the societal variance contains ten terms.

$$(4\text{-}14) \quad \sigma^2_{so} = \sigma^2_{wg} + \sigma^2_{we} + \sigma^2_{be} + \sigma^2_{bg} + r_{wg,we}\sigma_{wg}\sigma_{we} + r_{wg,be}\sigma_{wg}\sigma_{be}$$
$$+ r_{wg,bg}\sigma_{wg}\sigma_{bg} + r_{we,be}\sigma_{we}\sigma_{be} + r_{we,bg}\sigma_{we}\sigma_{bg} + r_{be,bg}\sigma_{be}\sigma_{bg}$$

Some of the correlation terms may properly be dropped because they do not correspond with real situations. For example, there is no reason why deviation from the family mean should be correlated with deviation of the family from the grand mean. Hence, $r_{wg,bg}$ and $r_{we,be}$ can be dropped. The other correlation terms may assume importance through *autogenic* mechanisms—the subject creates a different environment or migrates to it; or through social reaction— other individuals react differently to particular genotypes or isolate them. Racial segregation is an obvious example.

The essential feature of the multiple-variance method is the selection of various types of families whose variances may be considered as combinations of the fundamental variances. These equations are grouped in sets such that solutions for certain variance terms and correlations are possible. One set of family equations and its solution are given here as an example. Other sets may be found in Cattell (1957).

Components of Family Variance

(Identical twins together)

$$(4\text{-}15) \qquad \sigma^2_{ITT} = \sigma^2_{we'}$$

(Siblings together)

$$(4\text{-}16) \qquad \sigma^2_{ST} = \sigma^2_{wg} + \sigma^2_{we} + 2r_{wg,we}\sigma_{wg}\sigma_{we}$$

(Siblings apart, reared in different foster families. The term in parentheses allows for selective placement of genetically different children.)

$$(4\text{-}17) \qquad \sigma^2_{SA} = \sigma^2_{wg} + \sigma^2_{we} + \sigma^2_{be} + 2r_{wg,we}\sigma_{wg}\sigma_{we}(+\ 2r_{wg,be}\sigma_{wg}\sigma_{be})$$

(Unrelated children together)

$$(4\text{-}18) \qquad \sigma^2_{UT} = \sigma^2_{wg} + \sigma^2_{we} + \sigma^2_{bg} + 2r_{wg,we}\sigma_{wg}\sigma_{we} + 2r_{we,bg}\sigma_{we}\sigma_{bg}$$

(Unrelated children apart. The variance of the population determined by taking pairs at random.)

$$(4\text{-}19) \qquad \sigma^2_{UA} = \sigma^2_{wg} + \sigma^2_{we} + \sigma^2_{bg} + \sigma^2_{be} + 2r_{wg,we}\sigma_{wg}\sigma_{we} + 2r_{bg,be}\sigma_{bg}\sigma_{be}$$

Solutions for Fundamental Variances

$$(4\text{-}20) \qquad \sigma_{we} = \sqrt{\sigma^2_{ITT}}$$

$$(4\text{-}21) \qquad \sigma_{be} = \sqrt{\sigma^2_{SA} - \sigma^2_{ST}}$$

$$(4\text{-}22) \qquad \sigma_{wg} = -r_{we,wg}\sqrt{\sigma^2_{ST} + (r^2_{we,wg} - 1)\sigma^2_{ITT}}$$

$$(4\text{-}23) \qquad \sigma_{bg} = \sqrt{\sigma^2_{UT} - \sigma^2_{ST}}$$

$$(4\text{-}24) \qquad r_{be,bg} = 2\,\frac{\sigma^2_{UA} - \sigma^2_{UT} - \sigma^2_{SA} + \sigma^2_{ST}}{\sqrt{\sigma^2_{SA} - \sigma^2_{ST}}\,\sqrt{\sigma^2_{UT} - \sigma^2_{ST}}}$$

The solution of this group involves setting the values of each non-cancelling correlation coefficient at .1 intervals from -1.0 to $+1.0$ and finding which estimate gives the greatest internal consistency among variances which depend and do not depend upon it.

The method of multiple-variance analysis is capable of extension to include many variables of ostensible psychological importance: order of birth, sex of siblings, variations in age of subjects, age of parents, cultural subgroups, and the like. According to Cattell, it is primarily valuable for getting at developmental laws in situations where experimental control is impractical. Potentially, analysis of several diverse family types has more significance for the general nature-nurture problem than the results of twin studies. At the time of writing, only the originator of the method and his colleagues have employed it in psychological research. Further details of procedure and accounts of the derivation of the equations may be found in the cited publications.

Summary. Human genetics has become a specialized science with its own techniques and literature. Methods of studying human heredity have been best developed with respect to traits whose variance depends upon substitutions at a single locus. These are of value to psychological genetics in the investigation of certain sensory anomalies (color blindness, the taster phenomenon) and some types of neurological and psychiatric disorders. The effect of heredity on quantitative traits in man has been studied classically by the method of family correlations, the comparison of intrapair differences in monozygotic and dizygotic twins, and more recently by multiple variance analysis. At present, so-called nature-nurture ratios are not interpreted as universal constants, but as specific for a given population.

5

Variation in sensory and perceptual processes

An organism's capacity to behave adaptively is dependent upon the information collected by its receptors. The superb raptorial equipment of a hawk would be useless in capturing prey if it were not coupled with extraordinary visual acuity. A catfish has degenerate eyes, but taste buds on his body surface enable him to scavenge successfully on the river bottom. Many of the psychological differences between species are understandable in terms of the structure of their sense organs.

Within-species heritable anomalies of sense organs are extremely common in man and his domesticated animals (Roberts, 1940; Gates, 1946; Sorsby, 1953; Grüneberg, 1947). Many of these involve gross deformity or even the absence of a particular organ. In severe conditions such as amaurotic idiocy, there are concurrent anomalies of the central nervous system which directly impair intelligence.

We shall deal only briefly with sensory variations which result from major structural defects. Blindness and deafness have important psychological consequences, but in educational or psychotherapeutic work the genetic or non-genetic etiology of the condition is usually not important. The question of hereditary origin is more important to the genetic counselor who may have to advise on the probability of the trait appearing in siblings or offspring of the afflicted individual. Major emphasis here will be placed upon variations which are known only by their behavioral manifestations or which are most conveniently studied by psychological and psychophysical techniques.

Variations in sensory processes are deduced from behavior which may be a conditioned reflex, a change in rate of bar pressing, or a verbal report. Genetic studies in which the chief interest is the nature of the response itself are described in later chapters. Here we shall deal with researches in which emphasis is placed upon variations in the capacity to discriminate stimuli or in preference for particular stimulus configurations. Such variations may not represent processes limited to sense organs. Many variations in perceptual tests seem as much aspects of personality as of receptor quality. The decision to include some researches here rather than in the chapters dealing with personality has been somewhat arbitrary. In some instances the perceptual data have been summarized without detailing the particular personality theories of the investigators, since the theories were only remotely related to problems of heredity.

Variation in Temperature Preference. When a mouse is placed in an elongated compartment in which a temperature gradient is maintained, his position of rest in the apparatus fluctuates about a position characteristic of the individual and his strain. Herter (1936) used this method to determine the thermotactic optima of three strains of mice. The preferred temperatures of the strains were: gray (laboratory descendants of a wild stock), 37.36 ± 0.12°C.; white (obtained from a dealer in pet stock), 34.63 ± 0.2°C.; and dancing mice, 33.85 ± 0.13°C. The results of crossing the gray (G) and white (W) strains are illustrated in Figure 5-1. The thermotactic optimum of the F_1 was indistinguishable from that of the W parents. In the F_2 and in the backcross to G, segregation into two types of mice with different temperature preferences indicated that the difference was attributable to a single locus with the lower optimum (W type) completely dominant. In crosses between the G strain and dancers, a low thermotactic optimum again appeared to result from a single dominant Mendelian factor.

Anatomical differences between the strains were investigated by Herter (1938) and Herter and Sgonina (1938). They reported that the difference in behavior was not the result of a quantitative difference in sensitivity, but was related simply to the structure of the skin. Mice raised in warm environments had a reduced thermotactic optimum; those reared in cool environments had a higher one. Returning mice to the ordinary laboratory temperature restored their usual thermotactic optimum. Mice reared in a warm place had thinner skins and went to lower temperatures. Differences in the density of the ventral hairs were also found; gray mice had about 80% more hairs per unit area. The behavior of the hybrids was highly correlated with hair density.

In this example the influence of heredity upon behavior seems to be mediated in a straightforward manner through peripheral effects. Structural variation in the skin affects the rate of heat transfer and

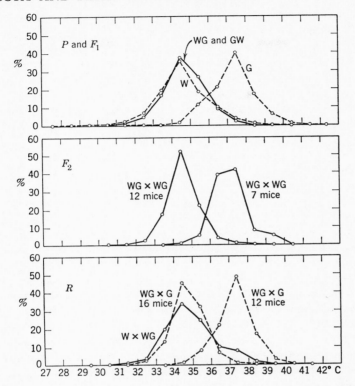

FIGURE 5-1. Thermotactic optima of gray (G) and white (W) mice; their F_1 hybrids WG and GW; the F_2 hybrid (WG $\times$ WG) and a backcross (WG $\times$ G) and (W $\times$ WG). (Herter, 1936.)

modifies the closeness of contact between the external surface and thermal receptors located in the deeper layers of the skin.

Taste Threshold Differences. In 1931, Snyder, Blakeslee, and Salmon independently announced that the inability to taste phenylthiocarbamide (PTC) was inherited as a monofactorial recessive. Snyder's data have already been presented as an example of the way in which Mendelian hypotheses can be tested in human populations (page 99). The stimulus for these researches had been provided by the accidental discovery (Fox, 1932) that the characterization of PTC in the chemical literature as "bitter tasting" could not be verified by all members of the laboratory staff.

Blakeslee and Fox (1932) and Setterfield, Schott, and Snyder (1936), using more precise methods, showed that "tasters" and "non-tasters" differ quantitatively rather than absolutely. The distribution of taste acuity is, however, distinctly bimodal, and there is no doubt that a major cause of individual differences is a recessive gene. The method of testing does influence the point at which the two phenotypes are separated, and thus slightly alters the proportion of tasters detected. The inaccuracy is not great, since very few individuals have taste thresholds for PTC in the intermediate range. Dry crystals, filter paper impregnated with PTC, and test solutions sampled through straws have all been used in surveys. The technique of Harris and Kalmus (1949) appears most adequate, though it is too complex for large-scale field investigations desirable for population genetics. Subjects are given a few cubic centimeters of test solution in a glass. The concentration is gradually raised until a positive response is given. A confirmatory test requires that the subject separate correctly eight glasses, four containing water and four the test concentration of PTC. Barnicot's data (1950) were obtained with this method (Figure 5-2). Large racial differences in the frequency of the non-taster gene are apparent. The use of threshold determination methods has also shown that young people are more sensitive to PTC and that women have lower thresholds than men. These effects are superimposed upon the effects of the "taster gene."

The non-taster of PTC is not deficient in general taste acuity. Blakeslee and Fox (1932) and Blakeslee and Salmon (1935) showed that the thresholds of a variety of substances, bitter, sweet, sour, and salty, varied unpredictably among individuals. There was little correlation between thresholds for different substances all classed as bitter. To Blakeslee this meant that "we live in different taste worlds." The inheritance of the ability to taste diphenyl-guanidine was reported as an independent trait by Snyder and Davidson (1937), and Barrows (1945) found that the ability to taste brucine was also inherited.

The PTC deficiency does extend to a number of related compounds, and the degree of chemical specificity has been investigated by a number of workers (Fox, 1932; Hopkins, 1942; Harris and Kalmus, 1949; Barnicot, Harris and Kalmus, 1951). The critical configuration seems to be $=N-C-$, and sensitivity to all compounds containing this

$$\underset{S}{\overset{\|}{}}$$

structure is strongly correlated with the ability to taste PTC. Fox (1932) showed that solubility was essential for tasting and hypothesized that the saliva of non-tasters contained some substance which reacted with PTC and rendered it insoluble. Cohen and Ogden (1949) stated

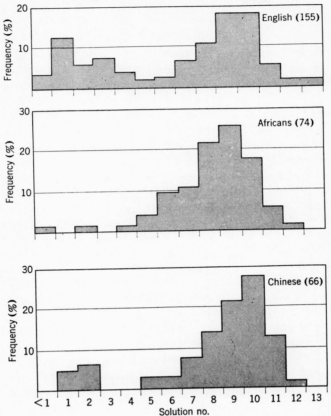

FIGURE 5-2. Taste thresholds for PTC in English males, Africans, and Chinese. Solution 1 is 0.13% PTC; each succeeding solution is one-half the concentration of the preceding. Bimodality of taste acuity is clearly shown in the English and Chinese samples. (Barnicot, 1950.)

that tasters could not detect PTC dissolved in saliva of non-tasters, or even in the saliva of other tasters. Only when PTC was dissolved in the subject's own saliva was a response elicited. The reasons for this astounding specificity are not clear.

The frequency of the taster gene varies in different populations (Cohen and Ogden, 1949; Boyd and Boyd, 1937; Boyd, 1951). If the most accurate methods are used, the percentage of non-tasters in north European populations is found to be about 32% (Denmark, Mohr, 1952). In non-Europeans it is much less.

An association of the non-taster trait with diabetes was reported by

Terry and Segall (1947), Segall (1948), and Terry (1948). This was not verified in the survey of Harris, Kalmus, and Trotter (1949). As Boyd states (1950), "A gene exists which enables its possessor to taste a synthetic substance not known to occur in nature. It is not too easy to understand how such a gene can exist or to guess what its function can be." He suggests that since the ability to taste certain antithyroid substances parallels the ability to taste PTC, the gene might protect against an excess of such substances in the diet.

The existence of different taste worlds seems adequately proved. Whether the various specific thresholds are each genetically determined; the extent to which thresholds are modified by age and by training; the possibility of polygenic determination of taste acuity: all these are questions which have been relatively neglected.

Taste Differences in Animals. Fish and Richter (1946) found that domestic rats had about 18% fewer fungiform papillae on their tongue than did wild rats. They suggested that this might be related to more stringent selection for acuity of taste in the wild variety, but no physiological or genetic data were presented.

Olfaction. Little research has been done on the genetics of olfactory acuity. In breeds of dogs selected for tracking ability, one finds enlarged nasal cavities, and it is reasonable to expect that olfactory sensitivity is also increased. Nevertheless, we know of no data comparing the olfactory thresholds of dog breeds. Temperamental qualities and the ability to learn fine discriminations may be more important in tracking than olfactory acuity *per se*.

The neglect of research on the genetics of olfaction probably arises from the more urgent need to understand the general mechanism of odor reception. A report of individual variation in sensitivity to the odor of verbenas (Blakeslee, 1918) was apparently not followed up by genetic studies. Glaser (1918) and Mainland (1945) have reported small pedigrees of anosmia. Glaser's pedigree is compatible with a sex-linked recessive mode of inheritance or an autosomal dominant with incomplete penetrance. The condition in Mainland's family appears to be caused by an autosomal dominant.

It is possible that a search for individual variations in olfactory ability combined with genetic studies might provide a key to many physiological puzzles. This approach has been very successful in the area of color vision. The occurrence of specific genetic lesions affecting color vision has facilitated psychophysical analysis. Possibly genes which produce analogous partial deficiencies in olfaction will prove useful in studying this elusive sensory modality.

Visual Functions in Man. An organ whose functioning is dependent upon precise correlated growth of many parts is extremely susceptible to environmental and genetic influences. An entire book has been published upon genetics in ophthalmology (Sorsby, 1951). The author makes the point that as standards of communicable disease control have improved, the importance of heredity as a factor in blindness has increased. In Liverpool in 1791 two-thirds of the applicants for admission to an institution for the blind were victims of smallpox. By 1951, smallpox had been eliminated from England. At the same institution, 21% of the patients at that time had blindness attributable to hereditary effects as contrasted with 44% associated with degenerative changes of age. However, the hereditary conditions accounted for more expected years of blindness and presented more serious educational problems.

We shall not attempt a catalog of the varieties of heritable eye anomalies of clinical importance (see Sorsby, 1951, 1953). The effects of visual handicaps upon intellectual and personality characteristics have been summarized by Anastasi (1958a, page 142). Provided there is no brain damage, intellectual retardation in properly educated blind children is not exceptionally large, and the average I.Q. seems to be about 90. The partially sighted child often has a more severe psychological handicap than the visually uneducable child. The state of the medical arts has a great deal to do with the classification of an individual. Before the invention of eyeglasses a child with severe inherited myopia would be greatly handicapped, but today he may have essentially normal vision.

The eye as an optical device is somewhat less precisely constructed than a fine camera. The refractory power of the cornea and lens varies considerably among individuals. There is a significant excess of severe myopia beyond that to be expected on the basis of a homogeneous population. This is evidence that specific genes are responsible for the extreme deviants. A more direct estimate of heritability of optometric constants has been provided by Hofstetter (1948) and Hofstetter and Rife (1953). In the first study the accommodative convergence index was determined by the author in 30 pairs of identical twins between 10 and 35 years of age. This index is the change of convergence of the lines of sight of the two eyes when accommodating for near vision. Only twins with 20/20 vision (correction by glasses was allowed) were selected. The intraclass correlation of .67 is significant at the .001 level and demonstrates a high degree of genetic determination. In the second paper of the series, data obtained from

27 MZ and 12 DZ pairs of twins were summarized. Tests were conducted by students in a school of optometry, and this multiplicity of testers undoubtedly produced some inaccuracy. MZ twins were much more alike than DZ pairs in interpupillary distance and errors of refraction. No significant difference was found in astigmatism or in accommodative convergence. The failure to confirm Hofstetter's earlier result is probably due to less experienced observers. The importance of heredity in determining the efficiency of the eye as an optical instrument is clear.

Genetic studies have played an important part in the development of theories of color vision. Red-green color blindness has been for years the most popular example in description of sex-linked inheritance. However the physiological and genetic situation is more complex than was indicated in Chapter 2. Red-green color blindness is not a unitary character but can be divided into at least four phenotypes on the basis of tests in which combinations of red ($\lambda = 665.6$ mμ) and green ($\lambda = 537.3$ mμ) are matched against yellow ($\lambda = 589.3$ mμ). For normal individuals the balance is attained at a rather uniform point. Protanopes ("red blind") can match like normals but can also match intensified yellow with green alone or reduced yellow with red alone. Protanomalous ("partially red blind") individuals cannot match at the normal equivalence point but report that the mixture is green. More red must be added to obtain balance. Deuteranopes ("green blind") can match yellow with red or green over a narrow range of intensities. Deuteranomalous ("partially green blind") individuals require additional green to match the standard.

Waaler (1927) showed in a survey of over 18,000 school children in Oslo that the same types of color blindness were found repeatedly in related individuals. He postulated that protanomaly and protanopia were due to alleles recessive to the normal allele which contributes something to the red-seeing system. Deuteranopia and deuteranomaly were shown to be expressions of alleles, probably at separate loci, but closely linked. Brunner (1930) and Franceschetti (1949) have confirmed Waaler's work in general and found evidence for intermediate conditions, extreme protanomaly and extreme deuteranomaly.

The critical test for the separation of the two allelic systems requires a woman who is heterozygous for both a protanoid and a deuteranoid effect. If the theory is correct, such a woman would have normal color vision, all her sons would be color blind, and two types of color blindness should be demonstrable among them. According to Walls (1955) four cases of double heterozygosity in women have been described in the literature, and three had normal color vision.

The fourth (Hylkema, 1943) was totally color blind, but Walls (*vide infra*) explains this in terms of his theory of a special action of the genes in some heterozygotes. Additional cases have been found by Franceschetti and Klein (1957).

Walls (1955; see also Walls and Mathews, 1952) has utilized data on the chromatic and brightness vision of protanoids and deuteranoids to construct a comprehensive color-vision scheme. His point of view is that each kind of hereditary defective color-vision system represents a normal system minus something, and that each may be considered as an experiment from which one can deduce the properties of the normal system. This approach is familiar in physiology, where it is hard to conceive of a science of endocrinology or neurology developed without the aid of surgical extirpation. Walls' hypothesis is derived from biochemical extirpations produced by mutant human genes.

Walls's scheme for normal color vision is shown in Figure 5-3. His original papers deal with the experimental argument for this theory. According to its originator, it provides an explanation for the different effects of color blindness (and various experimental procedures) upon brightness and chromaticity. A protanope, for example, is assumed

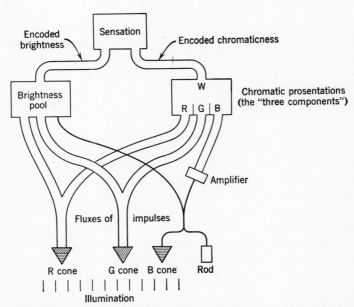

FIGURE 5-3. A schema for normal color vision based on data from color-blind subjects, an example of using genetic lesions to interpret normal functions. (Walls, 1955.)

to lack the R-cone system (sensitive to long wavelengths) and their associated paths to the brightness and chromaticity centers. A deuteranope has only G and R cones sensitive to long wavelengths, but not to short ones. Other rare anomalies of color vision can also be fitted into the hypothesis, including tritanopia (all chromaticity missing), which is inherited as an autosomal recessive.

Perhaps the most interesting part of Walls' hypothesis pertains to the effect in women of color-blindness genes in the heterozygous state. Some 5% of men are deuteranomalous and about 3% are deuteranopic, protanomalous, or protanopic in approximately equal proportions. Since women have two X-chromosomes while men have only one, it can be calculated that about 16% of all women are carriers of a color-vision defect gene. Most deuteranoid carriers cannot be distinguished as individuals, though as a group they show a statistical deviation in brightness sensitivity. Most protanoid carriers are seriously defective in brightness sensitivity to long waves, though their color vision is normal (Schmidt's sign). This is explained by postulating a central effect of the gene in the heterozygote; the contribution of the R cones to chromaticity remains, but their action upon the brightness center is impaired.

An especially interesting use of a genetic lesion is Graham and Hsia's (1958) study of a woman with unilateral deuteranopia. Genetics here must have been assisted by some unknown factor in development. From data acquired with this subject, who was able to compare colors seen with her normal and affected eye, the authors hypothesize that in the color-blind eye the sensitivities of the red and green receptors become similar while no change takes place in the central brain connections. Whatever the ultimate nature of theories of color vision, it is certain that the genetic lesions will contribute crucial evidence. The effects of color-blindness genes seem to be more extensive than interference with specific photoreceptive systems in the retina. To some extent the central nervous system appears to be involved. This is also strikingly shown when complex perceptual functions are studied from the genetic point of view.

Visual Perception. Much of the work on visual perception has been motivated by the idea that afterimages, flicker fusion, and susceptibility to illusions are valid indices of personality. Proof of the heritability of such functions has been sought in order to provide evidence for the importance of genetic influences upon personality. We shall not here enter into the argument regarding the validity of perceptual differences as personality measures. Instead the data will be presented as evidence for or against the heritability of perceptual differences. Most investigators have compared MZ and DZ twins. The major deficiency in the studies is the failure to determine possible effects of prior experience upon simple perceptions.

von Bracken (1939) tested 7 MZ pairs, 12 DZ pairs of like sex, and 8 of unlike sex with respect to the apparent size of afterimages. Subjects fixated on a 5-cm. red square on a neutral background for 30 seconds, then judged the size of the afterimage by "projecting" the afterimage to screens at greater or lesser distances than the fixation distance. MZ pairs were as variable as DZ pairs.

Smith (1949) carried out two series of tests on afterimage size. MZ pairs were more alike than DZ pairs when afterimages were projected upon screens at 50 and 200 cm. after fixation at 100 cm. The intraclass correlations for the MZ pairs on four tests were .71, .68, .98, .75; and for DZ pairs, .08, .00, .22, and .23. Not all attributes of afterimage formation seemed to be affected by heredity. The effective duration of the images was as variable between MZ pairs as between DZ pairs.

The eidetic-imagery indices of 13 male and 19 female MZ twins were more alike within pairs than those of 16 male and 13 female DZ twins. Imagery tests were conducted with a variety of complex visual stimuli such as pictures with large colored areas, and the degree of image persistence was determined by the subject's report. A composite eidetic score was calculated from the sum of several tests. Each stimulus was presented with and without intermittence (slight flicker). The MZ pairs averaged higher, probably because there were more girls in the sample, and eidetic imagery is stronger in females. The intraclass correlations are presented in Table 5-1.

TABLE 5-1

Eidetic Imagery in Monozygotic and Dizygotic Twins (Smith, 1949)

Conditions of Test	Intraclass Correlations	Significance
Eidetic index without intermittence:	$r_{MZ} = .496$	$p < .01$
	$r_{DZ} = .099$	$p > .2$
Eidetic index with intermittence:	$r_{MZ} = .657$	$p < .001$
	$r_{DZ} = .150$	$p > .2$
Difference between intermittence and no intermittence:	$r_{MZ} = .672$	$p < .001$
	$r_{DZ} = .050$	$p > .2$

Eysenck and Prell (1951) determined the frequency of critical flicker fusion in 25 MZ and 24 like-sexed DZ pairs. The intraclass correlations corrected for age were: $r_{MZ} = .705$, $r_{DZ} = .209$, giving a Holzinger H (heritability) value of .627.

The well-known Müller-Lyer illusion has been observed in twins (von Bracken, 1939; Smith, 1953). von Bracken adjusted the distance of the >—< figure until it was judged equal to the ↔ figure, whose center portion was objectively of the same length. The results were presented in terms of the average intratwin differences in estimations of length in millimeters (Table 5-2). The results with twins of unlike sex do not support the theory of hereditary determination of susceptibility to the illusion.

TABLE 5-2

Twin Responses to Müller-Lyer Illusion
(von Bracken, 1939)

	Type of Twin		
	MZ	DZ	DZ
		Like Sex	Unlike Sex
Number of pairs	16	11	12
Starting point "too long"	.43 mm.	.54 mm.	.29 mm.
Starting point "too short"	.46 mm.	.52 mm.	.36 mm.

Smith's study of the Müller-Lyer illusion was much more complex and emphasized serial analysis of the data. With continued exposure the illusion is less marked. This is consistent with Smith's belief that "peristatico-stability" is to be found in development and not in level of achievement. "Peristatico-stable" functions are roughly equivalent to environment-insensitive or endogenous functions which are little affected by ordinary environmental fluctuations.

Four series of tests on the Müller-Lyer illusion were given to 19 MZ and 22 like-sexed DZ twin pairs. Twins familiar with the illusion were not used. The subject could control the length of a straight line placed between the two Müller-Lyer figures and was required to alternately match its length with the right- and left-hand design. Ten trials on each design comprised each series. Conditions of each series were as follows:

Series	Left-Hand Design	Right-Hand Design	Instructions
1	←——————→	>——————<	"Work naturally"
2	·———————·	·——————·	"Try to imagine the oblique lines"
3	←——————→	>——————<	"Try to disregard the oblique lines"
4	←——————→	>——————<	"Work naturally and rapidly"

Intraclass correlations were calculated for the extent of errors of judgment under each set of conditions, and the results are summarized in Table 5-3. Intrapair differences for MZ twins were consistently less, but the significance of the differences is questionable.

TABLE 5-3

Twin Resemblance in Susceptibility to Müller-Lyer Illusion as Shown by Intraclass Correlations (Smith, 1953)

Series	MZ	DZ	Significance of Difference
1	.53	.39	n.s.
2	.55	.05	.05
3	.51	.37	n.s.
4	.57	.28	n.s.

When a measure of the change of the illusion with time was computed, greater MZ, DZ differences were found, as is shown in Table 5-4.

TABLE 5-4

Twin Resemblance in Müller-Lyer Illusion as Measured by Changes with Repeated Trials on Same Stimulus (Intraclass Correlations)

Stimulus	MZ	DZ	Significance of Difference
Left-hand design (1)	.61	.06	.05
Right-hand design (2)	.20	−.26	n.s.
(1) + (2)	.32	−.42	.01
(2) − (1)	.62	.12	.05

Smith concludes: "It seems advisable not to confine heredity-psychological investigations to traditional performance-level scores. . . . The concept of heredity in psychology must be looked upon as basically developmental." The developmental concept may apply to periods as short as an experimental test session or as long as the life span.

Other illusions have been studied in twins. Eysenck and Prell (1951) found that MZ twins were more alike in the autokinetic response. Intraclass correlations corrected for age were: MZ, .722; DZ, .210. Subjects were instructed to fixate on a stationary light and describe what they saw. If movement was reported, subjects traced the path and were scored by the length of line drawn. von Bracken (1939) required individuals to judge, with their heads laterally inclined, the perpendicularity of an illuminated straight line in a dark room. Errors of estimation are common in this situation (Aubert's illusion). Results were similar to those of his afterimage study. Unlike-sexed twins were most alike in response, a result which has no genetic significance.

Malan's (1940) experiment on spatial orientation in twins is not concerned with an illusion, but is similar in concept and methods. Subjects were oriented toward a light at a distance of about eight meters. They were then blindfolded and led away at various angles or in curved paths. At the end of each course they were required to point out the position of the light while still blindfolded and to make their way back to the starting point. A representative sample of Malan's data has been reassembled in Table 5-5. Monozygotic twins were consistently more similar in response.

TABLE 5-5

Spatial Orientation in 40 MZ and 40 DZ Twin Pairs (Malan, 1940)

Nature and Length of Path	Percent of Pairs with Large* Intrapair Difference		Significance of MZ, DZ Difference
	MZ	DZ	
Straight path to right, 2.6 m.	10	55	.001
Straight path to left, 2.6 m.	15	52	.001
Straight path to right, 4.6 m.	15	50	.001
Convex path, 4.0 m.	22	48	.02

* The size of a "large" deviation in degrees varied from test to test. In general, about one-third of all pairs had "large" differences.

Hereditary Deafness. Many types of deafness are inherited in simple fashion, and even deafness ascribed to infection may be more common in individuals inheriting a predisposing anatomical peculiarity (Lindenov, 1953). Many choreic mutants in the housemouse are deaf (Grüneberg, 1952), and hereditary deafness is found in dogs (Burns, 1952) and cats (Castle, 1940, page 157). We have been unable to locate reports of experiments on the inheritance of auditory acuity or discrimination in animals. The immense labor of training enough subjects to permit genetic analysis of individual differences has discouraged the efforts of scientists. Deafness, whether genetic or traumatic, has well-recognized psychological consequences in man. These have been discussed by Anastasi (1958a).

Auditory Discrimination. Several studies on auditory discrimination have been motivated by an interest in discovering an innate basis for musicality. Pitch discrimination is obviously valuable to a musician, though many other attributes are needed to make a fine performer or composer. Seashore developed a number of simple tests which were supposed to measure primary abilities essential for musicianship. The tests have been criticized with respect to their validity as predictors of musicality, but this does not necessarily detract from their value as indicators for genetic studies.

Stanton (1922) gave the Seashore tests of pitch, intensity, time, and interval discrimination to the families of six famous musicians. The basis of her sampling was obviously too narrow, but a larger-scale population survey might yield material of genetic value.

F. Mjoen (1925) administered a pitch discrimination test to a group of parents and offspring. His sample, too, was not representative, since the majority of parents were superior when compared with norms for a large test sample. He found, however, a strong correlation between midparent scores and children's scores. There is some dispute about the effects on the test scores of musical training and exposure to music. Seashore stated that practice had little effect (20 days of drill produced no improvement); the drill, however, may have been too late or of the wrong kind. Mjoen, like Stanton, proposed that pitch discrimination had a simple genetic basis, but this need not be taken seriously today.

A review of "absolute pitch" by Neu (1947) cites much evidence for the acquisition of pitch discrimination by training. He justifiably hits hard at the notion that a sense of absolute pitch (the ability to name tones when sounded) is an inherent faculty or quality determined by a particular gene or constellation of genes developing *in vacuo*. The tone, however, if not the exact words, of Neu's review implies that heredity is a static factor whose work is finished when an organism is born. Equal training in pitch discrimination might produce greater individual differences in pitch discrimination than no training. The possible genetic determinants of auditory discrimination must be sought by methods which will detect developmental processes. Rife (personal communication) has good evidence of MZ twin similarities on the Seashore pitch-discrimination test. It is likely that other investigations using adequate techniques would detect genetic effects upon auditory perception.

The most complex auditory discrimination which has attracted the attention of geneticists is "tune deafness" (Kalmus, 1949). Fifty characteristic phrases from songs popular in England and widely known were played on a record to each subject. Some were played correctly, others incorrectly. A score, $3 \times$ (wrong judged correct) − (correct judged wrong) gave a bimodal distribution in a school population. Tune deafness defined in this manner segregated in families and sib pairs in such a way as to suggest that much of the variation might be due to a single locus. The inheritance of simple musical memory has also been suggested by Ashman (1952).

Heredity and Sensory Preferences. Stimuli have several distinct functions in behavior. Sometimes they serve as cues to direct activity enabling an organism to maximize the probability of reinforcement. At other times stimuli simply arouse or alert an organism without affecting any particular behavior pattern. Heredity is unlikely to play much part in these functions aside from effects attributable to deficiencies in receptors. Organisms learn the pertinent cues in their surroundings; they are aroused by intense, unusual, or specifically meaningful stimuli.

Reinforcement is also a property of stimuli. Organisms behave so as to maximize (or sometimes to minimize) the probability of receiving certain stimuli. Often reinforcing stimuli are internal and contingent upon the composition of the blood or the distension of the viscera. One point of view is that all reinforcing properties of stimuli depend ultimately upon their association with the satisfaction of tissue need (Miller, 1957). Carried to its logical extreme, reinforcement must then be defined by the biochemist rather than the psychologist. If this is true, genetic variation in reinforcing properties of stimuli must be limited, for tissue needs are much the same in all organisms. Individual variation in appetites associated with all sensory modalities must then be considered as secondary to association of stimuli with metabolic processes. However, considerable evidence has accumulated that many stimuli have reinforcing properties which are not contingent upon biological needs (Harlow, 1953). In fact, possibly all stimuli may be considered to have reinforcing properties, although satiation (habituation) may be very rapid for many of these. Such a view of the general reinforcing properties of stimuli affords much scope for genetic variation, both within modalities ("sensory preference") and between modalities ("sensory dominance").

A fourth function of stimulation is the elicitation of specific behavior as exemplified by the "releasers" of the ethologists (Lorenz, 1935). The gaping reaction in young gulls is elicited by a variety of models shaped roughly like a bird's head with a dark spot at the base of the "bill" (Tinbergen and Perdeck, 1950). Models can be arranged in order of their capacity to elicit the gaping response. It is quite apparent that this attribute of stimuli differs between species. Puppies do not gape when presented with models of a gull's head, nor do gulls congregate about a bitch in heat. The extent of genetic differences within species with respect to the eliciting function of stimuli has been little studied. Some pertinent material will be found in our discussion of courtship and mating.

Sensory Preference. DaCunha et al. (1951) found that various subspecies of Drosophila were differentially attracted to various species of yeasts. They suggested that food preferences might lead to assortative mating and thus function in species formation. The experiment was conducted in the field, and experiential effects on food preference could not be excluded, since the previous history of the wild specimens was unknown.

In a laboratory experiment Mayer et al. (1951) offered genetically obese mice a choice of foods in cafeteria style. They found that obese animals (*ob/ob*) selected more fat than their (+/+) or (+/*ob*) littermates. Fuller and Jacoby (1955) compared the food intake of obese and non-obese mice on a stock diet and on stock diet diluted with cellulose, made bitter with quinine, and more palatable (to mice) by the addition of fat. They found similar food preferences in both kinds of mice. Obese mice ate more fat, but this could be accounted for by a defect in the mechanism which stops eating when caloric needs are met.

The extent to which "private taste worlds," to use Blakeslee's provocative phrase, determine human food preference is unknown. Boyd (1950) has suggested that the taster gene protects its possessors against antithyroid substances similar to PTC which occur in certain plants. Otherwise, Blakeslee's lead does not seem to have been taken up by sensory psychologists or physiologists.

Visual color preferences in poultry were investigated by Ermisch

(1936). He noted that hens of northern (Nordic) races tended to eat first from dishes of short wave colors; hens of southern races preferred food from dishes of long wave colors. His paper is interesting in its use of Nazi racial concepts in comparative psychology.

Luth (1935) studied color-form dominance in visual perception. He observed 64 children in 19 families and some unrelated individuals. Eight stimuli were presented tachistoscopically, each a geometric form on a colored background. Subjects were simply directed to report what they saw, and their reports were scored on the basis of both color and form. In other experiments, subjects were required to select the best match of a stimulus which could only be matched with respect to color or form, not with both. The data were inadequately analyzed, but family differences were shown. The primary objective of Luth's experiment was to find objective evidence for Kretchmer's personality types. A more empirical approach with better genetic methods might yield interesting results.

Habitat Preferences. In nature every species is found within a more or less limited set of environmental conditions. For mobile animals the choice of a habitat is an active process. Survival is dependent upon adequate responses to environmental factors. Organism-environment interactions are the domain of ecology, and they have some interest for the evolutionist. If mutations can effect changes in habitat selection, they could lead to genetic isolation, which is an important factor in evolution. In the field, both genetic and environmental factors fluctuate so widely that controlled studies are impossible. Hence evidence that genes can influence habitat choice has been sought in the laboratory. The response of being in a particular place is taken as an indication that the corresponding constellation of environmental factors is discriminated as more comfortable than the other choices. When experiments are carried out for a prolonged period, provision is made in all environments for the biological needs of the species. In principle these experiments are similar to those of Herter (1936) on thermotactic preferences, but discrimination is made to a complex group of stimuli which may span several modalities.

An example of this approach is the work of Waddington et al. (1954) on environment selection by Drosophila mutants. Seven different stocks were allowed choice of access to eight environments, which consisted of all possible combinations of three alternative pairs of attributes, humid-dry, cold-warm, and light-dark. Substantial differences were found. Purple and apricot stocks were strongly attracted to light, whereas aristaless and black were slightly influenced by this modality. Rough and apricot favored the dry environment, whereas all others spent more time in the humid chambers. The authors point out that such preferences would lead to a stable polymorphism if there were some migration between subpopulations in which selection was proceeding in opposite directions. If the separation on the basis of sensory preference were more complete, evolution might lead to quite divergent species.

The experiments of Harris (1952) on habitat preference in the deer-mouse, Peromyscus, also involve many sensory modalities. Laboratory-reared specimens of two subspecies, *P. maniculatus bairdii* and *P. m. gracilis,* were offered an opportunity to select between two artificial habitats, one simulated forest, the other simulated grass lands. Food, water, and an activity wheel were present in both habitats. In nature, *bairdii* is a meadow species and *gracilis* a frequenter of woodlands. In the laboratory the indices of selection, food and water intake and rotation of the activity wheels, showed a carryover of the natural habitat preference (Figure 5-4). Selection was not impaired in darkness or when vibrissae were removed or when the positions of the environments were exchanged. When an intermediate "jungle" environment was matched against the "forest" and "grass lands," results

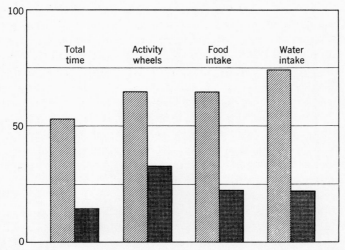

FIGURE 5-4. Four measures of habitat preference in *Peromyscus maniculatus gracilis* (oblique shading) and *P. m. bairdii* (cross-hatched). The height of each column represents the percentage of activity taking place in the "tree" habitat; the remaining activity occurred in the "grass" habitat. (Drawn from data of Harris, 1952.)

were ambiguous. They suggested, however, that *gracilis* was positively attracted to "trees" and *bairdii* to "grass," rather than repelled by the opposite.

Summary and Discussion. Sensory and perceptual processes are generally more alike in related individuals. Heritability is not limited to anatomical defects (blindness, deafness), or to chemical defects (color blindness), but is found less clearly in more-complex perceptual processes. Few studies, however, have been carried out with adequate controls for environmental effects.

It has been claimed that heritability can be more readily demonstrated for the time course of an illusion than for the strength of the illusion at a given instant. Psychogenetic investigations in this area should ideally be longitudinal studies of individual differences, not single measures at an arbitrarily selected time. Such research is needed to counter the argument that the improvement by training of an ability such as pitch discrimination disproves the significance of heredity. It is equally conceivable that training increases rather than decreases the difference between genotypes. It may be hoped that current longitudinal twin studies will include a variety of sensory and perceptual measures.

Another possibility is that mass-screening methods such as the method described by Hirsch and Tryon (1956) will make it feasible to broaden behavior-genetic investigations in animals to include the heritability of differences in discrimination. Methods which require laborious individual training are unsuitable to behavior genetics, and progress in this area must await the development of suitable techniques.

6

Response processes

This chapter is concerned with a rather heterogeneous collection of studies on diverse aspects of behavior in many species. For convenience the material has been divided into "simple" and "complex" sections, although this classification does not imply any fundamental difference in the level of organization at which gene action occurs. The common feature of the research reported here is a concern with reflexes, taxes, physiological variation, or deviant motor activity. The investigation of such responses has been predominantly the domain of biologists rather than psychologists. One might expect such responses to have simpler relationships to genes than do general traits like intelligence and temperament. If so, they would have especial importance for behavior genetics. This expectation is sometimes verified, but there is no reason to assume that behavioral and genetic complexity always run in parallel. Perhaps the most important generalization to be drawn from the variety of studies summarized here is the ubiquity of genetic effects. Quantitative measurement of behavior combined with genetic techniques finds an influence of heredity in insects, rats, and men, both in behavior which is relatively unmodifiable in pattern and in behavior which is the outcome of a long period of development under specified conditions.

SIMPLE RESPONSES

Circling and Choreic Behavior. A considerable number of "behavior mutants" have been described in mammals and birds. The inheritance of these conditions has always proved to be of the monohybrid type. In those cases which have been thoroughly investigated, lesions of the nervous system have been found associated with the behavioral anomaly. Some of these mutations reduce viability so that the affected class of offspring is numerically deficient or shows impaired life span.

Others affect motor responses without serious effects on general health.

Behavior mutants are generally characterized by circling or choreic behavior, sometimes of an epileptiform character. Although these deviant types are known in many species, our main discussion will be confined to the mouse, *Mus musculus*. This species has been most extensively investigated and will illustrate general principles. Much of our account has been drawn from Grüneberg (1952), who may be consulted for references to original sources and for a more detailed description of the anatomical findings.

The Japanese waltzing or dancing mouse has been maintained for years by animal fanciers as a curiosity. In 1907 Yerkes published a descriptive study of this variety which is still useful. Some of the conflicting literature which he cited was undoubtedly the outcome of confusion between waltzing and other genes which produce similar phenotypes. Waltzers are characterized by a syndrome of peculiarities, running in tight circles, head shaking, deafness, lack of rotational dizziness, and inability to balance on an edge or slanting surface. All of these symptoms point to a defect in the vestibular and cochlear apparatus, and this is confirmed by histological examination. Cerebral degeneration has also been reported, but it is not clear whether this is primary or secondary. Waltzers are delicate mice, and in breeding experiments one finds a deficiency of the homozygous recessives.

A number of other genes produce the shaker-circling syndrome, more or less faithfully mimicking *waltzing*. Considerable ingenuity has been expended in selecting such appropriate names as *shaker-1, shaker-2, jerker, pirouette, kreisler, fidget, shaker-short,* and *shaker with syndactylism*. All are monohybrid recessives, and many have been placed in known linkage groups. In all but fidget, deafness is reported as part of the syndrome. In shaker-short and shaker with syndactylism a non-neural structural anomaly accompanies the nervous-system defect. Presumably all of these genes interfere with some metabolic process important to central nervous-system maturation. Shaker-1 is reported to show some summation of effects with waltzer (*v*). Mice with the formula sh-$1/+$, $v/+$ are said to be deaf although otherwise normal (Lord and Gates, 1929).

Another series of mutations in mice is characterized by convulsive seizures at some stage in development in addition to neuromuscular abnormalities. The seizures occur with minimal stimulation and are distinct from the audiogenic seizures described below. Such colorful terms as *varitint-waddler, trembler, wabbler-lethal, jittery,* and *reeler* convey a picture of the behavioral defect. The first three genes in this list are dominant, the other two are recessive. Still other genes such as *pallid* and *short-ear,* though named for their structural effects, produce some neurological abnormalities. *Vaccilans* (Sirlin, 1956) is another recessive gene whose behavioral effects include erratic movements, excessive docility, and poor parental care. Sirlin notes that the syndrome resembles vitamin E deficiency.

Most research on these behavior mutants has been concentrated on their genetics and linkage relationships or on the relationship of their neuropathology to peculiarities of motor behavior. Even though detailed neuropathological studies are not available for all of them, it is clear that the genes produce localized lesions in the central nervous system which result in specific behavioral deficiencies. A few investigations have been concerned with learning ability in mutants. Vicari (1929) found that Japanese waltzers performed poorly on a maze-learning problem. Other learning tasks might be less affected by the motor handicap. Curtis (1956) measured circling behavior as affected by experience and environmental factors. Rate of circling increased as the test enclosure was made larger. Curtis' circling stock was obtained by selection, and the trait is probably not controlled by a single gene. The use of standard quantitative procedures for measuring intensity of circling and the preparation of stocks carrying behavior mutations upon a common genetic background are essential for further progress in this area.

Geotaxic Orientation in Rats. A series of papers by Crozier and Pincus (1929–1936) reported a number of experiments on the inheritance of the angle of orientation of young rats climbing up an inclined surface. The nature of the test and the terminology of the angles involved are shown in Figure 6-1. As the angle of inclination,

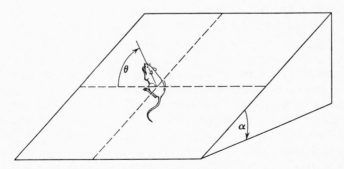

FIGURE 6-1. The negative geotactic response of young rats. The angle of inclination, α, and the angle of inclination, θ, are shown. (After Crozier and Pincus, 1929.)

α, changes, the angle of orientation, θ, is considered to vary according to the following equation.

$$(6\text{-}1) \qquad\qquad \cos \theta = a + b \sin \alpha$$

As the inclination of the plane is increased (sin α increases) the rats tend to climb more directly upward, and cosine θ approaches zero.

This series of experiments represents one of the most elaborate analyses ever attempted in behavior genetics, and the methodological issues raised have wide ramifications. In the original reports the genetic material is interwoven with a theoretical analysis of tropistic behavior which is of secondary importance for our purposes. Essentially, Crozier and Pincus were attempting to prove Loeb's theory of forced movements, which postulated that the angle of upward orientation was adjusted to produce equal tension in the proprioceptors of the symmetrical limbs.

The objectives of the experiment were: (1) to study the inheritance of strain variation in the geotactic response, and (2) to use the resultant genetic criteria to test a particular functional interpretation of the original differences. Genetics was used as a tool for manipulating an organic substratum (the proprioceptors of the limbs) inaccessible by other techniques. If the geotactic behavior of hybrids could be predicted from a theory of the inheritance of specific proprioceptive components, the genetic experiment (so argued the authors) could be considered as a validation of the original physiological hypothesis.

Crozier and Pincus conceived of a behavioral trait as a dynamic mode of adjustment to varying stimuli. Instead of comparing their strains of rats under one set of standard conditions, each subject was tested using widely different angles of inclination. From the relationship between θ and α, the constants a and b were calculated for each individual. A comparison between the geotactic response of three strains, A, B, and K, is illustrated in Figure 6-2. Strains A and B, derived from the same stock, respond similarly to increasing slope, but the absolute angles of orientation are different. Strain K's response curve crosses both of the others and has a distinctly different slope. Clearly a comparison of these strains at a single angle of inclination would be inadequate and misleading. When strains A and K were crossed, the F_1 was close to A in its average angle of orientation but resembled K in its increased sensitivity to change in inclination.

The relationship between cos θ and sin α was not precisely linear over the entire range of angle α. The authors chose to describe the actual curves as composed of three portions corresponding to slight, medium, and extreme inclination of the plane. In each section, it was

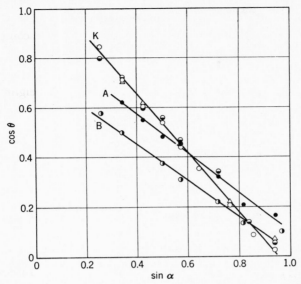

FIGURE 6-2. Geotropic orientation of young rats of three genetically distinct races, K, A, and B, presented in terms of the linear relationship between cos θ and sin α, where α is the slope of the surface and θ is the angle of oriented progression on the surface. (Crozier and Pincus, 1929.)

hypothesized, a separate set of proprioceptors assumed the dominant role in controlling the angle of orientation. The symbols I, II, and III were used to designate the portions of the genotype of strain K concerned with the sets of receptors. Similarly for strain A, the symbols i, ii, and iii were used. By assuming dominance of i, ii, and III, the response curve for the F_1 (A × K) could be derived. The behavior of the backcrosses was also found to agree with the theory.

Still another parameter investigated by genetic techniques was response variability. This was defined by a variability number (VN), which measured the change in variability (essentially two-thirds the coefficient of variation) as a function of changing inclination of the plane.

$$(6\text{-}2) \qquad VN = \Delta \frac{\text{P. E. } \theta}{\theta} \cdot \frac{1}{\Delta \log \sin \alpha}$$

As might be expected, variability in θ was systematically greater at low slopes; thus part of the response variability could be attributed to α. For each strain it was possible to partition variability into an α-dependent component and an error component ("wobble"). The α-dependent variability for strain K was 85% of the total, for strain B, 74%, and for strain A, 56%. F_1 hybrids (A × B) oriented like B's, but their variability was like A's (Crozier and Pincus, 1932).

The tenth paper in the series (1936) dealt with a backcross of F_1 (A × B) to A rats. Forty-one subjects were tested and classified in an experiment designed to "supply a searching test of the competence of the whole analysis." The classification was based upon the previously described tripartite divisions of the response curve corresponding to low, medium, and high values of angle α. Each section was considered to be controlled by a separate set of alleles. Thus, eight classes of curves, recognizable by the presence of irregularities between the three sections, were equally probable according to the genetic hypothesis. A $B_l B_m A_u$ curve should have a break between the middle and upper portions, whereas a $B_l A_m B_u$ curve would have breaks at the lower-middle and middle-upper boundaries. In agreement with expectation, the obtained curves could be classified into eight groups in the proportions 5:5:6:6:5:4:4:6, an unusually close fit to the theoretical ratio.

This series of studies has been described at some length because it represents the concept of a behavioral trait at a dynamic response system, a concept that is still not widely enough employed in psychological genetics. Despite the importance of this contribution, the genetic analysis is subject to serious criticism. Interlitter differences are mentioned by the authors, but apparently no attempt was made to allow for them in the calculations. The classification of curves by eye appears highly subjective, and the determination of inflection points is certainly risky. The conclusion that geotactic orientation in rats is affected by genotype is definitely upheld. Further evidence is required to establish the hypothesis of separate proprioceptive systems.

The technique of Crozier and Pincus was applied by Clark (1936) to a number of arboreal and non-arboreal subspecies of deermice (Peromyscus). Arboreal races climbed upward at a steeper angle and oriented at a lesser inclination of the plane. Since all individuals were laboratory reared, it was concluded that selection for a well-developed orientation response was part of the evolutionary history of arboreal forms.

Silk Spinning in Mealworms. *Ephestia kühniella* is a common mealworm which can be reared on cornmeal and has been used in experimental genetics. Larval cultures of one stock maintained homozygous for genes a and rt were observed to produce webs of silk rather than the tangled mass of threads characteristic of the species (Caspari, 1951). Genetic analysis presents some difficulty since the trait is shown only in cultures and not by individuals. However the results of crossing web-forming by non-web-forming strains were compatible with a multiple-factor mode of inheritance with the non-web-forming character dominant. By selection it was possible to produce a non-web-forming strain homozygous for *rt* and *a*, thus proving the behavioral trait to be independent of these genes.

Web-forming behavior depends upon a specified genotype, a particular type of food, and darkness. In light the negatively phototropic larvae burrow in their food and do not spin a surface web. Spinning occurs in commercial cornmeal but not in ground whole corn. This suggests that a nutritional deficiency is involved. Observations on the life history of the larvae show that spinning is restricted to the last larval *instar* (intermoult period) and that the duration of this phase is inordinately prolonged in the spinning strain on a deficient diet. Hence the larvae have a longer period of spinning and crawling over their limited habitat. The web is a fortuitous outcome of genetic control of rate of development. This study is a particularly good example of the relationship between genetic, environmental, and behavioral systems, and may well be a model for other situations. Perhaps the most interesting feature is the dependence of a behavioral character upon modification of the rate of maturation.

Phototaxis in Insects. A number of biologists have studied the effect of specific mutations upon phototaxis in Drosophila. These flies tend to move toward brightly illuminated areas. The most widely used method has been to place a group of flies in a tube, shine a light into one end, and measure the rate of progression towards the light. This method does not separate the photokinetic effect of light (stimulated activity) from its phototactic effect (directing locomotion). Some of the earlier workers, including McEwen (1918, 1925) and Cole (1922), compared stocks carrying various mutations but did not distinguish effects of particular genes from other genetic differences between the stocks. Scott (1943) prepared special inbred stocks segregating for white (*w*) and brown (*br*) eye. The wild-type and mutant types in each stock could be assumed to be genetically identical except for the named gene and its closely linked neighbors. Phototaxis was measured by the median rate of crawling over a measured course. The results are summarized in Table 6-1.

The effects of the sex-linked gene, *w*, were conspicuous, but brown flies did not differ from wild type of the same stock. Particularly notable is the great difference between the wild-type individuals from the two stocks.

Scott's experiment did not separate the effects of photokinesis from

TABLE 6-1

Effects of Single Genes upon Phototaxis in Drosophila
(Scott, 1943)

Genotype	No.	Mean Time, sec.	σ, sec.	Significance of Difference
bw/bw	68	11.4	3.0	
				N.S.
bw/+	66	11.5	2.6	
w/	47	21.2	5.8	
				.001
+/	46	32.0	18.1	

those of phototaxis. In the study of Brown and Hall (1936) this was accomplished by changing the form of apparatus. A Y-tube was used, one arm of which was illuminated. Flies inserted into the stem of the Y were observed at the choice point against an opal red light to which they did not respond. The threshold was defined as the level of illumination at which entries into the light and dark tube were equal. Full and bar-eyed (eye reduced in size) flies with red or white pigmentation were tested. The results are summarized in Table 6-2.

TABLE 6-2

Thresholds in Foot-Candles for Phototactic Response in Drosophila
(Brown and Hall, 1936)

Type of Fly	Threshold	Area of Eye, mm.²
Red-bar	.178	.016
White-bar	.09	.023
White-full	.00058	.097
Red-full	.0001	.113

The difference between the different types of flies is a direct result of the greater number of receptors in full-sized eyes. The difference between red and white eyes is shown in column three to be merely the consequence of gene interaction whereby "pigment" genes modify eye size. A linear relationship was found between the logarithm of light intensity at threshold and the surface area of the eye.

In a more recent study, Dürrwachter (1957) has described differences in angle of orientation of Drosophila mutants crawling over blotting paper in the path of a directed light beam. Strongest positive phototaxis was found in the wild type; stocks carrying defective wings (curled, vestigial) were significantly less positive. Since wild-type flies were tested after partial removal of their wings, the effect of the mutation is presumably independent of its structural features. Rearing Drosophila in continuous darkness increases the degree of positive phototaxis; in continuous light the opposite effect is found. Dürrwachter claims that the effect is progressive from generation to generation in the absence of selection. The data given in his paper do not permit statistical evaluation of the significance of the changes, since values are given only for the average strength of response in selected generations. Although no theoretical explanation for the phenomenon is offered, an adaptive genetic modification is implied. In view of the past history of such ideas, all reported cases must be viewed skeptically.

Hereditary variation in phototaxis in grain weevils, *Calandra granaria,* has been reported by Richards (1951). The chance observation of some aberrant individuals who were not negatively phototactic stimulated a selection experiment. After two generations there was a separation into a strongly negative strain and one relatively indifferent to light. The parent-offspring correlation of mean angle of orientation to a directed light beam was .473 ($p = .02$). How common such genetic psychophysiological variation may be is unknown, since few observers analyze the sources of variation in their material by conducting breeding experiments.

Phototaxis in *Drosophila melanogaster* is responsive to selections in both directions. In experiments by Hirsch and Boudreau (1958) selection was carried out for 29 generations, using the mass-screening technique of Hirsch and Tryon (see page 74). In the foundation population 50% of subjects entered the lighted side of a Y-maze during a 30-second test period. At the end of the experiment about 80% of the high line and 15% of the low line were responding positively. It was predicted that progress in changing the population by selection would cease as the variance of the selected lines approached the error of measurement, and the hypothesis was verified. In the foundation population the variance of the phototaxic scores (which ranged from zero to ten) was 6.38. The average variance of the last two generations of both high and low lines was 2.77. If the second value is considered to represent variability in an isogenic line, it must be of environmental origin; thus heritability in the foundation stock can be computed as $(6.38 - 2.77)/6.38 = .566$. The authors comment: "Since present data have been obtained with a laboratory stock considered to be rather inbred and therefore not very heterogeneous genetically, it is to be expected that larger genetic variance would be found in a less-inbred natural population."

The Dance of the Bees. Worker bees are apparently able to stimulate other workers in the hive so that they find food more readily than the original discoverer. The technique of stimulation ("the language of the bees") is a type of dance movement whose pattern and orientation are related to the flight distance and the relative location of the sun and the food (von Frisch, 1950). The nature of the dance varies in different races of bees (von Frisch, 1951; Baltzer, 1952). In dark-colored Swiss and Austrian races a characteristic undirected "round dance" was executed when the food was nearby (Figure 6-3a). This is the form of behavior reported originally by von Frisch. Only when food is at a distance of 50 to 100 meters is a directed form of dance executed. However, light-colored workers from an Italian strain performed a directed "sickle-dance" when food was only 10 to 20 meters

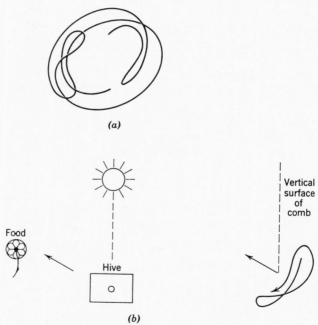

FIGURE 6-3. (a) The undirected "round dance," circling with reversals, characteristic of Swiss bees (*carnica* strain) on returning to hive from a nearby food source. (b) The oriented "sickle-dance" of "ligustica" bees. The mid-sickle angle with the vertical equals the angle between the directions of the food and the sun. (After Baltzer, 1952.)

from the hive. (Figure 6-3b). The behavior trait did not follow the body color when the strains were hybridized, but appeared to be somewhat intermediate. Following von Frisch's terminology, one might consider these dance forms as heritable dialects.

Even if this behavior is not thought to merit the designation of "language," it is certainly a more complex response than the phototaxes and geotaxes we have discussed previously. Whether the difference in dance form has any selective value has not been investigated to our knowledge.

Functional Activity of the Nervous System. In the strict sense, the studies described in this section deal with the heredity of physiological rather than behavioral traits. There can be little doubt, however, that functional activity of the nervous system is correlated with behavior, even though psychology has not yet become a branch of neurophysiology. The neurophysiological trait whose genetics has been investigated most extensively is the electroencephalogram (EEG). Patterns of activity recorded from the cortex tend to be characteristic of an individual over many years of his adult life. A difficulty of EEG studies is that the judgment of similarity between records is somewhat subjective and requires considerable experience. Gottlober (1938) reported failure of four judges to correctly group records of fifteen families, each including parents and two or more children. He concluded that hereditary effects were absent, or of minor importance. His method, however, seems unsuitable for studying the heritability of any quantitative trait. In contrast, Lennox et al. (1945) reported that MZ and DZ twins could be correctly diagnosed almost as readily from EEG tracings as by a complete examination (Table 6-3). Raney (1939)

TABLE 6-3

Judgments of Zygosity of Twins from EEG Tracings (Lennox et al., 1945)

Actual Type of Twin Pair	Judgments		
	MZ	DZ	?
55 MZ pairs	47	2	6
19 DZ pairs	1	18	0

reported that the EEG's of members of MZ-twin pairs were more alike than those of subjects taken at random with respect to the percentage of time alpha waves were present, amplitude of alpha, and frequency of alpha corrected for age. A tendency for lateral dominance of the EEG to be reversed between members of a pair was also found.

The inheritance of EEG patterns has received some attention in its relation to psychiatry. EEG abnormalities are often found associated with epilepsy and possibly with psychopathic personality and primary behavior disorders (Chapter 9). Lennox (1946) reported on the EEG's of 66 pairs of twins with seizures. It was difficult to detect seizure patterns in a short section of record, for all the subjects had received therapy and typical seizure waves may occur only during an attack. However, over 50% of MZ twins were concordant in EEG abnormality, while DZ pairs were concordant in less than 20% of the cases. The judgments were made by an electroencephalographer not familiar with the twins.

Gottlieb et al. (1947) and Knott et al. (1953) took records on a large sample of patients with primary behavior disorder and psychopathic personality. These patients had character defects such as egocentric motivation and poor judgment of the outcome of deviant behavior. The EEG's of 86 patients had significantly more fast and slow rhythms than Gibb's extensive sample of normal subjects. One hundred and seventy-two parents also differed significantly from Gibb's standard, though to a lesser degree than their offspring. If the parental pairs are classified according to normality of the EEG of each partner, evidence of hereditary effects is clear. Kennard (1949) has reported similar findings.

TABLE 6-4

**EEG's of Patients and Parents
(Gottlieb et al., 1947)**

Parent's EEG	Number	Patient's EEG	
		Normal	Abnormal
Normal × normal	22	15 (68%)	7 (32%)
Normal × abnormal	17	4 (24%)	13 (76%)

The weight of evidence points to a degree of hereditary determination of the EEG pattern, both in its normal and abnormal aspects. All of this research, however, has been carried out on specialized samples so that generalization to a larger population is impossible. The criteria used for classification also lack precision. More quantitative measures of the EEG are possible and might yield results of greater genetic significance.

Autonomic Responses. Homeostatic regulation in the higher vertebrates depends upon a system of reflexes involving the sympathetic and parasympathetic divisions of the autonomic nervous system. When an organism is aroused psychologically, some of these reflexes may be activated. Thus some psychologists have attempted to measure emotionality in terms of heart-rate changes, defecation and urination, or acidity of the gastric juice. Defining a trait of emotionality or fearfulness in terms of an autonomic response is justifiable only as an approximation (Bindra and Thompson, 1953). These authors found non-significant correlations between emotional elimination and performance in tests of timidity and fearfulness. The lack of general validity does not detract from the usefulness of the autonomic-response measures in behavior genetics. As shown below, abundant evidence exists for the genetic control of patterns of autonomic response. From the viewpoint of medicine, similar psychodynamic processes may lead to different somatic manifestations depending upon the inherited characteristics of the autonomic system (Sontag, 1950). Unfortunately, the factual basis for such a hypothesis is slim. Individual variability in response patterns is well established, but relatively few researches have demonstrated the hereditary nature of the variations.

Perhaps the most comprehensive work on the heritability of visceral reactivity is Hall's investigation (1941, 1951) of emotional elimination in the rat. Selection for frequency of defecation and urination in an open-field situation was highly successful. This experiment is considered more fully in the chapter on temperament, since the objective was to produce emotional or timid rats. But without making any assumptions with respect to the psychological significance of elimination, we can see that visceral reactivity was greatly influenced by heredity. Hall's results have been substantially confirmed by another selection experiment (Broadhurst, 1958b).

Breed differences in cardio-acceleration as a response to various types of stimulation have been reported in dogs (Fuller, 1953). As set forth in Table 6-5, it is apparent that the same objective stimulus elicits quantitatively different autonomic responses. Even the direction of the change may vary, as the results with basenjis and cocker spaniels demonstrate. Basenjis show cardio-acceleration when the experimenter enters the test enclosure; the spaniels show deceleration. Both respond equally to a loud bell. These findings suggest that part of the difference between the breeds is an outgrowth of conditioning to human handling.

In experiments of this type many factors operate simultaneously upon the heart rate. Cardio-acceleration is a function of the reactivity

TABLE 6-5

Heart-Rate Changes in Breeds of Dogs Following Stimulation (Fuller, 1953)

Breed	Stimulus	
	Entrance of Experimenter	Sound of Bell
Basenji	15.0 ± 3.6	25.1 ± 2.7
Cocker spaniel	−5.2 ± 1.9	25.8 ± 3.0
Shetland sheep dog	−0.2 ± 5.1	49.8 ± 5.0
Fox terrier	7.5 ± 3.3	34.4 ± 3.1
Significance of differences	$p < .001$	$p < .001$

of peripheral effectors, of central emotional arousal, and of secondary effects of motor activity. The existence of a physiological differentiation of breeds is clear, but its psychological significance is a matter for hypothesis and experimentation.

Some research has been carried out on autonomic-response specificity in man (Lacey, Bateman, and Van Lehn, 1953). Individual male college students were characterized by definite patterns of autonomic response which might emphasize changes in blood pressure, in galvanic skin reflex, or in salivary secretion. By implication these are usually considered as inherited, though the argument is chiefly that acquisition of autonomic-response patterns has not been demonstrated. More definite evidence for the heritability of autonomic nervous-system variation in man is afforded by the observation of Jost and Sontag (1944) in the Fels Institute studies of longitudinal growth in children. Measurements were made on persistence of skin reddening following pressure, rate of production of saliva, heart rate, blood pressure, skin conductance, and rate of respiration. An index of autonomic balance was computed from a weighted sum of the scores on separate measures. The correlations of the autonomic-balance measure for three successive years show a strong familial effect (Table 6-6).

The data on autonomic response specificity suggest caution in using any one response as an indicator of the intensity of some psychological process conceptualized as emotionality. Changes in autonomic function do, of course, accompany behavioral arousal, but the nature and intensity of such reactions probably are as much a function of inherited effector sensitivity as of differential "emotionality." This hypothesis could explain the apparent contradiction between the re-

TABLE 6-6

Correlation of Autonomic Balance Measures in Pairs
of Different Degrees of Relationship
(Jost and Sontag, 1944)

Year	Twins		Sibs		Unrelated	
	N	r	N	r	N	r
1940	5	.434	10	.255	361	.164
1941	5	.470	19	.406	364	.017
1942	6	.489	25	.288	300	.080

sults of Hall and those of Bindra and Thompson. Hall in his selection program for increased emotional elimination might have carried along genes favoring both effector sensitivity and central excitability, since both would lead to a high defecation score. In such a strain one would expect a good correlation between emotional elimination and other tests of fearfulness. In strains of different origin the two responses might be associated randomly. It would be of interest to attempt by the selection technique to produce a negative correlation between elimination scores and other behavioral indices of emotional arousal.

Audiogenic Seizures. A convulsion is caused by a massive discharge of motor neurones in a relatively uncoordinated pattern. In milder seizures the number of neurones involved and the degree of uncoordination are less. Susceptibility to convulsions is thus one indicator of the level of excitability of certain parts of the nervous system. High fever, electroshock, injections of metrazol or picrotoxin, and traumatic injury to the brain are well-known examples of seizure-inducing agents. Psychological interest is limited to convulsions which appear as the result of excessive stimulation. It is not unreasonable to surmise that such seizures represent a failure of the inhibitory systems involved in the patterning of ordinary responses. Stimulation spreads so widely through the nervous system that adaptive responses are overwhelmed. Audiogenic seizures in rats, mice, and rabbits and epileptic seizures in man have been intensively studied in relation to genetics. For many psychologists, interest in audiogenic seizures was stimulated by their designation by Maier (1943) as a "neurotic pattern." The descriptive terms "audiogenic seizure" or "sound-induced convulsion" are preferable, since the relationship to neurosis is tenuous at best.

Audiogenic seizures are induced by exposing a susceptible subject to intense high-pitched (5,000–20,000 cycles per second) sound. After a short latent period, the subject runs wildly about the test enclosure. The running attack may culminate in a standing spasm of several seconds, or the subject may fall on his side and kick rhythmically (clonic convulsion). Frequently this passes into a tonic convulsion in which the limbs are stiff and the respiratory muscles fixed in the inspiratory position. Tonic seizures are often fatal. Any of the more severe seizures may be followed by a varying period of ataxia and apparent perceptual derangement.

Dice (1935) and Watson (1939) considered that seizures in *Peromyscus maniculatus artemisiae* were inherited as a simple recessive in some stocks. On an outcrossed background the proportion of susceptible subjects was less than predicted. The discrepancy was considered due to modifiers. A similar genetic mechanism has been proposed for seizure susceptibility in rabbits (Antonitis et al., 1954).

Differences in the susceptibility of various strains of rats were reported by Maier and Glaser (1940) and Maier (1943) during the active phase of investigation of the "neurotic pattern." Selection for two generations was carried out on two stocks, one containing relatively few susceptibles (the "stable" stock), the other containing many susceptibles (the "unstable" stock). The results in Table 6-7 show

TABLE 6-7

Selection for Susceptibility to Audiogenic Seizures in Rats (Maier, 1943)

Strain	Selection for:	Litters	Offspring	% Susceptible
Unstable	Susceptibility	10	48	83
	Resistance	5	37	69
Stable	Susceptibility	4	34	56
	Resistance	4	37	3

that selection was much more effective in the "stable" strain. Griffiths (1942) was only moderately successful in selecting for high seizure susceptibility, but the intensity of selection appears to have been rather low.

A more extensive selection program in mice has been reported by Frings and Frings (1953). Starting with a stock of mongrel Swiss albino mice, they succeeded in producing strains with high and low incidence of convulsions and with high survival rates for convulsers. At the start of their study, research was handicapped by high mortality from the convulsions. Figure 6-4 shows the course of selection for high incidence. After only two generations of selection the proportion of susceptibles was greatly increased, almost to the maximum attained. However, mean latency of seizures (taken to start of running) continued to fall throughout seven generations of selection. Similarly, seizure incidence fell sharply after only two generations of selection, but the length of the susceptible-age period, in those subjects who did convulse, continued to fall. Such results are typical of selection for a quantitative character. A major effect may be noted with only a few generations of selection, but slow changes in the same direction may be noted for a considerable period as modifying genes are gradually concentrated in the selected lines.

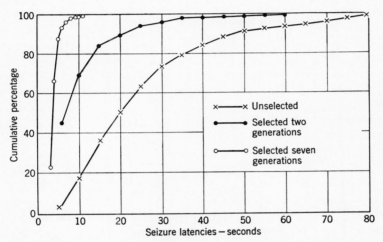

FIGURE 6-4. Changes in seizure latencies in a strain of mice selected for high incidence of seizures. In only two generations the median latency (among animals having seizures) was reduced from 22 to 7 seconds. Five additional generations of selection produced lowering of latencies to a median value of less than four seconds. In the seventh generation about 90% of the population consisted of individuals comparable to the most susceptible one per cent in the original stock. (Drawn from data in Frings and Frings, 1953.)

Differences in seizure susceptibility have been related to other behavioral characteristics. Martin and Hall (1941) found that Hall's "non-emotional" rats had more convulsive attacks than his "emotional" strain. Farris and Yeakel (1943) found fewer susceptibles among inbred gray Norway rats than among Wistar albino rats. As judged by other criteria, the grays were more emotional. Griffiths (1944) tested wild Norway and Alexandrine rats. None had seizures. The wild rats attacked the nozzle of the air-blast apparatus used to generate sound, rather than running from it. However, wild rats fed on a magnesium-deficient diet did convulse (Griffiths, 1947). All wild rats survived convulsions, but domesticated controls on the deficient diet died in seizure. Inbred mouse strains have found much use in audiogenic seizure research since Hall's (1947) report that the DBA strain was almost 100% susceptible at 30 days of age, whereas the C57BL strain was very resistant under the same conditions. Lindzey (1951) compared the frequency of audiogenic seizures and emotional defecation in five strains (Table 6-8), and found the two measures to be independent.

TABLE 6-8

Emotional Defecation and Audiogenic Seizures in Five Inbred Mouse Strains (Lindzey, 1951)

(Strain names have been changed to accord with current terminology.)

Strain	DBA	C57BL	C3H	BALB/c	A
Number tested	100	100	100	100	100
Number defecating	68	37	72	75	61
Number convulsing	80	0	0	9	21

The mechanism of genetic transmission of seizure susceptibility in the rat appears to be multifactorial, and most investigators have accepted this view. Witt and Hall (1949) postulated that in the mouse susceptibility was caused by a single dominant gene. Later studies by Fuller et al. (1950), Frings et al. (1956), and Ginsburg and Miller (personal communication) have supported a more complex mode of determination. The matter is of interest because it illustrates some of the methodological problems of behavior genetics (see also page 88).

Witt and Hall performed a standard breeding experiment crossing highly susceptible DBA/1 mice with slightly susceptible C57BL mice. Test trials were given daily, beginning at 30 days of age. Subjects responding by a seizure within four trials were classified as "reactors"; other subjects were classified as "non-reactors." Their results (Table 6-9) were generally in satisfactory agreement with the hypothesis of determination by a single dominant gene, if one allows for a small percentage of overlaps in both the As/As and as/as genotypes. However, it will be noted that the backcross to the DBA's had less severe convulsions than the pure DBA, although they should be indistin-

TABLE 6-9

Audiogenic Seizures in Crosses between DBA and C57BL Mice
(Witt and Hall, 1949)

Group	No.	% Observed	% Expected*	% Observed†		
				Intensity of Seizure		
				WR	C	F
C57BL (B)	38	5.3 ± 3.6	0	0	0	5
DBA (D)	30	93 ± 4.7	100	0	6	87
F_1 (B × D)	81	90 ± 3.3	100	7	17	65
F_2 (F_1 × F_1)	70	77 ± 5.0	75	1	9	67
F_1 × B	70	53 ± 6.0	50	4	6	43
F_1 × D	22	91 ± 6.1	100	0	32	59
Critical backcross‡	48	25 ± 6.2	0	23	0	2

* Expected on basis of dominant gene hypothesis

† Maximum seizure intensity, WR = wild running; C = convulsion; F = fatal convulsion

‡ Non-reactors from (F_1 × B) crossed with B

guishable according to the hypothesis. The offspring from the "critical backcross" of non-reactors from the first backcross to C57BL showed a high proportion of mild seizures, though the hypothesis called for them to be free of the *As* gene.

The study of Fuller, Easler, and Smith (1950) on the same strains did not support the hypothesis of dominance, for the F_1 was distinctly less susceptible than the DBA's. Although the data did not contraindicate the hypothesis that a single gene controls susceptibility (*As/As* producing about 99% susceptibility and *As/as* about 75%), preference was given to Wright's threshold theory as a descriptive model. According to this formulation, seizure susceptibility is considered to be related to a genetically controlled variable of continuous distribution. Under appropriate circumstances a multiple-factor genetic system can yield ratios of individuals above and below the susceptibility threshold which mimic ratios of simpler genetic systems. Continuous backcrossing of susceptible hybrids into the C57BL stock was used to test between the single-factor and multiple-factor hypotheses. Under the former the proportion of susceptible subjects should remain constant as each successive backcross is merely a repetition of an *As/as* × *as/as* mating. The *As/as*'s are the selected re-actors; the *as/as*'s, the resistant strain. Actually the proportion of reactors fell rapidly as the DBA gene contribution was diluted, and the experiment was terminated at the fourth backcross because of the lack of reactors to continue the breeding program.

Frings, Frings, and Hamilton (1956) have stressed the fact that the age distribution of susceptibility varies with genetic background. In supporting a multiple-factor hypothesis they comment on the dangers of basing genetic conclusions on data drawn from a single standard test at a single age: "It is obvious that with restricted testing periods or with systems of classification which designate mice merely as susceptible or non-susceptible, it would be possible to get almost any ratios."

Ginsburg and Miller (personal communication) have compared crosses involving two closely related susceptible strains, DBA/1 and DBA/2, and two resistant strains, C57BL/6 and C57BL/10. They have proposed a two-locus system of control with rather complex relationships between the two loci and the residual genetic background. A number of assumptions were made which were related to their hypotheses regarding genic control of specific metabolic reactions. Evaluation of their hypothesis must await a more complete report of their results.

Research on the genetics of audiogenic seizures has led to experiments particularly designed to define the pathway between genes as metabolic agents and susceptibility as a behavioral character. These ideas will be developed in Chapter 10. It can be indicated here that most physiological research on audiogenic seizures tends to place the genetic effect somewhere in the central nervous system. The relationship between otitis media and convulsions described by Patton (1947) has not been found by other workers to be a general phenomenon (Frings and Frings, 1951).

Finer degrees of strain differences in seizure susceptibility can be brought out by techniques such as prestimulation (Fuller and Williams, 1951; Fuller and Smith, 1953). DBA/2 mice, for example, are highly susceptible (95%), whereas A mice are moderately susceptible (25%) when continuously stimulated. Their F_1 hybrids show 94% seizures under the same conditions, and this high incidence superficially leads to the characterization of susceptibility as a completely dominant condition. Prestimulation by 10 seconds of sound, however, greatly retards the onset of seizures in the hybrids but has little effect on the pure strain DBA's. A trait which appears to be a clearcut dichotomy can be shown to be more truly continuous when more precise measurements are taken, and the hybrids can actually be demonstrated to be intermediate to their parents. The prestimulation technique has also led to an interpretation of genetic differences in seizure susceptibility in terms of differential rates of recruitment and blocking of neurones (Fuller and Smith, 1953).

Laterality. Human beings are predominantly right-handed, but between 5 and 10% of tested individuals are more skilled with their left hand. Handedness is only part of the functional asymmetry characteristic of our species. Most individuals have a dominant eye and a dominant foot. Psychological interest in laterality was stimulated early in the century by theories that speech, reading ability, and personality were deleteriously affected by attempts to change naturally left-handed children into right-handers. Recognition of naturally left-handed children implies genetic control of the trait. Considerable opposition to this view has been voiced. The human infant shows no hand dominance. Handedness develops as he acquires more and more skilled movements. The question is whether genes control growth in such a way that dextrality is more readily acquired by most children and sinistrality by a small but rather constant percentage. Alternatively the causes of left-handedness must be sought in differential early experience. A strong statement of the environmentalist position will be found in Hildreth (1949–1950). Unfortunately, her critique in this paper of the hereditary theory contains serious errors. For example, she states that the theory that left-handedness is a Mendelian recessive means that one-fourth of the population should be naturally sinistral, and her expressed dichotomy between hereditary and developmental processes reflects an old conceptual fallacy.

Pedigree studies of the inheritance of left-handedness have been reported by Ramaley (1913), Chamberlain (1928), Rife (1940), and Merrell (1957). All of these investigators report a substantial excess of left-handed children in the offspring of left-handed parents. The data of the three earlier studies as summarized by Trankell (1955) are presented in an earlier chapter (Table 4-5) as an example of methodology in human behavior genetics. Trankell argues for the hypothesis that left-handedness occurs in homozygous recessives (r/r), but that a substantial proportion of "native" left-handers are modified by cultural pressures to become right-handed. The best estimate of the frequency of gene r is about .413, which would under random mating yield 17% of r/r individuals. About half of these would become phenotypically right-handed.

Merrell (1957) and Rife (1950) have proposed a different genetic mechanism in which R/R individuals are right-handed; r/r, left-handed; and R/r labile so that approximately 50% become right-handed. In Merrell's study, handedness was determined for the tasks of writing, striking a match, and threading a needle. The preferred kicking foot and the dominant eye as indicated by a sighting test were determined on the same sample of 577 subjects. Individuals were largely right-sided or left-sided for all motor tasks, although about 10% of otherwise right-handed subjects used their left hands in needle threading, a task which may be less culturally stylized, hence more likely to elicit unmodified hand preference. No marked association was found between eye and hand dominance, if only subjects with unambiguous classification on both tests were used (Table 6-10).

TABLE 6-10

Relationship between Dominant Eye and Dominant Hand (Merrell, 1957)

Dominant Eye	Dominant Hand	
	Right	Left
Right	287	9
Left	118	11

Pedigree analysis of Merrell's material confirmed other studies in finding a higher percentage of left-handedness in families with left-handed parents. His data and that of Rife (1940, 1950) are in accord with the hypothesis that left-handedness is a simple Mendelian recessive (r/r), and that the heterozygotes (R/r) are developmentally labile so that 50% become left-handed (Table 6-11).

TABLE 6-11

Observed and Predicted Occurrence of Left-Handedness in Various Types of Marriages (Merrell, 1957; Data from Rife, 1940)

Mating	Expected Percentage	Observed Percentage
R × R	6.0	7.6
R × L	31.0	24.3
L × L	56.0	54.5

There is evidence that heredity plays a part in determining eye dominance, although the mechanism must be independent of that controlling handedness (Table 6-12). Litinsky (cited by Ludwig, 1932) obtained similar data from a small sample.

TABLE 6-12

Eye Dominance of Parents and Offspring
(Merrell, 1957)

Mating Type	No. of Families	No. of Offspring	Percentage Left Eye Dominant
R × R	56	151	23.7
R × L	36	82	43.9
L × L	11	24	54.2

It might be thought that data from twins would be conclusive with respect to the heritability of handedness, but unfortunately the fact of being a twin has some relationship to the probability of being left-handed. Wilson and Jones (1932) found the percentage of left-handedness among MZ twins to be 10.7 ± 1.8; in like-sexed DZ pairs, 10.9 ± 1.8; mixed sex DZ pairs, 12.0 ± 2.2; and single born, 6.5 ± 0.7. Newman, Freeman, and Holzinger (1937) summarized their own observations with those of several European investigators. A tendency for increased discordance of MZ pairs was evidence. Rife (1940) brought together a number of studies (Table 6-13) and proposed a

TABLE 6-13

Handedness of Twin Pairs in Various Investigations
(Rife, 1940)

Investigators			Newman	Wilson and Jones	Rife
Criteria			Tapping, Testimony	Writing, Throwing	Ten tasks: Throwing, Sewing, Use of Spoon, etc.
MZ	R-R	No.	30	56	176
		%	60	80	80
	R-L	No.	17	13	41
		%	34	19	18
	L-L	No.	3	1	6
		%	6	1	2
DZ	R-R	No.	39	97	104
		%	78	89	71
	R-L	No.	11	24	39
		%	22	20	27
	L-L	No.	0	2	3
		%	0	2	2

hypothesis for the nature-nurture interaction involved in the modification of handedness in genetically alike MZ pairs. He also pointed out a significantly higher percentage of left-handed relatives in the families of discordant twins (Table 6-14). Rife's study demonstrates

TABLE 6-14

Frequency of Left-Handed Relatives of MZ Twins Discordant and Concordant for Handedness
(Rife, 1940)

Handedness of Parents and Sibs	Handedness of the Pair	
	RR	RL
None left-handed	105	25
One or more left-handed	26	22

Chi-square $= 12.8$; $P < .001$

that whatever the factors may be which predispose towards left-handedness, they are strongest in families with left-handed members. The discordant MZ pairs may be R/r genotypes, which are functionally labile, and the concordant pairs could be R/R or r/r. The data are not good enough to allow a rigorous distinction between the several genetic hypotheses which have been proposed. A multiple-factor explanation is not contraindicated, although the simpler models seem to provide an adequate description. One difficulty lies in the obvious modifiability of the trait both by learning and by biological accidents. As the path between gene and character is lengthened, formal genetic hypotheses are more difficult to prove. However, the effect of the genes is not obliterated. Supplementary evidence on the problem of lateral dominance is provided by the large number of inherited and acquired biological asymmetries (see Ludwig, 1932, for an extensive literature).

There are indications that the reversed lateral dominance often reported in identical twins is reflected in the *phi-phenomenon,* direction of apparent movement of a stationary visual stimulus, even more markedly than in handedness tests (Raney, 1938). Identical-twin pairs showing the most pronounced discordance in tests of handedness and the phi-phenomenon were also notable in the bilateral differentiation of their EEG patterns. Alpha activity was greater on the non-dominant side, which was different for each twin. These variations were, of course, not genetic since they were found between members of MZ-twin pairs. They do furnish objective support to a theory of cerebral dominance as a determinant of handedness.

Cromwell and Rife (1942) found slight but consistent differences in the skin-ridge patterns of right- and left-handed persons. These appear to be structural manifestations of a biological asymmetry. The experiments of Cole (1955) on paw preference in cats suggest a possible neural basis for lateral dominance. Among 60 cats, 20% were right-handed, 38.3% left-handed, and the remainder ambidextrous. The hypothesis that feeding habits produced these preferences was not supported. However, minute lesions of the motor cortex contralateral to the preferred side were effective in reversing laterality. A gene-produced asymmetry in the central nervous system, either metabolic or structural, is certainly a plausible explanation of handedness, though direct proof is still lacking. This asymmetry may be of little importance as long as the organism is restricted to relatively crude movements. When greater precision is required responses are made with both hands, but those of one side are more efficient and hence differentially reinforced. Thus hand dominance develops. In the absence of special training, the differential reinforcement arises from internal sources. The child, however, is susceptible to other types of reward. Falek (1959) found that children from homes of left-handed white-collar workers showed evidence that the trait was heritable. A deficiency of left-handed children was found in families from working-class homes, particularly where the father was left-handed. This deficiency apparently was correlated with the parents' belief that the trait was a disadvantage when working with tools and machinery designed for right-handers.

In closing this brief account of heredity and handedness, some mention should be made of the psychological significance of laterality. Vernon's text (1957) contains much information on the relationship of handedness to speech and reading defects. A small but definite association between left-handedness and language difficulties has been reported from many countries. Lynn and Lynn (1943) related smile and hand dominance to personality traits in a group of psychiatric patients. Individuals whose smile and hand dominance were homolateral rated higher on traits described as "aggressiveness," "independence," and "high effectivity," whereas their score was low on a group of dependency traits.

Motor Skills. Individual variation in manual dexterity, speed, and steadiness are easily observable. Motor skill is not a unitary factor, and the correlations between different tests are usually lower than those between parts of intelligence tests. An extensive study of twin resemblances in five motor skills was conducted by McNemar (1933) on 98 pairs of twin boys of junior high-school age. The tests employed were (1) the Koerth pursuit rotor, a measure of hand-eye coordination; (2) the Whipple steadiness test; (3) the Miles speed hand-drill; (4) the Brown spool sorter; and (5) a test of card-sorting speed. Tests (1), (4) and (5) were repeated to measure practice effects.

The correlations given in Table 6-15 have been corrected for at-

TABLE 6-15

**Twin Resemblance on Five Tests of Motor Skill
(McNemar, 1933)**

| | | Intraclass Correlation (corrected) | | |
| | | | Practice Effect | |
Test	Twin Type	Total Score	Initial	Final
Pursuit rotor	DZ	.51	.45	.61
	MZ	.95	.90	.89
Steadiness	DZ	.43		
	MZ	.84		
Speed drill	DZ	.56		
	MZ	.82		
Spool packing	DZ	.44	.41	.59
	MZ	.71	.62	.61
Card sorting	DZ	.39	.61	.54
	MZ	.84	.86	.82

tenuation and adjusted for range. It is evident that the within-pair correlations are much higher for MZ pairs, thus making a strong case for heredity. McNemar also found that the within-pair divergence of DZ twins was less than that of individuals paired at random. The effect might represent common experiences or the effect of common heredity. In the two right-hand columns of Table 6-15 are correlations for the initial and final trials on three tests used for practice effects. There is a hint on two tests of a closure of the gap between DZ pairs as a result of practice, but the effect is reversed in card sorting. Practice has no general effect upon the relative importance of hereditary differences; it simply alters the level at which they are manifested.

A similar study by Brody (1937) employed four forms of the Minnesota form board, two being repeated in order to observe the effects of practice. On every comparison MZ pairs were significantly more alike than DZ pairs. As in McNemar's experiment, there was no consistent effect of practice on the degree of difference in resemblance between the two types of twins.

COMPLEX RESPONSES

Individual differences frequently involve modifications in a group of behavior patterns related to a particular motivational state. Courtship behavior, for example, may involve elaborate ritualistic posturing, abortive copulatory activity, eventual mating, and characteristic post-copulatory grooming. These components usually appear in a regular sequence and may have common physiological dependency upon the presence of sex hormones.

Hereditary differences in such sequences could arise in two ways. The peripheral sensory and motor components of the system might vary independently, and the outcome in terms of behavior would be the resultant of the interplay of separately varying parts. Such an arrangement would be complex psychologically and genetically. Alternatively, a wide range of effects upon behavior could derive from genetic influences upon a single part with widely ramifying relationships. Variation in a neural center or in hormone output might have a simple genetic basis but extensive effects upon behavior. These mechanisms are not exclusive, and a reasonable hypothesis is that both coexist in most organisms.

The present section deals with courtship and parental behavior, eating, and hoarding. Hormones are known to influence courtship and the care of young, and nuclei in the hypothalamus have been proved to have critical importance for ingestive and sexual activity. A close relationship between physiological status and behavior offers particularly favorable opportunities for studying the mechanisms by which genes contribute to individual differences. Research on this aspect of behavior genetics is just beginning. No sharp line divides the activities treated in this section and the emotional, temperamental, and social characteristics discussed in following chapters. Activity, aggression, and timidity are also affected by hormones and have special relationships to known neural systems. These temperamental differences, however, affect a wider range of activities and are manifested by the responses to a wider and more individualistic variety of stimuli. Eating and sexual behavior are more stimulus-bound than fear or anger. This distinction is more valid for the rat than for man, and classifying rat and human courtship in the same rubric because they both lead to copulation and reproduction results in the juxtaposition of unlike psychological mechanisms. We have used this arrangement, not to imply a behavioral taxonomy based upon homology, but as a convenient means of organizing a variety of researches concerned with complex biological phenomena.

The phrase "complex behavior patterns" embraces much that has been called instinctive or innate behavior. Instinctive behavior in genetic terms is behavior so highly determined by genes that it occurs uniformly under practically any condition which will permit survival. A rigid distinction between innate and learned components of behavior is difficult (Verplanck, 1955), and the "instinct problem" appears in modern times to be not one problem, but many separate problems concerned with the development of specific responses. The vast literature in this area is beyond the scope of this work, except for a few instances in which experimental genetic techniques have been used. Usually the heritability of "innate behavior patterns" has been inferred from developmental studies, since interest has centered on interspecific differences, and interspecific hybrids are difficult to obtain. A few studies (Clark et al., 1954; von Hörmann-Heck, 1957) have utilized hybrids between related species, but the majority have dealt with race and strain differences among domestic and laboratory animals. Lorenz (1950) has criticized the generality of results obtained with domestic animals on the ground that selection may eliminate the physiological basis for behavior patterns characteristic of wild ancestors. The criticism has merit, but the requirements of experimental genetics are best met with domestic species in which maximum intraspecific variation has been introduced through selection. The limitation and powers of genetic techniques are illustrated by the literature cited in the remainder of this chapter.

Sexual Selection and Psychosexual Isolation. Darwin considered sexual selection to be a major factor in the evolution of such features as the brilliant plumage of some male birds. Many naturalists have been critical of this idea and have stated that the colors are more important in the maintenance of territory against other males than in attracting the favor of a coy mate. Modern work on Drosophila and other species which can be conveniently maintained in the laboratory has reinforced the evidence for sexual selection. Some of the studies have pertinence for behavior genetics.

Courtship and mating have a special adaptive and evolutionary significance. In addition to the need for reproductive competence adequate for species survival, there is a possibility that variation in courtship patterns may lead to assortative mating and thus function as an isolating mechanism. A number of authors (Huxley, 1942; Spieth, 1952) have assigned to psychosexual isolation a prominent role in evolution. Another problem is genetic control of the intensity of sex behavior and the nature of the physiological channels through which control operates. A few miscellaneous researches dealing with heredity and sex have also been included in this section.

In order to avoid confusion between the biological and psychological meanings of the word "selection," we shall use it solely in its biological sense. Selection occurs whenever a particular genotype manages to leave more descendants than other competing genotypes. This may be the result of greater vigor, greater fertility and fecundity, or because the males of this genotype are more acceptable as mates. The word "choice" will be used with reference to a discriminative response between potential available mates. Selection may be caused by many factors in addition to behavior, whereas choice is a psychological process which may result in selection.

Methods for Studying Sexual Selection. All techniques for studying these phenomena involve comparisons between the number of matings of like types (homogamic) and the number of matings of unlike types (heterogamic) under prescribed conditions. Three classes of methods have been used. (1) In the *no-choice* method males and females of like and unlike stocks are placed together and the occurrence of mating verified by direct examination of the female genital tract or by the production of offspring. This method is of minimal value in analyzing the behavioral basis of isolation. (2) In *choice* methods one type of male is placed with two types of females, or one type of female with two types of males. Verification of mating is made as in no-choice methods, although genetic tags must be used if choice by females is studied, since the spermatozoa of different stocks are not microscopically distinguishable. (3) Direct observation of courtship and mating has been used by a number of investigators, sometimes in combination with other techniques. These studies are of particular interest for behavior genetics.

The most extensive work on sexual isolation has been conducted with various species of Drosophila. Since the orientation of much of this research is towards evolutionary rather than psychological problems, only selected papers will be reviewed here.

Measurement of isolation is conveniently made by means of a standard index. Stalker (1942) introduced the following formula for experiments in which males of one strain are placed with two types of females, one conspecific and the other alien:

$$I = (C - A)/(C + A)$$

where C = percentage of conspecific females inseminated
A = percentage of alien females inseminated

An index of $+1$ signifies complete isolation; an index of zero, no choice; and one of -1, exclusive cross mating. Bateman (1949) pointed out that this index often gives contradictory results depending upon which type of male is used. For example, strain 1 males may show high positive isolation with strain 1 and 2 females, but strain 2 males may mate more frequently with strain 1 females and give a negative index. If "male-choice" experiments are interpreted in terms of male discrimination of favored mates, the frequency of reversed isolation is unexpectedly high. However, the direct and indirect evidence is contrary to this interpretation. Streisinger (1948) showed that males would readily mate with etherized females of strains against which there was almost complete isolation when normal females were used. The determining factor in male-choice matings is the degree to which the two strains of females repel the same males. Bateman (1949) proposed the use of complementary mating indices which separate the effects of sexual isolation (assortative mating) and mating propensity.

This is done by combining the isolation indices of complementary matings such as: (strain 1 + strain 2 females) × strain 1 males; and (strain 1 + strain 2 females) × strain 2 males. If $I_{1,2}$ symbolizes the isolation index for the first mating, and $I_{2,1}$ is the index for the second mating, the complementary isolation index is:

$$I = (I_{1,2} + I_{2,1})/2$$

A measure of the difference in mating propensity between the females of strains 1 and 2 is given by:

$$M = (I_{1,2} - I_{2,1})/2$$

The indices can be computed in a comparable manner for female-choice experiments.

These indices suffer from the fact that their values depend upon the duration of the experiment. Over a long period of time even the less receptive females will become inseminated, and the index of isolation will approach zero. This disadvantage can be avoided by stopping the experiment after mating is observed, which is feasible when one male and two females only are employed (Sturtevant, 1915). In mass-choice experiments the investigator must adjust the procedure so that about 50% of the females in each subgroup are inseminated. If this requirement is not met the indices are not comparable from experiment to experiment.

Levene (1949) has proposed an index based upon the numbers of non-inseminated females. His index is less sensitive to the duration of the experiment, and its standard error can be calculated. These factors are advantageous in comparing the intensity of isolation, but simpler indices combined with observation are equally useful for studying the nature of isolation.

Effects of Single Genes upon Mating Success. The effects of single genes upon sexual selection in *D. melanogaster* were studied by Sturtevant (1915). He directly observed courtship and mating using (*A*) one male of either type 1 or 2 with two females of types 1 and 2, or (*B*) two males of types 1 and 2 with one female of either type. The mutants employed were white eye, yellow body color, curved wings (wings of males always held in courting posture), and vermilion eyes. Only the latter appeared to be as active as the wild type in culture bottles. The results with all mutants were similar and may be illustrated by the crosses between white eye and red eye (wild type) (Table 6-16). If Bateman's formulae are used, the complementary isolation

TABLE 6-16

Selective Mating between White-Eyed and Wild-Type *Drosophila melanogaster* (Sturtevant, 1915)

"Chooser"	Number of Mating Choices of Each Type	
Wild-type male	Wild-type female, 54	White-eyed female, 82
White-eyed male	Wild-type female, 40	White-eyed female, 93
Wild-type female	Wild-type male, 53	White-eyed male, 14
White-eyed female	Wild-type male, 62	White-eyed male, 19

index in the male-choice experiments can be calculated as .097. In the female-choice experiments it is .026. The mating propensity of wild-type females compared with whites is −.303, but the wild-type males surpassed the mutants by .558. Sturtevant, although he did not use this method of expressing his results, concluded that there was no evidence for choice of mates. The results were interpretable in terms of genetic determiners of the vigor of sexual behavior.

Merrell (1949) made quantitative estimates in *D. melanogaster* of the effect upon mating success of four sex-linked recessive mutations singly and in combination. Both male-choice and female-choice experiments were conducted and the results evaluated by the types of offspring produced. The use of genetic markers makes female-choice experiments possible as illustrated in the following example. A wild-type female heterozygous for raspberry (*rs*) was placed with wild-type and raspberry males. The types of offspring resulting from the success of each male in achieving insemination are shown below (Table 6-17). The appearance of mutant females indicates success of the mutant male.

TABLE 6-17

Effects of *ras* Gene on Success in Mating
(Merrell, 1949)

		ras/Y Male Successful		+/Y Male Successful	
		ras	Y	+	Y
Male gametes		*ras*	Y	+	Y
Female gametes	*ras*	*ras*/*ras*	*ras*/Y	*ras*/+	*ras*/Y
	+	*ras*/+	+/Y	+/+	+/Y

The results of female-preference experiments showed that wild-type males were much more successful than yellow males and moderately more successful than cut and raspberry males. Forked males were equal to wild type in mating success. In general, the effects of multiple mutant genes were additive, although *ct ras* males were superior to *ct* or *ras* males. This implies some compensating effect of the combination. The behavior of the females was primarily responsible for non-random mating. Where "male choice" was found, it could be interpreted as caused by rejection of less-vigorous males by the less-receptive type of female. Hence the male was more successful in his courtship of the other female though he did not choose her. In line with this hypothesis, "male choice" was most evident in the less vigorous males; furthermore it was consistently in the same direction for all males tested with the same choice of females. Merrell concluded that within *D. melanogaster* there is selective, but not assortative, mating. In a later experiment (1953) he showed that the rate of elimination of mutant genes from a population followed time curves predicted from the effects of each gene upon selective-mating behavior.

A more detailed analysis of the behavioral components of sexual isolation has been reported by Bastock (1956), who approached the problem in the framework of the European school of ethology. She confirmed previous workers in finding that yellow *D. melanogaster* are less successful than wild type in mating. (For a description of mating and methods of quantifying observations see Bastock and Manning, 1955.) Visual stimuli seemed to be unimportant since the relative success of yellow males was the same in light or darkness. Wingless males were less successful than intact males when paired with normal females, but were equal to intact males when paired with females lacking antennae. Stimuli produced by wing vibration must be important in courtship, and must be received by the female's antennae.

In an established stock of yellow melanogaster, males were inferior to wild type with both types of females, but yellow females were more receptive than wild type with both kinds of males. When the yellow gene was placed on a new background by crossing repeatedly to wild type, the effect in males persisted, but the outcrossed yellow females were no more receptive than wild type. The effect in males was interpreted as a primary action of the y gene; the increased receptivity of yellow females from the original stock was ascribed to compensatory selection, since only the more passive females would be fertilized by the yellow males.

Courtship of yellow males differed quantitatively from that of wild type and was particularly deficient in those elements most closely related to copulation. More wing vibrations and less licking of the female genitals were characteristic of yellow males. No evidence could be found for negative reactions against the males as such, for when their courtship was adequate females of either type accepted them readily.

The net result of the studies on mate selection within *D. melanogaster* is the depreciation of the significance of discrimination in both sexes, though some contrary evidence has been obtained by Tebb and Thoday (1956). The results are intelligible on the assumption that the vigor of the courtship of each male can be expressed by a positive valence and the resistance of each female by a negative valence. Different genotypes vary in average valence. When an encounter between a male and a female involves a positive sum of valences, mating occurs; when the sum is negative, there is no mating. This is not a very interesting situation from the psychological point of view, but more complex hypotheses do not seem necessary to explain intraspecific selective mating.

Strain and Subspecies Isolation. When barriers between the mating of different species and races are considered, there is evidence for true discrimination. In terms of the valence model, a male might be $+5$ for one female and $+12$ for another instead of having the same value in all encounters. Dobzhansky has been particularly active in the investigation of sexual isolation between various subspecies and species of Drosophila. (See, for example, Dobzhansky and Koller, 1938; Dobzhansky and Streisinger, 1944; Mayr, 1946.)

Indirect methods prove the existence of sexual isolation and its heritability, but direct observation is needed to interpret isolation in behavioral terms. Stalker (1942) made parallel studies using both techniques on the species complex, *Drosophila virilis*. His subjects included several stocks of *D. americana* and a stock of *virilis*. All combinations will hybridize, but sexual isolation was demonstrated in both no-choice and choice experiments. Observations with a hand lens showed that qualitatively the courtship of the two species was very similar and involved wing vibration by the male as well as licking the abdomen and ovipositor of the female. However, the two species seemed to require different amounts of warm-up activity, and adjustment of these needs to a partner of alien type was limited.

Spieth (1951) observed mating in the same group of Drosophila, using a binocular microscope instead of a hand lens. A coding system was employed so that the observer did not know the source of the stocks whose behavior was being evaluated. Five species of the *virilis* complex subdivided into 14 substrains were used as subjects. Several features of the results were notable. *Virilis* males were ineffective with all but their own females; *virilis* females were fairly receptive to alien males, but much more so to *virilis* males. Males of certain strains were above average in success in cross-strain matings, but their females were inseminated less often in such combinations. Perhaps compensatory selection is involved.

Spieth stated that the only detectable variation between strains was the degree of activity or passivity. Sexual isolation was considered to be a function of (1) courtship discrimination and (2) strength of sexual drive. Discrimination was largely the province of the males. Those females which were courted most were the most receptive. Males tended to court females of a like stock more vigorously. Within strains there is a fine balance between the amount of discrimination and the strength of sex drive in the two sexes. When the genotypic differences are larger (as between species) the behavior of the males becomes more important in producing isolation, and assortative as well as selective mating is the result.

An extensive survey by Spieth (1952) of over 100 species of Drosophila indicates that evolutionary processes in this genus have led to differences in the emphasis placed upon various sensory modalities in courtship. Thus in *D. subobscura* and *D. auraria,* mating cannot take place in the dark. In the *virilis* group wing vibration is apparently effective at a greater distance than in other species, and auditory stimuli are suspected to be more important. An odor-dispersing function of wing vibration is postulated for *D. persimilis* and *D. pseudoobscura*. Spieth believes that such differences are important in evolution: "The first stage in the evolution of mating behavior must occur at the sensory and psychological levels rather than at the mechanical and physical action levels."

Since the single-gene differences thus far investigated do not result in assortative mating, it is likely that some form of isolation other than sexual may be necessary for the accumulation of genetic differences which eventually produce psychosexual isolation. Work on other species casts some light upon the inheritance of the individual components of courtship patterns. There is more possibility for variation in complex patterns where interaction between the sexes involves mutual stimulation.

Inheritance of Specific Courtship Movements. The inheritance of patterns of courtship in cricket hybrids has been reported by von Hörmann-Heck (1957). Female *Gryllus bimaculatus* and male *G. campestris* interbreed readily and produce fertile hybrids. The barrier to reciprocal mating is behavioral rather than physical or genetic. Certain aspects of courtship and mating were chosen for study in the hybrids: (1) Vibration of antennae after pairing, a characteristic of *campestris* males which is almost absent in *bimaculatus;* (2) pendular movements of the anterior body regions during copulation characteristic of *campestris;* (3) precourtship sounds produced by raising and lowering the elytrae. These are produced only by *bimaculatus; campestris* males raise their elytrae in a single quiet movement. Each trait appeared to be inherited independently, and a different genetic model was postulated for each. Vibration of antennae was hypothesized to depend upon a single Mendelian dominant gene, pendular movements were considered to be the expression of a complex polygenic system, and the production of beating sounds by the hybrids fitted a monohybrid model in which the heterozygote was intermediate in phenotype.

Interspecific hybrids between the platyfish, *Xiphiphorus maculatus,* and the swordtail, *X. helleri,* were subjects in an experiment of Clark, Aronson, and Gordon (1954) on the nature of isolating mechanisms. These species, both well known to aquarium fanciers, do not hybridize in nature but will do so in the laboratory. Fertilization is internal, and male courtship patterns are highly specialized. Swordtail, platyfish, and F_1 males were tested with females of their own genotype. Males of other generations were tested with essentially passive platyfish females in order to avoid complications caused by segregation of behavioral traits in the females as well as in the males.

Two pairs of alternative patterns clearly differentiated the precourtship behavior of the two species. Platyfish males pecked at the sand on the bottom of the aquaria, and swordtail males nibbled at the female. Platyfish males approached the female, then suddenly backed away with body limp and fins folded, a sequence known as *retiring*. The corresponding behavior in swordtails was a distinctly different pattern called *backing*. Males approached a female by swimming backward and usually touched her with their tail tip. Table 6-18 gives

TABLE 6-18

Precourtship Patterns of Behavior in Platyfish, Swordtail, and Hybrid Males
(Clark, Aronson, and Gordon, 1954)

Genetic Group	No.	Percentage Showing Indicated Behavior			
		Pecking	Nibbling	Retiring	Backing
Platyfish	33	82	0	73	0
Swordtail	21	0	71	0	95
F_1 (P × S)	5	0	0	20	40
F_2 (F_1 × F_1)	61	39	15	23	67
F_1 × P	10	20	10	10	0
F_1 × S	10	0	40	0	90

the percentage of the various genetic classes of males showing each of these forms of behavior. The number of tested F_1's was small, because the sex ratio in the hybrids strongly favors females. No simple Mendelian ratios were obtained but there was strong indication of genetic effects.

The effectiveness of the total behavior pattern may be expressed in terms of the percentage of females inseminated. These figures were: platyfish, 86%; swordtail, 39%; F_1, 64%; F_2, 24%; backcross to platyfish, 9%; backcross to swordtail, 0.0%. Backcross males showed sexual arousal, but seldom coordinated the separate actions of the mating pattern to achieve copulation. The disruption of courtship patterns in hybrids is apparently quite general in species which have rather stereotyped behavior. Examples may be cited from sticklebacks (Leiner, 1940), a duck-goose hybrid (Poulsen, 1950), and English finches (Hinde, 1956).

Sexual Isolation in Mammals. Psychosexual isolation in a mammalian species complex was studied by Blair and Howard (1944). Species of the *Peromyscus maniculatus* complex, native to widely separated regions of North America, were employed as subjects, *P.m. leucocephalus* from a Florida island, *P.m. albifrons* from Alabama, and light and dark strains of *P.m. blandus* from New Mexico. Experimental subjects were born and reared in the laboratory. Mixed groups consisting of a male and female of each of two varieties were placed together in living quarters consisting of four separate nesting compartments. Daily observations were made on the association of the mice in these nesting compartments and on pregnancy in the females. The parentage of most litters could be accurately determined. The original data were analyzed by an inappropriate chi-square procedure and have been reanalyzed by the present authors. Each group of four mice has been considered as an individual contributing one degree of freedom to the total. The number of times that mixed-species male-female pairs were reported in each group has been subtracted from the number of times that same-species male-female pairs were found in the same group. The significance of these difference scores has been evaluated by a *t*-test and the results summarized in Table 6-19.

TABLE 6-19

Sexual Isolation in *Peromyscus maniculatus* (Recalculated from Data of Blair and Howard, 1944)

Comparison between	No. of Groups	Mean Like Pairings	Mean Unlike Pairings	Differ- ence	t	p
Light + dark blandus	14	11.4	7.3	4.1	1.41	> .10
Blandus + leucocephalus	17	36.8	1.5	35.5	9.49	< .01
Blandus + albifrons	17	13.2	6.0	7.2	1.93	< .10
Blandus + F_1 (b × l)	10	10.4	7.7	3.7	0.81	> .10
Leucocephalus + F_1 (b × l)	10	16.0	4.5	11.5	2.31	< .05

There is no evidence of psychological isolation between light and dark *blandus* or between *blandus* and *blandus-leucocephalus* hybrids. In the other three combinations the degree of isolation is variable, but only in the *leucocephalus-blandus* combination does it reach definite significance. *Blandus* is an aggressive species and *leucocephalus* a peaceful one. This supports the original authors' conclusion that the intensity of sexual isolation is a function of differences in social behavior. They also concluded, on the basis of the results with hybrids, that if mating barriers were broken down in nature, genes would flow more freely from *leucocephalus* into *blandus* than in the opposite direction. Strains of the domestic mouse have also been shown to differ in reproductive vigor under competitive conditions (Levine, 1958). As in Drosophila, however, there is little evidence for assortative mating based upon discrimination.

Summary: Psychosexual Isolation. The reality of psychosexual isolation is well established in nature (Blair, 1951; Clark et al., 1954) as well as in the laboratory. Such isolation might be related to genotype in a variety of ways. Primary psychological isolation could result from the failure of a male to carry out certain acts necessary to arouse a female or to lower her resistance to mating. Reciprocally, a female might fail to provide adequate stimuli to activate masculine courtship. Primary psychological sexual isolation implies heritability of a rather specific set of interlocking social releasers in the sense of Tinbergen (1951) and Lorenz (1935). The experiments of Clark et al. (1954) and von Hörmann-Heck (1957) show that the separate components of courtship patterns are independently heritable though the genetic mechanisms may be complex.

Deficiencies in the mating patterns may be more important in the sex which plays the more active role in courtship. However, reduced sexual vigor in itself does not necessarily lead to discrimination and choice responses. Many mutant males of *D. melanogaster* are less successful than wild-type males, but this is not due to negative discrimination by females. Being less vigorous they court less; those which court are acceptable. Nor do mutants in general appear to be more attracted to their own phenotypes (Sturtevant, 1915; Bastock, 1956). Only when wider taxonomic differences are involved has evidence been found for a higher "releasing" value of conspecific over alien females (Stalker, 1942; Spieth, 1951; Clark et al., 1954).

Heredity, Sex Hormones, and Sex Behavior. It is well known that courtship and mating in vertebrates are dependent upon an adequate supply of sex hormones (Beach, 1948). Breeders of laboratory mammals are well aware that the vigor of sexual activity varies in different genetic stocks. A program of research initiated at the University of Kansas by W. C. Young has for its objective the determination of the relationship between genetic, hormonal, and stimulus factors in controlling the sex behavior of guinea pigs. In addition, early experience has been introduced as an additional variable in some experiments.

The sexual behavior of the male guinea pig is particularly suitable for genetic studies, since reproductive behavior of individuals is qualitatively and quantitatively consistent over long periods of time (Grunt and Young, 1952, 1953). The sequence of actions with a receptive female follows a predictable order leading towards copulation. A system was devised under which the sexual activity of a male could be quantitatively evaluated on a scale of zero to twenty. Empirically, animals averaging over 8.50 in ten tests were classified as high drive, those scoring below 6.25 as low drive, and those with intermediate scores as medium drive. When castrated all subjects became sexually inactive. Injections of testosterone propionate restored sex drive in all individuals but only to the level characteristic of that individual preoperatively. The basis of individual differences in sexual activity seemed to be a matter of somatic response to androgenic hormones rather than of the amount of hormone secreted by the intact animal.

The hereditary nature of the individual differences was not demonstrated in the above experiment, though the results strongly suggest a genetic interpretation. Valenstein, Riss, and Young (1954) compared sex activity in two highly inbred guinea-pig lines and in a genetically heterogeneous stock. Both inbred strains had lower sex drive than the heterogeneous stock and on the scale employed were less variable. A more detailed comparison between the behavior of the two inbred strains was made by comparing the frequency per minute of scored items. These results, summarized in Table 6-20, showed characteristic

TABLE 6-20

Comparison of Inbred Strains of Guinea Pigs
on Separate Components of Male Sexual Behavior
(Valenstein, Riss, and Young, 1954)

Group	Frequency of Observed Behavior per Minute						
	Sniffs Nibbles	Nuzzles	Abortive Mounts	Mounts	Intro-mission	Ejacu-lates	Sum of All Scores
Family 2	0.797	1.089	0.465	0.162	0.107	0.007	2.627
Family 13	0.839	0.731	0.287	0.346	0.174	0.019	2.396
t	0.22	2.84	2.24	2.63	1.30	2.50	1.01
p	—	.01	.03	.02	—	.02	—
Diff. favors	—	Fam. 2	Fam. 2	Fam. 13	—	Fam. 13	—

differences between the strains which were not brought out by the average-score method of comparison. In general, strain 2 surpassed strain 13 in the amount of preliminary courtship behavior, whereas strain 13 had higher frequencies of behavior in the categories related to actual impregnation.

Goy and Young (1957*a,b*) have studied the intensity of sexual activity in females of the same stocks. In order to control the time of occurrence of estrus, subjects were spayed and brought into heat by injections of 100 I.U. of estradiol benzoate followed by 0.2 I.U. of progesterone. The indicator of estrus was arching of the back (lordosis) when the animal was clasped. Measures used were: (1) latency or time between progesterone injection and the first lordosis; (2) the number of hours during which lordosis could be elicited; (3) maximum duration of lordosis in seconds, a measure of postural maintenance; (4) the frequency of male-like mountings of other animals; and (5) the percentage of females brought into heat by the hormones.

Genetic differences were clearly shown in the results which are presented in Table 6-21. All differences between pairs of strains were

TABLE 6-21

Strain Differences in the Responses of Female Guinea Pigs to Estradiol Benzoate plus Progesterone (Goy and Young, 1956)

		Mean Score on Tests of Sex Behavior				
Strain	No.	(1)	(2)	(3)	(4)	(5)
Strain 2	15	3.4	7.2	15.9	1.0	97.8
Heterogenous	21	5.9	4.3	11.7	7.3	96.8
Strain 13	17	5.7	5.0	25.2	37.7	90.2

Description of Measures:
(1) Time in hours between progesterone injection and first lordosis
(2) Number of hours during which lordosis was elicitable
(3) Duration of maximum lordosis in seconds
(4) Number of male-like mounting attempts
(5) Percentage of females brought into heat by hormones

significant except the latency difference betwen strain 13 and heterogenous females and the percentage of animals brought into heat.

In an experiment in which the dosage of estradiol benzoate was varied, the larger doses produced a quicker and longer-lasting response but did not alter the vigor of the behavior itself. These results were interpreted as signifying that, as in males of this species, individual differences depend upon the somatic response to hormones.

In comparison with the males of the same strains, the differences between females are more striking. Interestingly, the measures of vigor (duration of estrus, duration of postural maintenance, and occurrence of male-like mounting) tend to favor the inbred rather than the random bred strains. As in Drosophila, there appears to be compensatory selection for sexually receptive females in stocks whose males are lacking in sexual vigor.

Interaction of Genetic and Experiential Factors. Guinea-pig genotypes respond differentially to hormones as measured by the activation of courtship and mating behavior. Do they also react differentially to experiential factors? Valenstein, Riss, and Young (1955) investigated this problem by comparing within these strains the sexual behavior of males isolated from the age of 25 days with that of controls reared with a group of females. As each subject attained the age of 77 days a series of tests with estrous females was instituted. Several measures of sexual activity were recorded, but the scores for ejaculation are probably most significant. The percentages of animals reaching this level in the several groups were: strain 2, isolates 6%, controls 84%; strain 13, isolates 0%, controls 57%; heterogenous strain, isolates 71%, controls 100%. Conditions of rearing had a much greater effect in the inbred strains than in the non-inbred strain. However, when heterogenous males were isolated at ten days of age, their sexual performance as adults was significantly inferior to that of socially reared males. The difference between heterogenous and inbred males was not in the need for social experience, but in the age range during which this experience was effective. The possibility that the performance of strain 13 males might be improved by providing them with large doses of androgenic hormones during early development was tested in another experiment. Two groups of this strain were castrated at birth and then given large daily doses of testosterone propionate. One group was reared in isolation, the other with females. Even supernormal amounts of male hormone failed to improve the isolated animals' sexual scores, but there was some evidence of increased activity in the social group. In another related experiment, males reared with other males were compared in sexual activity with isolate-reared and female-group-reared males. The sex composition of the social group was not a significant factor in the results. Confirmatory results with strain 2 guinea pigs (also inbred) have been reported (Riss et al., 1955).

The authors believe that these experiments can best be explained in terms of two semi-autonomous components of mating behavior, arousal and organization. The organization of sexual responses in such a way that they will be biologically effective is dependent upon social experience during certain periods of development. These experiences are of a general nature, and are not specifically sexual. Strain differences in the organization component are concerned with the rate of attaining sufficient maturity to profit from associations with other animals. Males of the heterogenous strain are mature in this sense earlier than inbred males. The arousal component, shown overtly by sexual responses in the presence of an estrous female, is not as much affected by learning. Isolated males were obviously aroused in the test situation, but did not organize their responses into a coherent effective pattern. Strain 13 appears to be genetically deficient in the arousal component, even under optimal social and hormonal conditions. The value of simultaneously varying genetic, physiological, and experiential factors is well demonstrated in this series of experiments.

Physiological Correlates of Sexual Behavior Differences. One explanation offered for the failure of the inbred guinea-pig males to respond behaviorally to testosterone was that their metabolism was low. Riss (1955) made direct observations on the correlation between sex-drive ratings and oxygen consumption under anesthesia. The strains with high drive also tended to have a higher metabolic rate, but within strains there was no evidence of correlation between these two variables. Administering thyroxin to strain 13 males raised their oxygen consumption above that of heterogenous males but did not significantly increase sex activity. Energy output may set an upper limit for any form of behavior, but low metabolism was not the primary determinant of low sex drive in the deficient strains.

Further evidence on the physiological pathways by which genes exercise control over sexual activity is provided by experiments with cockerels (Wood-Gush and Osborne, 1956). Subjects in these experiments were 15 pairs of full sibs comprising 6 sets of half sibs (6 sire-families). All subjects were given four independent behavior tests, and individual response levels proved to be highly consistent. Response levels of sire families varied over a threefold range and differences were significant. No clear effects of the dam were detected. Full sibs tended to be alike in their scores. Since all subjects had common experiences in the flock, it was concluded that heredity contributes significantly to sexual performance.

The comb heights of the cockerels in this experiment were measured, since this character is known to be a measure of androgenic hormone production. The correlation coefficient, $-.43$, is significant. The regression of matings on comb height was determined for 27 of the 30 cockerels with the following results (Table 6-22). Part of the differences in mating frequency arise from factors common to behavior

TABLE 6-22

Regression Analysis of Comb Height and Mating Frequency in Cockerels
(Wood-Gush and Osborne, 1956)

Source of Variation	D.F.	M.S.	F	p
Linear regression	1	258.00	8.18	< .01
Deviations from linearity	25	31.44	4.04	< .01
Error	81	7.79		

and comb development. This may be hormone production or sensitivity to hormones. A significant part of the individual differences in behavior appears unrelated to the comb response. Selection based upon sexual responses was successful (Wood-Gush, 1958).

Human beings, according to the reports by Kinsey, Pomeroy, and Martin (1948), probably vary as greatly in their sexual behavior as do cockerels and guinea pigs. Experiential and physiological factors contribute to this variability, but nothing is known of their possible interactions with genotype. Hormones are less important determinants of human sex behavior than of rodent sex behavior (Beach, 1947), but hereditary effects upon behavior need not depend upon hormones. In the absence of data, differences in the sexual activity of man should not be ascribed by default to heredity. Unless genetic differences can be excluded, however, similar conservatism should be exercised with respect to purely cultural hypotheses of the origin of variations.

Parental Behavior. Examples of the inheritance of parental caretaking behavior have been selected from three major groups of animals: birds, mammals, and insects. In the latter group, biologists will recognize that the worker bees of our example are not parents. We have included them here because the social significance of worker activity seems equivalent to the parental care of birds and mammals. Despite the importance of care-taking behavior to species survival, it has been investigated very little from a genetic point of view.

Broodiness. Economic interest has stimulated much genetic work on broodiness in the domestic fowl. Hens who do not take time out from laying to incubate their eggs return more money to their owner. Selection against broodiness has been practiced for years, and certain breeds, White Leghorns for example, are known as non-broody. Actually most fowl of non-broody strains can be induced to incubate eggs if proper conditions are established (Burrows and Byerly, 1938). There is no doubt, however, that the threshold of stimulation necessary to produce broody behavior varies tremendously among breeds. Many birds which are non-broody during their pullet year become broody later. This creates a problem when geneticists try to fit individuals into a dichotomous classification. Goodale, Sanborn, and White (1920) noted that the strength of the "broody character" might vary in two ways, (1) in the frequency of broody episodes and (2) in the duration of the episodes. Obviously, broodiness seems to be best considered as a quantitative character, and one would expect it to be controlled by many genes (Lerner, 1950). Early hypotheses which postulated one to three Mendelian factors to account for the occurrence of broodiness do not seem adequate today.

The heritability of broodiness is indicated by its response to selection in experiments carried out for 18 years at the Massachusetts Agricultural Experiment Station (Hays, 1933, 1940). The average number of broody episodes per broody individual fell from 3.5 to 1.1, and the percentage of broody fowl was reduced from 86 to 5. A correlation between the behavior of dams and daughters was noted (Table 6-23).

TABLE 6-23

Broodiness in Daughters as Related to Broodiness in Dams (Hays, 1940)

Dams	No.	No. Daughters	% Broody
Broody first year	27	187	52.5
Not broody first year	183	1580	10.3

Hays reported no evidence for sex-linked genes affecting broodiness, but several investigators have found the contrary. In fowl the males are homogametic (ZZ) and the females heterogametic (WZ). Females must receive their Z-chromosome from their sire. If this chromosome carries factors affecting broodiness, the genotype of the sire will have the predominant influence upon the offspring (Table 6-24).

The data of most investigators summarized in Table 6-24 support the hypothesis that sex-linked factors have an important effect upon broodiness. Kaufman also showed that autosomal factors must be involved. If all relevant genes were sex-linked, broodiness in dams and offspring would be uncorrelated, since the female's Z-chromosome goes only to her sons. Actually broody mothers had 67% broody daughters, and non-broody mothers had 31% broody daughters.

Whether the sex-chromosome effect is produced by a single gene,

TABLE 6-24

Results of Reciprocal Crosses between Broody and Non-Broody Breeds of Fowl

Dam	Sire	Percent Broody Offspring	Reference
Br. Leghorn	*Langshan*	29	Punnett and Bailey, 1920
Langshan	Br. Leghorn	50	Punnett and Bailey, 1920
Wh. Leghorn	*Cornish*	88	Roberts and Card, 1934
Cornish	Wh. Leghorn	37	Roberts and Card, 1934
Rh. Id. Red	*Plymouth Rock*	40, 39	Knox and Olsen, 1938
Plymouth Rock	Rh. Id. Red	12, 46	Knox and Olsen, 1938
Wh. Leghorn	*Plymouth Rock*	42	Knox and Olsen, 1938
Plymouth Rock	Wh. Leghorn	12	Knox and Olsen, 1938
Leghorn	*Greenleg*	78	Kaufman, 1948
Greenleg	Leghorn	0	Kaufman, 1948

Broody breeds identified by italics.

or a block of synergistically acting genes is uncertain. Apparently broodiness in some breeds is not sex-linked, so that it is incorrect to speak of a single mechanism for inheritance of broodiness. Selection within various breeds may have operated upon totally different genetic systems.

Maternal Behavior in Rabbits. Animal breeders are aware that races or strains vary in the adequacy of maternal care. Racial differences in the domestic rabbit have been described by Sawin and Curran (1952) and Sawin and Crary (1953). Females of race X characteristically prepare a nest before giving birth to young, whereas in other races nest building is commonly delayed until after parturition. Cannibalism and scattering of young are more prevalent in race IIIc. The authors have hypothesized that the behavior of race X may reflect hypopituitarism and that race IIIc may exhibit a hyperpituitarism. Although racial differences are significant, there is much individual variation which may reflect heterozygosity within the races or the operation of environmental factors. Confirmation or rejection of the endocrine basis of racial differences should be feasible with modern techniques of hormone assay, and such studies are reported to be in progress.

Hygienic Behavior in Bees. To designate the care of bee larvae as "parental behavior" would be a biological misnomer, for the caretaking activity is a function of the sterile workers, not of the parents.

It may well be included here, however, under the broader category of *epimiletic* (care giving) behavior (Scott, 1958). Regardless of nomenclature, worker bees do vary in their efficiency in tending the hive and removing diseased larvae (Rothenbuhler, 1958). This discovery came from observations on two inbred lines selected respectively for resistance and susceptibility to the disease, American foulbrood. The resistant-line workers uncovered the cells of diseased larvae and removed them from the hive. This, Rothenbuhler called hygienic behavior. Susceptible-line workers left inoculated larvae in place so that the disease spread widely. The F_1 workers were unhygienic, but a backcross to the resistant line (presumably recessive) yielded four types of offspring in equal numbers. One-fourth showed the complete hygienic pattern; one-fourth had none of it. Another fourth would uncap the cells of diseased larvae but not remove them, and still another fourth would remove larvae after the experimenter had uncapped the cells. The data are compatible with a dihybrid system in which uncapping and removal behavior are independently disrupted by two dominant genes. Rothenbuhler's hypothesis can be illustrated in genetic symbols:

Unhygienic line	*UURR*
Hygienic line	*uurr*
F_1 (non-hygienic)	*UuRr*

Crossing *UuRr* × *uurr* yields:

¼ non-hygienic	*UURR*
¼ hygienic	*uurr*
¼ uncover, do not remove	*uuRr*
¼ remove, do not uncover	*Uurr*

Such experiments illustrate the elegant simplicity of results which are sometimes obtained from non-mammalian species. Where behavior is determined by structures whose development is invariant with respect to most environmental occurrences, genes have a more definite relationship to specific behavior patterns. The most interesting feature of the Rothenbuhler experiment is the independent determination of two closely related acts. Breaking up complex patterns into specific movements is one way of finding units suitable for the genetic analysis of behavior.

Ingestive Behavior. The need for food and water is so universal that little variation in ingestive behavior can be tolerated. Domesticated species show some differentiation between breeds with respect to nutritive requirements (Williams, 1956, Chapter 10), but ingestive behavior itself has been little investigated from the genetic point of view. It is not certain, for example, that depriving animals for the same period of time equalizes hunger. Though eating problems in children are fairly common, psychiatrists treat these as manifestations of emotional disturbance, not as the outcome of specific constitutional variables. In animals, however, there is clear evidence that overeating sufficient to cause gross obesity is characteristic of certain genotypes. In addition, considerable research has been devoted to the hypothesis that "perverted appetites" may be the behavioral response to inherited biochemical deficiencies. A well known example, Williams' geneto-trophic hypothesis of alcoholism, has evoked considerable research and discussion.

Genetic Obesity in Mice. Body size in mice is affected by many coat-color genes. The yellow gene, A^y, is lethal when homozygous; in the heterozygous state it predisposes to obesity. Yellow mice are re-ported to have increased appetite and reduced activity (Dickerson and Gowen, 1947). Weitze (1940) showed that a yellow mouse in para-biosis with a normal mouse did not become fat. Hence the obesity was ascribed to deficiency in a hormone which was alleviated by cross-circulation.

More extreme obesity is found in mice homozygous for the obese gene, ob/ob. Reared under standard conditions, these animals eat heavily and are relatively inactive. The weight gain and the charac-teristic infertility may be prevented by restricting available food (Runner and Gates, 1954; Lane and Dickie, 1954) and can be largely overcome by combining the waltzing gene and the obese gene (Mayer, 1953). Compulsive activity in such animals compensates for the high caloric intake.

The question may be raised as to whether increased food intake (*hyperphagia*) represents a stronger hunger drive or a failure of a satiation mechanism. Miller, Bailey, and Stevenson (1950) demon-strated on rats made hyperphagic by hypothalamic lesions that meas-ures of consummatory activity (food intake) did not correspond with measures of drive (energy expended in crossing barriers). This is also true of the genetically obese mouse. If food is diluted with an inert filler, normal mice adjust their bulk intake upward to maintain ca-loric intake constant. Obese mice do this less well (Fuller and Jacoby, 1955). Obese mice are also less efficient in adjusting intake to need when the diet is made unpalatable by a bitter additive or increased in palatability by the addition of fat. On the first day of a changed diet both genotypes responded similarly. After several days on a diet, normal mice ingested about the same number of calories as usual, while obese mice were still responding more to palatability than to caloric content (Table 6-25). Although the eating behavior of this mouse is similar to that of the rat with hypothalamic lesions, no histological abnormalities have been detected.

TABLE 6-25

Nutritive Intake (in Percentage of Stable Control Level) of Obese and Normal Mice Given Special Diets (Fuller and Jacoby, 1955)

Diet	Group	First Day	Stabilized	Return to Standard
Bitter	Obese	56	72	109
Bitter	Normal	58	93	148
Excess fat	Obese	177	126	79
Excess fat	Normal	168	95	84

Continuous recording of the food intake of genetically obese mice revealed the absence of the 24-hour cycle of eating and quiescence characteristic of normal mice (Anliker and Mayer, 1956). Mature obese mice showed a short cycle periodicity, similar, but not identical to, irregularities shown by other experimentally obese subjects. Eating behavior in the genetically obese mouse is more under the immediate stimulus control of the nature of the diet and is less affected by nutritive status. Failure of the satiation mechanism when the diet is highly palatable, rather than increased hunger drive, appears to be the behavioral explanation of genetic obesity. Whether the failure derives from an undetected neurological anomaly or from a biochemical defect has not been settled.

Experimental Alcoholism. Men and animals select food and drink for reasons other than nutritive value. Appetites for specific substances are generally considered to be acquired. A genetic basis, however, has been proposed for the appetite for alcohol (Williams et al., 1949a,b). This hypothesis has aroused considerable interest because of the social significance of alcoholism in many cultures.

Williams' genetotrophic theory holds that certain individuals possess distinct inherited metabolic patterns which predispose them to alcoholism (Williams et al., 1950). A genetic block or partial block leads to diminished enzyme production, impairment of the ability to use one or more essential nutrients, and thence to augmented appetite for alcohol. Several experiments have been reported in support of this view. Williams et al. (1949b) reported that rats on a vitamin-deficient diet drank more alcohol in a water–10% alcohol choice situation than when the basic diet was more adequate. Two strains, O and H, were used. Feeding O rats with a vitamin supplement reduced alcohol consumption, but the same regimen had little effect on H rats. Alcohol solutions provide calories, and increased alcohol "preference" might simply be a response to a caloric deficiency induced by the fact that vitamin-free test diets are generally less palatable than stock diets. To combat this criticism, Williams et al. (1955) gave rats on a vitamin-deficient diet a choice between water and 10% sucrose and followed this by a period with water–10% alcohol choice. Experimental rats drank more sucrose solution and more alcohol solution than controls. However, consumption of sugar and alcohol was not correlated within individuals.

Success in selection for alcohol consumption in rats receiving deficient diets has been reported (Mardones, 1952; Mardones et al., 1953). Combined results for generations 3 through 7 are given in Table 6-26.

TABLE 6-26

Alcohol Intake of Offspring of Rats Selected with Respect to Alcohol Consumption
(Mardones et al., 1953)

Parents' Consumption	Number Litters	Number Offspring	Percentage of Offspring Whose Alcohol Consumption Falls within Indicated Range			
			.00–.19	.20–.39	.40–.59	.60+
.00–.19	24	189	61.4	29.6	5.8	3.2
.20–.39	16	71	29.6	42.4	22.5	5.6
.40–.59	11	69	27.6	31.9	26.1	14.5
.60+	6	36	25.0	19.5	22.3	33.3

Consumption measured in ml./100 gm. body weight/day.

Subjects were tested after 60 days on a diet deficient in "factor N," the thermolabile component of yeast. Reed (1951) reported significant strain differences in voluntary alcohol consumption in rats, but was unable to correlate these with excretion patterns of amino acids.

The Williams group has not specifically described the mechanism whereby vitamin deficiency could lead to an increased appetite for alcohol. In a weak form of the theory, alcohol might become reinforcing by an analgesic effect upon the malaise produced by malnutrition. As thus stated, the nutritional source of discomfort becomes fortuitous, and other relieving agents could be substituted for alcohol ingestion. A stronger version of the genetotrophic hypothesis calls for a more specific effect of particular deficiencies upon appetite. One gains the impression that Williams favors the stronger version, although he recognizes that decisive evidence is lacking. Research by Dember and Kristofferson (1955) supports the idea that a connection exists between free-choice alcohol consumption and emotionality as measured by audiogenic seizure latencies. Albino rats with low seizure latencies (considered to be more emotional) were significantly higher in alcohol consumption.

Most workers in the field of alcoholism place more emphasis upon psychosocial etiological agents than upon genetotrophic factors (Popham, 1953). No real confirmation of the genetotrophic hypothesis has been found in human material. In fact, the demonstration of its validity for experimental alcoholism in rats is far from complete. Scattered observations are in agreement, but more rigorous proof is needed. It is our opinion that the strong form of the hypothesis is unlikely to be true; the weak form which assigns non-specific motivating properties to partial genetic blocks deserves consideration.

Hoarding in Rats. Many species of mammals, among them the laboratory rat, transport food material to their nests where it is stored. Hoarding behavior is affected by the deprivation state of the animal and his early experience with transportable objects. A number of studies have dealt with the effects of these variables. Heredity is also a significant factor. Strains of rats differ in the latency of onset of hoarding after being placed in a suitable test apparatus and also in the average number of pellets transported in a standard test period (Stamm, 1954). Subjects of these experiments were three inbred strains distinguishable by their color patterns as black-hooded (*BlH*), brown-hooded (*BrH*), and Irish. Results of the tests under food deprivation are summarized in Table 6-27.

TABLE 6-27

Latency and Quantity of Hoarding in Rats
(Stamm, 1954)

Strain	Latency in Days		Pellets per Day	
	Mean	S.D.	Mean	S.D.
BlH	4.2	2.5	43.7	17.6
BrH	12.8	9.3	31.3	14.2
Irish	10.7	2.8	10.7	6.1

Differences in latency and amount of hoarding between black-hooded and Irish rats were highly significant. When the rats were fed to satiation, hoarding fell rapidly in the Irish and brown-hooded strains but persisted for several days in the black-hooded strain. All three indices of hoarding behavior showed consistent differences between the two extreme strains. The brown-hooded rats, however, were highly variable.

In a later experiment (Stamm, 1956), similar tests were conducted on Irish $\times$ BlH F_1 hybrids and $F_1 \times$ Irish backcrosses. Subjects were compared during a 12-day period of stabilized hoarding. In order to make the variances of the hoarding measures of the parental stocks reasonably similar, pellet counts (P) were transformed to hoarding scores (H) by the equation:

$$H = 10 \, (\log P + 1) - 3$$

The F_1 subjects hoarded like their black-hooded parents. The mean of the backcross was intermediate between the parents, and an increased variance suggested segregation of genetic determinants. It is possible that increased hoarding is a consequence of the greater activity of the black-hooded strain. No relationship was found between hoarding scores and a measure of dominance (Stamm, 1955).

Conclusion. A great number of response processes in a variety of species have been observed in behavior genetics. The high frequency of success in demonstrating inheritance of behavioral variation indicates that heredity must be a common source of variation in nature.

Undoubtedly more forms of behavior variation in more species will be shown to be subject to some degree of genetic determination. For traits of practical importance research of this kind is certainly useful. By itself, however, the accumulation of additional observations of strain differences will not improve the theoretical structure of behavior genetics. More useful experiments would sample the behavioral significance of the genetic variability existent in wild populations. Such studies, if carried out on a sufficiently wide range of species, might yield important general laws relating the heritability of behavior to breeding structure, phylogenetic status, and intensity of selection.

Equally needed are investigations of the pathways between genes and response patterns. Strain differences and breeding experiments may be useful tools in analyzing the physiological basis of individual differences in behavior.

7

Intellectual abilities

In this chapter we shall consider evidence relating to the inheritance of intellectual abilities in man and the lower animals. We shall look first at the meaning of the term "intelligence" and the ways of measuring it; second, at studies purporting to show its inherited components; third, we shall discuss the relation of inherited intelligence to other psychological and physiological variables; and finally, we shall present several theories that have been formulated on the genetic mode of transmission of intelligence and attempt to show their adequacies and inadequacies in the light of existing data.

THE NATURE OF INTELLIGENCE

Although intelligence is a widely used term, it is one that most psychologists find difficult to define satisfactorily. Interest in it can be traced far back in history—like many other problems, at least to the Greeks. Until about the nineteenth century, attention was directed to intelligence largely as a special attribute of man and as a power enabling him to know reality. The primary orientation was metaphysical and epistemological rather than empirical. Thus for Aristotle and later for medieval thinkers, intelligence was a special faculty pertaining to the essence of man as opposed to lower animals and was the means by which he could abstract from sensory data and arrive at concepts. Little attempt was made to look for differences between individuals in this respect, since all possessed it by virtue of being human.

Scientific interest in individual difference in mental ability can be dated from Sir Francis Galton, who later came to be known to some as the "father of mental testing." Galton did not go to any lengths to define intelligence exactly, much less measure it adequately. But he did deal with it in a general way in his studies of the inheritance of natural abilities, eminence, and genius, whch will be discussed later. His definition of high intelligence was, in many ways, a completely operational one. For example, to belong to Galton's more select group a man "should have distinguished himself pretty frequently either by purely original work or as a leader of opinion" (Galton, 1883b, page 9).

Under the influence of Galton and later of Binet, the mental-testing movement grew rapidly, especially in America, and it became a popular pastime among psychologists to offer different definitions of intelligence. Binet suggested that intelligence involved the ability to select and maintain a definite direction, the ability to make adaptations leading to a desired end, and the ability to criticize one's own behavior. Spearman reduced it to the ability to educe relations and correlates. Thorndike regarded it as the power of making good responses from the standpoint of truth or fact, whereas Terman, in more classical style, defined it as the ability to abstract. Useful summaries of these and other definitions have been made by Spearman (1927), Knight (1933), Mann (1946), and Goodenough (1949).

Eventually American behaviorism supplied at least a partial answer to the problem by suggesting that no further speculations be made as to the nature of intelligence, but rather that it be regarded simply as that which an intelligence test measures (Goodenough, 1949). This definition may seem circular and arbitrary, but actually it is not, provided that the test is made up on the basis of some clear postulational definition. Given such a test, we may then proceed to analyze in detail the nature of the functions it involves and the pattern of their relationships. In this way hypotheses may be generated which can then be examined and corrected until a satisfactory understanding of mental ability is achieved. This a posteriori approach is implicit in most of the factor-analytic work which we may now discuss briefly.

The originator of the technique of factor analysis was Charles S. Spearman (1927). He was perhaps the first to explore and develop the idea implicit in Pearson's coefficient of correlation, which suggested that if two traits or abilities vary together, they have something in common. Spearman noted that practically all tests, when corrected for their lack of reliability (correction for attenuation), intercorrelated to a high degree. From this fact he reasoned that all intellectual tasks must have some basic common element—an element he called G, or general mental ability. The fact that correlation between tests was not perfect, he explained by suggesting that each test had a specific as well as a general character. He conceived of these specifics as being the particular "engines" through which G was expressed.

Since Spearman's day, factor techniques and factor theory have both changed a good deal, though the essential idea remains the same. One of the most outstanding developments was made by Thurstone (1947) in America. Rather than postulating one general factor, Thurstone explained test intercorrelations by a multiple-factor hypothesis. Thus intelligence was conceived as being made up of a number of "primary mental abilities," such as spatial ability, reasoning, verbal fluency, numerical ability, and others. At the present time there are many ways of describing a correlation matrix factorially. There appears to be no absolutely "best" solution, though some solutions have won more popularity than others. The major problem is that of relating factors to independent empirical criteria (see page 338). If factor analysis is to be used at all inferentially rather than merely descriptively (Eysenck, 1950), relating factors in this manner is necessary. In summary, the factor-analytic definition of intelligence takes little for granted. It is largely operational and a *posteriori*. For these reasons it has much to recommend it.

A final approach that should be mentioned briefly is that involved in the so-called "culture-free" test. It has been assumed by some workers, such as Rulon, Cattell, Raven, and others (Anastasi, 1954), that there is some basic stratum of intelligence that underlies its expression through any particular cultural medium. If local sociocultural elements can then be eliminated, there should remain only this essential aspect. Thus Vernon (1954) has suggested that the ability to follow "oral directions" of a greater or lesser complexity represents a basic intellectual ability that is demanded by all societies and that is probably little affected by differences in educational background. Obviously, this approach to defining intelligence is almost as a *priori* as that followed by early workers in the field. At the same time, it cannot be dismissed entirely. If we use an "iterative" procedure, constantly checking and rechecking our initial definition against empirical data, it is possible that we may eventually arrive at a genuinely basic definition of intellectual ability.

In this chapter, we wish to establish that the tests used in psychology to measure intelligence agree with certain genetic criteria, such as twin and family resemblances; that is, we wish to establish that this trait depends on or is correlated with hereditary factors. Clearly, not all of those who have worked on this problem have used the same tests or have defined intelligence in the same way.

The next section deals with empirical studies on the inheritance of intellectual ability. We shall consider separately experiments using human and animal subjects. We shall not restrict ourselves to studies based on formal intelligence tests but shall also consider the inheritance of achievement and academic abilities.

THE INHERITANCE OF INTELLIGENCE IN MAN

As stated in Chapter 4, three main methods have been used in studying the inheritance of psychological characters in human beings. These are the pedigree method, the familial correlational method, and the twin method. We shall now look at some of the data obtained by each.

Pedigree Studies. Although many people had traced family pedigrees before him, Galton (1883a) was the first to do so in a way that can be called scientific. He was particularly impressed with what he called eminence, or unusually high intellectual endowment, and considered this trait so rare as to have an incidence in the population of only 0.025%. On the basis of reputation and available records he constructed pedigrees of distinguished statesmen, commanders, literary men, scientists, poets, musicians, painters, divines, and even university oarsmen and "North Country wrestlers." An example of one of his ancestral charts is shown in modified form in Table 7-1. To allow

TABLE 7-1

Example of a Pedigree of Rowing Families Described by Galton (Galton, 1883a, page 310)

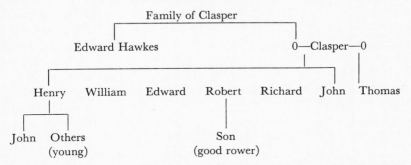

All those mentioned in the pedigree except one were able or excellent oarsmen.

more quantitative examination of these pedigrees, he used a rough scale based on a normal curve with eighteen intervals ranging from eminent to idiot and imbecile. Since Galton found from his data that the chances of an eminent man having an eminent relative were rather high, he inferred that intellectual ability was clearly inherited. Furthermore, after a careful examination of the environmentalist hypothesis, he concluded that true capacity could not be altered by lack of opportunity and would always overcome social barriers and unfavorable circumstances. It is interesting or amusing, according to one's viewpoint, that one of his arguments for this involved a comparison of British and American eminence. According to his judgment, the number of really able men was higher in England in spite of the more repressive social life in that country. If the more democratic form of society in America in which education and opportunity were more available to the masses did not produce proportionately more ability, then, obviously, environment could not make much difference. This general conclusion can be seriously questioned. Be that as it may, his analysis of pedigrees stands as a milestone on the road to understanding psychological inheritance.

Since Galton's day the pedigree method has been used widely, although for quantitative traits it has been largely replaced by correlational methods. Such men as Gun (1930*a,b*), van Bemmelen (1927), and Bramwell (1944) have presented pedigrees of Royal families, holders of the Order of Merit, and various other similar classes that cannot be easily described in exact terms but are nonetheless worth examination. In the realm of special abilities we have a great many pedigree studies devoted to musical talent. One of the most famous of musical families is, of course, the Bach family, which was studied first by Galton (1883*a*) and later by many others (Terry, 1929). Although the problem of separating nature from nurture complicates matters, the amount of musical ability that consistently appears in the Bachs for a number of generations is strongly suggestive of hereditary factors at work.

Inasmuch as pedigree studies represented a first step in psychological genetics, they have considerable historical importance. Their value is reduced, of course, by the fact that they usually do not show the operation of heredity independent of environmental influences. Intelligent parents supply their offspring not only genes for high intellectual capacity, but also a type of environment which is stimulating to mental development. By the pedigree method we cannot separate the two kinds of variables. It may be mentioned that, from one standpoint, we need not concern ourselves with this problem (Thompson, 1957*b*). If we are interested simply in the results of transmission from parents to offspring, it is not necessary to separate all the factors at work.

Correlational Studies. The next important development in the study of the genetics of intelligence was the introduction of correlation techniques by Galton and Karl Pearson. With this statistical tool the resemblance between parents and offspring and between the offspring themselves can be expressed in a concise quantitative form. Studies of intelligence will be considered separately from those dealing with special abilities.

Familial Correlation in Intelligence. The first systematic examination of familial correlation with respect to mental ability was made by Karl Pearson, who started his work around the turn of the century. Using teachers' rankings based on a seven-point scale of intellectual capacity, he found that the correlation between brothers was .52, between sisters .51, and between brother and sister .52. Since these values were approximately the same as those obtained with physical characteristics such as health, hair color, cephalic index, and others, Pearson concluded that psychical traits are inherited in the same way and to the same degree (1904). Woods (1906), using a rating scale of 1 to 10 for intellectual and moral excellence, analyzed some Royal-Family pedigrees. He obtained a parent-child correlation of .30. Schuster and Elderton (1907), using the records of academic performance at Charterhouse, Harrow, and Oxford, were able to establish a parental correlation of .31 and fraternal correlations of around .40.

One of the first to use standardized mental tests was Gordon (1919), who found a sibling correlation of .61 with the first Stanford revision of the Binet-Simon test. Both Pearson (1918) and Elderton (1923) reworked her data (correction for age, use of all possible sib pairs, etc.) and obtained a correlation nearer to .50. Around the same time Pintner (1918) and Madsen (1924) contributed to knowledge in the field by introducing control correlations between unrelated pairs. Since these turned out to be rather low (between .19 and −.04), the case for the inheritance of intellectual ability was strengthened.

Research in the area since this time has been concerned with three major problems: (1) the relative influence of heredity and environment in the determination of familial resemblance; (2) the degree of resemblance for different kinds of populations such as groups differing in mean intellectual level, different age groups, and different sociological groups; (3) the study of family resemblances with respect to different kinds of, or components of, intelligence. Since the three categories overlap this division is evidently to some extent an artificial one. But it provides a general framework that may facilitate understanding of the large amount of research done in the area.

In the first place, many studies that have been done subsequent to Pearson have tended to corroborate his original findings. Most workers have found sib and parent-child correlations ranging from .40 up to .70 or slightly higher. For example, Thorndike (1928) found a sib correlation of .70 (.60 when corrected for sample homogeneity) for

812 pairs of high-school students. In two later papers (1944*a,b*) he re-examined and added to these early data, and he concluded that his previous estimates and those of most of the workers in the field had been too low. Jones (1928) obtained a sib correlation of .49, and later Conrad and Jones (1940), using the Army Alpha and the 1916 revision of the Stanford-Binet for 269 family groups, obtained the same correlation both for sibs and for parents and their children. Gray and Moshinsky (1933) obtained correlations somewhat lower than those to be expected genetically. This comparison is shown in Table 7-2. It will become quite clear as the discussion proceeds that these figures are fairly typical.

TABLE 7-2

A Comparison of Actual Correlations for the Otis Test of Intelligence with Expected Genetic Correlations (Gray and Moshinsky, 1933)

		Obtained Correlations	Genetic Correlations Expected in a System of Random Mating	
			Autosomal	Sex-Linked
Siblings				
	All pairs	.35 ± .05	.50	.40
	Female pairs	.47 ± .08	.50	.75
	Male pairs	.33 ± .09	.50	.50
	Mixed pairs	.26 ± .10	.50	.35
First Cousins				
	All pairs	.16 ± .06	.125	.112
	Female pairs	.17 ± .10	.125	.172
	Male pairs	.16 ± .09	.125	.047
	Mixed pairs	.10 ± .03	.125	.104

Factors Modifying Correlations. Several approaches have been made to the problem of separating hereditary from environmental factors in the determination of similarity. Both always operate, usually exerting effects in the same direction. Freeman, Holzinger, and Mitchell (1928) found that the correlation between real parents and their children (.35) was actually somewhat less than that between foster parents and their foster children (.39). This could be accounted for at least partly by selective placement of the child in a home appropriate to his intellectual level. The same authors found also that the correlation for sibs reared apart was .34, a figure lower than those usually reported.

Taken in conjunction, these two findings do suggest that similarity of environment can do much to produce similarity of intelligence. The first finding of Freeman et al., however, was not supported by Burks (1928), who found that the relationship of a child with its true parent on a number of indices (mental age, vocabulary score, school grade attained) was much greater than it was with a foster parent. She concluded that the influence of environment was far less than that of heredity in determining intellectual level.

An interesting study taking a somewhat different tack (Lawrence, 1931) has also tended to favor the importance of hereditary over environmental factors. Two important points established were first, that even in children living in an orphanage, which might be considered a very homogeneous environment, variability of intelligence was as high as that found in children living in homes; and, second, that correlation between intelligence of children and socio-economic class of parent was low at the time the children entered the orphanage (at an early age), but tended to increase as the children grew older. These points mean that homogeneity of environment does not necessarily produce homogeneity of population intelligence and that the influence of social class may operate primarily through genetic rather than educational factors.

Quite a large number of studies have examined the effects of age disparities on family resemblances. It is assumed that since children of different age groups occupy different environments, the intellectual similarities between sibs of different ages should be less marked than between sibs of about the same age if environment is, in fact, of importance. If environment is of little importance, on the other hand, sib correlations should not be greatly affected by age differences. On the whole, the evidence appears to favor the second alternative. Conrad (1931) found that age differences between siblings did not appreciably affect their similarity on the Army Alpha. Likewise, Finch (1933), using 1023 pairs, found a correlation of .49 that was not much changed by age differences within sib pairs up to 11 years. Similarly, artificially "twinning" sibs by using only their I.Q. scores taken at identical ages had no effect on resemblance (Richardson, 1936). One study that appears to indicate the opposite conclusion is that of Sims (1931), who artificially paired unrelated children according to socio-economic background, age, and school. The correlation between these unrelated "sibs" was .35, a figure not much lower than that obtained by many investigators with real siblings. Consequently, the problem of age effects is not altogether solved, though the weight of the evidence indicates that they are not serious complications.

Correlations in Different Populations. The second line of work on familial correlations has dealt with degree of resemblance in different populations. Hart (1924) attempted to compare sibling correlations in three groups, a random selection of public-school children, a rural group of lower mean intellectual level, and a group selected for high intelligence. The three correlations were respectively .45, .46, and .40. Another study by Hildreth (1925) involving three schools, two of which differed in intellectual level, has supported the conclusion that differences between groups with respect to size of sib correlations depend on group homogeneity, rather than level of intelligence. Correlations in mental ability were lower in the more selected or homogeneous groups, and a composite correlation taken over the three schools together, was higher than that of any one school separately. Hildreth's data are summarized in Table 7-3. Outhit

TABLE 7-3

Resemblance in Intelligence of Siblings in Three Different Schools (Hildreth, 1925)

School Type	No.	Sib Correlation	Sib Correlation Age Constant
1. Average, heterogeneous	450	.63	.47
2. Superior, homogeneous	325	.32	.08
3. Average, homogeneous	253	.27	.13
4. Composite	1028	.68	.42

(1933), using the Stanford-Binet and the Army Alpha examined parental and sibling correlations in 51 families drawn from the city, the small town, and the country. Most of the coefficients she obtained were higher than others had found previously. All sib correlations (computed by different pairing methods) were in excess of .50, and the midparent-midchild correlation turned out to be .80. It seems likely that these figures are the result of using a rather heterogeneous sample. There did not appear to be any differences between the various groups, nor was there any correlation between parental ability and variability of offspring. It should be mentioned in passing that Outhit has an excellent review of the literature prior to 1933.

Several studies deal with culture and family structure respectively. Cattell and Willson (1938) attempted to discover the extent of family resemblance with cultural differences held constant. To this end, they used a so-called culture-free test of intelligence. After correction for age, for attenuation, for scatter, and for skewness the figures they obtained were .91 for parent-child, and .77 for sibling correlation. The authors concluded on the basis of these data that parents and children have nine-tenths of their respective intellectual levels in common and that four-fifths of the variability in intelligence among families is due to heredity. Whether their test was really culture-free is problematical; nevertheless, the correlations they obtained are higher than those found by any other workers, a fact which suggests that cultural differences may well produce artificially low estimates of family resemblance.

Griffits (1926) examined the resemblance between adjacent versus non-adjacent siblings with respect to modal school grades. He found that adjacent children were more alike than non-adjacent and that average fraternal correlations were smaller in families of four (.25) than in families of three children (.47). He attributed these results to environmental factors. Some support was given to this conclusion by the data of Huestis and Otto (1927). Using 100 sibling pairs at the University of Oregon, they found that although correlations between brother and brother and between sister and sister were high for school grades (.71 and .74, respectively), the average correlation between brothers and sisters was very low (.04). Since no reliable differences in general intelligence exist between males and females, these results can be construed as giving support to experience rather than to heredity. Dexter (see Carter, 1932), however, in a very similar study obtained quite different results from those of Huestis and Otto. He found no difference in the size of fraternal correlations in scholastic ability between like-sexed as opposed to unlike-sexed pairs. Both were close to .40.

Special Abilities. The final problem to be considered here deals with family resemblance for different components of intelligence and for different special abilities. Most of the relevant studies have been concerned with scholastic achievements. Two early studies (Earle, 1903; Pearson, 1910) obtained fraternal and parent-child correlations for various school abilities about as large as those commonly found for general intelligence. Another study (Starch, 1915) yielded a mean fraternal correlation for general scholastic ability of .52. In this and in a subsequent study (Starch, 1917), Starch also examined sib correlations in a variety of special abilities. These varied in size a good deal, being generally higher at older age levels. One notable finding was that the mean correlation for abilities not much affected by school work (e.g., memory, cancellation) was as high as those that were affected (e.g., reading, writing, arithmetic). For this reason, Starch concluded that heredity rather than training causes resemblances in families. Both Cobb (1917) and Banker (1928) supported this conclusion with further empirical data. Willoughby (1927) found somewhat stronger family resemblance in verbal as against non-verbal abilities. All correlations tended to be lower than those found by most investigators.

Perhaps the most exhaustive study in this area is Carter's (1932), directed at family resemblances in verbal and numerical abilities. His main data for these two classes are shown in Table 7-4. There is

TABLE 7-4

Family Resemblance in Verbal and Numerical Abilities (Carter, 1932)

Child with

	Like Sib	Unlike Sib	Midparent	Like Parent	Unlike Parent
Average verbal	.38	.31	.22	.54	−.11
Average numerical	.24	.17	.20	.64	−.28

a tendency for members of like-sexed pairs to resemble each other more strongly than unlike-sexed pairs. On the whole, specific correlations obtained were rather low. He attributed this result to the homogeneity of the group with which he worked and to the absence of a high degree of assortative mating within it. At the same time, by breaking down his data according to proportions of above-average and below-average children having both or one parent of above- or below-average ability, Carter made a fairly strong case for inheritance. Thus, if both parents were superior they tended to have a high proportion of superior children; if one or both were inferior this proportion was correspondingly less. Since this study has some aspects that bear on the problem of the genetic transmission of intelligence, it will be referred to again.

From the discussion above, several tentative conclusions are indicated. In the first place, resemblance in intelligence appears to depend in most populations more on hereditary than environmental or experiential factors. Second, degree of resemblance is not very different in different kinds of populations, such as urban or rural, superior or average, except insofar as these may influence the homogeneity of the sample. If cultural influences on test score are eliminated (Cattell and Willson, 1938), degree of resemblance is increased. Third, there is some evidence to show that resemblances even in school abilities are affected by heredity at least as much as those in general intelligence.

Twin Studies. Galton again must receive credit for introducing the twin method to the scientific study of inheritance. In his book *Inquiries into Human Faculty* (1883b) he describes the results of questionnaire data obtained from a large number of pairs of twins, about eighty of which indicated close similarity between the members of the pair with respect to many different characters. Some reports that suggested dissimilarity Galton tended to discount on the grounds of "the tendency of relatives to dwell unconsciously on distinctive peculiarities and to disregard the far more numerous points of likeness that would first attract the notice of a stranger." His final conclusion is that "nature prevails enormously over nurture when the differences of nurture do not exceed what is commonly to be found among persons of the same rank of society and in the same county" (Galton, 1883b, page 241).

Galton's data were rather meager and lacked objectivity, but the inferences he drew from them have been in most part substantiated by ensuing work. One of the earliest contributors on this continent was Thorndike (1905), who examined resemblances in fifty pairs of twins on a number of tests involving partly intellectual and academic and partly mechanical performance. On six such tests correlations ranged from .69 for a task of marking out A's in a page of capital letters to .90 for a test of "opposites." Addition and multiplication tests gave correlations of .75 and .84 respectively. Thorndike argued that since younger pairs showed as strong a resemblance as older pairs, environment played no important part in producing twin likenesses. It will be noted, of course, that the opposite argument also has cogency—that is, environment might act so as to bring out dissimilarities rather than similarities, in which case older pairs should be less alike than younger. The data actually support either hypothesis.

Resemblance in I.Q. Since this time a great deal of work has been done. We shall first consider studies done on resemblance in general intelligence for twins reared together and apart and then pass on to the matter of resemblance in special abilities. Before techniques of establishing zygosity became well standardized, most investigations dealt with comparisons between like-sexed and unlike-sexed twins. Typical of these is the study of Merriman (1924), who published one of the first incisive monographs on intellectual resemblances of twins. He used three well-standardized intelligence tests (the Stanford-Binet, the Army Beta, and the National Intelligence Test) as well as teachers' estimates. Merriman concluded that (1) environment has little effect on the size of the correlations, since older and younger pairs are not consistently different in this respect; (2) twins, as a group, do not show any obvious intellectual handicap; (3) correlations between like-sexed pairs are significantly higher than those between unlike-sexed pairs; (4) the resemblance in the case of unlike-sexed pairs is close to that between ordinary siblings.

Lauterbach (1925) confirmed and added to the earlier work in a study involving 212 pairs of twins, 149 being of like sex, 63 being of unlike sex. On the Binet I.Q. test he obtained correlations of .77 and .56 respectively for these two groups. The correlations tended to be lower at a younger age. Lauterbach also examined resemblances on various scholastic tasks, but we shall consider these separately in a later section.

One of the first to deal with MZ-DZ twin comparison was Tallman (1928), who found that the mean intrapair difference in I.Q. was 5.08 for identicals, 7.37 for like-sexed fraternals, 8.48 for unlike-sexed fraternals, and 13.14 for siblings. His findings were in agreement with earlier data and were supported in the same year by the results of Kramer and Lauterbach (1928).

Wingfield and Sandiford (1928) made a useful summary of intellectual similarity in twins as compared with unrelated individuals reared in a very uniform environment. They tested 102 pairs of twins, observing intrapair resemblance at two ages, eight to eleven years and twelve to fifteen years, with respect to I.Q., A.Q. (achievement quotient), and E.Q. (education quotient). Pupils from an orphanage constituted their control group. A correlation of greater than .70 on all these measures was found in the twins, and there was little variation in resemblance with age. The children who lived in an orphanage, in spite of their homogeneous environment, turned out to be no more alike than unrelated children in the general population.

Holzinger (1929) compared a population of MZ twins with a population of DZ twins on a number of indices of mental and scholastic ability and personality traits. Correlations for MZ twins on the Binet I.Q. and the Otis I.Q. were .88 and .92, respectively, and the corresponding coefficients for DZ twins were .63 and .62. Age did not affect similarity. On the basis of a subsequent analysis of these data he concluded that nature and nurture are about equally effective in producing twin differences, but nature is more effective in producing variability of such differences.

Continued work in the 1930's followed the lines developed above. Stocks and Karn (1933) found Stanford-Binet correlations to be .84 for MZ and .65 for DZ twin pairs, figures somewhat higher than those found later by Byrns and Healy (1936). The latter investigators also found that on the Henmon-Nelson Test of Mental Ability their twin population, numbering 412 pairs, had a mean percentile score of only 39.73 as compared with 50.00 for the rest of the high-school sample of 119,850 from which they were drawn. Furthermore, this retardation tended to be more marked in like-sexed (supposedly identical) twins than in unlike-sexed twins.

Hermann and Hogben (1933) published a paper on twin resemblances with respect to Otis score. Differences were found to be greater in the case of DZ than MZ twin pairs. In addition to their empirical work, the authors attempted to develop methodology for examining the relative influences of nature and nurture.

Three well-known studies of multiple births are also worth noting. Anderson and Scheidmann (1933) found varying degrees of similarity in the three sets of triplets with which they dealt. Gardner and Newman (1943) reported an intensive case study of the Morlock quadruplets, who were regarded as "unquestionably monozygotic." For the most part, the quadruplets proved to be remarkably alike in intellectual capacity, though one tended to be consistently inferior. Differences between them on Stanford-Binet I.Q. ranged from one to nine points. On the Army Beta three obtained identical scores, whereas the fourth was only three points lower. We shall come back to this study in considering twin resemblances in special abilities. The third study by Blatz (1937) of the famous Dionne quintuplets also supplies much information on a very rare genetic occurrence.

Components of Intelligence. The following three studies to be reviewed here represent attempts to study twin similarities by means of more refined measures of intellectual capacity. One of these, by Blewett (1954), used the Thurstone Test of Primary Mental Abilities and the Nufferno Tests of Intellectual Level and Intellectual Speed. The subjects finally chosen for analysis were 52 twin pairs. These included 26 monozygotic and 26 dizygotic pairs and 26 male and 26 female pairs. Blewett hypothesized first that the second-order factor derived from the primary abilities should represent predominantly hereditary influences and second that the heritability of the second-order factor should be greater than that of the primary factors. Thus he regarded *G*, or general ability, as a "core" of inherited intellectual capacity on which "environmental influences impose a consistent though diverse pressure leading to the relative hyper-development of certain facets of ability." Analysis of his results tended to support only the first of these hypotheses. Data are summarized in Table 7-5. Scores

TABLE 7-5

The Inheritance of Primary Factors of Mental Abilities and of Second-Order General Intelligence
(Blewett, 1954)

P.M.A. Factor	Intra-identical Correlation	Intra-fraternal Correlation	h^2 Value
Verbal	.726	.145	.680
Space	.630	.248	.508
Number	.489	.449	.073
Reason	.708	.188	.640
Fluency	.734	.257	.642
Composite 1*	.583	.369	.339
Composite 2†	.754	.394	.594
Composite 3‡	.732	.406	.549

* P.M.A. total score from formula $V + S + 2N + 2R + W$.

† P.M.A. total score calculated on the basis of the square of Thurstone's second-order factor loadings.

‡ P.M.A. total score calculated on the basis of weights derived from the present experimental group.

weighted in accordance with second-order factors certainly reflected heredity in that they gave rise to a correlation of over .70 for identicals and around .40 for fraternals, but this tendency was no more marked than with the use of primary-factor scores. It is of some interest that tests of verbal fluency, verbal comprehension, and reasoning showed determination by heredity to a much greater extent than number and space abilities. The author speculates that possibly good art students are born, whereas mathematicians, engineers, and statisticians are made by training. If true, this conclusion is a most important one.

Another important study by Thurstone, Thurstone, and Strandskov (Strandskov, 1954) attempted to show concordance for a large number of tests including the Primary Mental Abilities test much in the same manner as did Blewett's study. The authors used 48 MZ and 55 DZ

pairs. Their main results for P.M.A. tests are reproduced in Table
7-6. It is of interest that the results of this study do not altogether

TABLE 7-6

The Inheritance of Primary Factors of Mental Ability
(Strandskov, 1954)

P.M.A. Factor	Chi Square	p
Space	14.38	<.01
Verbal	12.93	<.01
Fluency	5.25	<.01
Memory	4.09	<.05
Number	2.12	<.10
Reasoning	0.40	<.30

High chi-square value for differences between MZ and
DZ twins indicates strong hereditary influence.

agree with those of Blewett. Space ability shows a very strong hereditary determination; reasoning shows the least dependence on genotype.
There is fairly good agreement between the two studies with respect
to the other factors, however.

Vandenberg (1956) examined 45 MZ and 37 DZ twin pairs with a
large battery of tests. Although the results he reported were not in
quantified form, they did indicate hereditary control for a number
of intellectual functions. These included P.M.A. number and P.M.A.
verbal comprehension. Performance on the Raven Progressive Ma-
trices, a non-verbal test rather similar to that used by Cattell and
Willson (1938), also showed genetic determination.

It is clear from the above discussion that MZ twins show much
greater similarity than DZ pairs on most tests of intelligence. In fact,
their likeness is about as great as the test-retest reliabiliy of a single
individual (Schwesinger, 1933). Nonetheless, it is still possible that this
similarity is partly due to their occupying more similar environments
than do fraternal twins (Jones, 1946). The work on twins reared apart
has attacked this problem directly.

Twins Reared Apart. Newman (1930) published an important study
which compared 50 pairs of DZ twins, 50 pairs of MZ twins reared together, and 3 MZ pairs reared apart. For fraternals, the average I.Q.
(Stanford-Binet) difference was 9.9 points, for identicals 5.9 points,
and for the three identicals reared apart about 9 points. Two of the

identical twins reared apart differed 12 points, although the members of one of the pairs had had very similar, and the members of the other pair very different educational environments. The members of the third pair differed only 3 points and had had similar environments. These kinds of results made it difficult to draw general conclusions.

The most significant piece of work to appear on the subject was the extensive study by Newman, Freeman, and Holzinger (1937) comparing identical twins reared together, fraternals reared together, and 19 pairs of identicals reared apart. These varied in their ages from 11 to 35 years, with one pair being 53 years old at the time of testing. Nine of these cases had been separated before the age of 1 year, 6 pairs were separated during the second year, 2 during the third year, 1 at 6½, and 1 at 8 years. Differences in amount of education between members of each pair were also considerable. The results of the comparisons made by the authors are summarized in Table 7-7. It

TABLE 7-7

Intellectual Resemblances of DZ Twins
with MZ Twins Reared Together and Apart
(Newman et al., 1937)

Test	Intra-pair Correlations		
	MZ		DZ
	Together	Apart	
Binet	.910	.670	.640
Otis	.922	.727	.621
Stanford Achievement	.955	.507	.883

will be noted that correlations for Binet and Otis I.Q. test results for identicals reared apart fall between those for identicals reared together and those for fraternals. In respect to the Stanford Achievement Test, however, the separated twins proved to be less alike than fraternals.

Newman, Freeman, and Holzinger conclude that social and educational environment is a crucial factor in producing resemblances and that variations in it will tend to reduce sharply the similarity given by genotype. This is perhaps too strong a conclusion. Certainly the range in I.Q. differences in the separated pairs is great, going from 1 up to 24 I.Q. points. It is true that in the case of this largest discrepancy (the twins Gladys and Helen) the amount of difference in education was great, and that on the whole there is a correlation of .79 between discrepancy in educational advantage and discrepancy in Binet I.Q. (.55 for Otis) (Anastasi and Foley, 1949). But in at least one case, notably the pair Richard and Raymond, the difference in intellectual ability is only one I.Q. point, even though one of these boys was raised by a truck farmer and the other by a well-to-do physician respectively. Consequently, we must be rather cautious about any blanket interpretations put on the general results. Good reviews of this experiment as well as other work on twins were made by Burks (1938) and by Woodworth (1940).

Gardner and Newman (1940) later added two more cases (numbers 20 and 21) of identical twins reared apart to their original list of 19 and drew the same conclusions as before. Four other case studies on MZ twins reared apart have also appeared. A rather large I.Q. difference of 19 points was found in one of these studies (Gates and Brash, 1941) but almost no differences in the other three (Saudek, 1934; Burks, 1942; Stephens and Thompson, 1943). It is likely that the definite inferiority of one member of the first pair was related to his poorer physical build and general health.

In summary, the evidence on twins reared apart supports the hereditary hypothesis, though there is also little doubt that large differences in environment can affect similarity of MZ twins. There is also the further difficulty that the same environment may act differently on different genotypes. This is a recurring problem for the behavior geneticist.

Special Abilities. Having discussed the studies of intellectual resemblance in twins, we may now turn to work concerned with their resemblances in special abilities. Many of the workers discussed above dealt with special skills as well as with intelligence. Thorndike (1905) found strong resemblances in twins for ability in various school subjects, including spelling, addition, and multiplication—resemblances as strong, in fact, as those found in intellectual capacity. Merriman (1924) later showed, however, that twins show rather less similarity in respect to teachers' estimates of their ability. Correlations were .69 and .37 at ages 5 to 9 years and 10 to 16 years respectively.

Lauterbach (1925), who found smaller than usual resemblance in the I.Q.'s of twins, also found less likeness in school subjects. His correlations for six school subjects at two ages are shown in Table 7-8. There do not appear to be many definite changes with development and, in effect, none on the average.

TABLE 7-8

Twin Resemblances in Various School Subjects Taken at Two Ages
(Lauterbach, 1925)

	Months	
	90–156	157–238
Reading quotient	.44	.57
Arithmetic accuracy	.59	.50
Arithmetic speed	.59	.57
Memory for digits	.36	.34
Handwriting quality	.49	.58
Handwriting speed	.66	.55
Average	.54	.55

Somewhat higher correlations for arithmetic ability were found by Wingfield and Sandiford (1928). They found correlations of .89 at age 8 to 11 and .73 at age 12 to 15. Waardenburg (1929) reported data on the resemblances in scholastic ability of identical and non-identical pairs. His finding that likeness was greater between identicals was given support by Holzinger (1929), who used among other indices five tests of school ability, namely word meaning, arithmetic, nature study, history and literature, and spelling. Correlations ranged from .73 to .87 for identicals and .56 to .73 for fraternals. Degree of resemblance was not noticeably less for these subjects than for intelligence test performances.

Newman, Freeman, and Holzinger (1937) showed that similarity of environment might be an important factor in producing resemblances between members of MZ-twin pairs. On the Stanford Achievement Test the mean difference between MZ twins reared together was 6.38 but was 16.26 between those reared apart. Corresponding correlations were .955 and .507. It is significant that the differences between the two groups were much less with respect to measured intelligence. Consequently, there are some grounds for supposing that although twins may show as much resemblance in scholastic ability as in intellectual capacity, the causes of this resemblance may be quite different for the two. This conclusion is supported to some extent by the Gardner and Newman quadruplet study (1940), which showed more dissimilarities among the members of the group with respect to Stanford Achievement Test scores than with respect to I.Q. scores.

In addition to the studies described above, dealing mainly with scholastic ability, there is a large collection of papers on a variety of particular skills and abilities in twins, such as skill in chess playing, mathematical ability, creative-writing ability, and others (Reinöhl, 1939).

Summary. In summary, it may be said that the data gathered with human subjects point to heredity as an important determiner of intellectual level though certainly not the only one. From the size of the correlations alone, however, we can infer very little about the extent of its importance, even in very particular cases. Even if all the many relevant variables that may affect the phenotypic expression of intelligence were known, the knotty problem of disentangling heredity and environment would still remain. Nor is this only a pseudo-problem as many writers appear to believe. There are ways of approaching it, some of which we have already discussed (Chapter 4). We shall turn now to the animal evidence on the inheritance of intelligence.

INHERITANCE OF INTELLIGENCE IN ANIMALS

We shall consider animal experiments on the inheritance of intelligence under two heads: first, work using the method of selective breeding; and, second, work using the method of strain differences. It should be mentioned before going further that the term "intelligence" is even more difficult to define in animals than in human beings. At least with persons, test scores can be related to various empirical criteria for validation purposes, but with animals this is usually not possible.

Selection Studies. One of the first workers to examine the inheritance of behavior in animals was E. C. Tolman (1924). Starting with a rather heterogeneous stock of animals, he selectively bred "bright" and "dull" animals on the basis of performance (time, errors, and perfect runs) in a maze. His results, summarized in Table 7-9, indicate that selection was not very successful. There is some separation in the G_1, but this diminishes in the G_2 where there is little tendency for the brights to get brighter or the dulls to get duller. Significant positive correlations between the generations, however, were obtained for error scores and number of perfect runs, though not for speed. A sib correlation for maze learning of approximately the same order (.31) was later found by Burlingame and Stone (1928). In view of the unreliability of the maze, the small number of animals used, and

TABLE 7-9

Selection for Maze Learning in Rats, Summary
of Three Generations
(Tolman, 1924)

	Errors (Trials 3–10)		Times (Trials 3–10)		Perfect Runs (10 Trials)	
	Mean	Standard Deviation	Mean	Standard Deviation	Mean	Standard Deviation
Parents	12.1	5.6	19.1	11.9	3.6	1.5
G_1 Bright	6.2	3.5	17.6	13.9	5.0	1.5
G_1 Dull	15.7	13.9	26.7	24.1	2.5	1.7
G_2 Bright	10.5	4.9	17.5	6.1	3.9	1.7
G_2 Dull	14.4	7.7	19.5	9.9	2.2	1.8

the limited control of inbreeding, not too much weight can be given to the data. The experiment is chiefly of historical importance.

Tryon has summarized a long series of experiments dealing directly with the inheritance of maze-learning ability in rats (1940a). The experiments extended over a period of almost 20 years and are still being continued in part. He bred the rats selectively for performance on 19 trials in a specialized automatic maze. Phenotypic as well as genotypic selection was used, the brightest being mated with the brightest and the dullest with the dullest. Results up to G_8 are presented in Figure 7-1 (Tryon, 1942). It will be seen that the two groups separate gradually until in G_8 they virtually do not overlap.

There is no doubt in view of these results that intelligence as measured by Tryon is genetically based. There is considerable question, however, as to its nature and complexity. In point of fact, the particular ability involved is apparently rather specific inasmuch as "brights" and "dulls" give reverse results on other maze tests (Searle, 1949). In three out of five maze measures, dulls were either equal to or better than brights. Consequently, we cannot speak of the two groups as being different in general intelligence or learning capacity. Furthermore, they differed in many other ways. Brights were more "food-driven," low in motivation to escape water, timid in an open-field situation, and more purposive or less distractible. Dulls, on the other hand, were not particularly food driven, were average or better in motivation to escape from water, and fearful of mechanical-apparatus features.

The data just presented do not necessarily contradict Tryon's interpretation of bright-dull differences. Some recent unpublished work (Tryon, personal communication) shows that the difference in learning ability between the groups is not abolished by drastically altering their motivational level. Nevertheless, we should be careful not to place too definite an interpretation on his data. Tryon himself was quite aware of this difficulty and spent many years attempting to deal with it by his method of "component analysis" (1940b). By this procedure, he accounted for performance on the maze by means of ten components—direction-sets, food-pointing, short-cut tendencies, counter-tendencies, centrifugal swing, adaptation, lassitude, exit gradients, initial-inertia gradients, and conflict. The first five of these he considered to be major components, the second five, minor components. Interestingly enough, the relative importance of specific components varies both for bright and dull rats at various stages of learning. The change from early to late component patterns occurred sooner for brights. This strain also utilized the components, food pointing and exit gradient, to a greater degree during the transition stage. Tryon interpreted this to mean that "brights elicit the more abstract cognitive types earlier than do the dulls."

Wherry (1941) also undertook to investigate the component abilities involved in rat learning, using two different mazes. He obtained, by his methods, three factors—forward-going tendencies, food pointing, and goal gradients. Results were consistent for both types of mazes and for Tryon's bright and dull rats. The utilization of these three components by the two groups of animals, however, was different at different stages of learning. This point is illustrated in Figure 7-2. It will be seen that brights are predominantly "insightful" inasmuch as the factor of goal gradient appears strongly in the third period of learning, while for dulls, it only gradually gains any ascendance and, even then, is not as influential as food pointing. Wherry related his finding to those of Krechevsky (1932, 1933) who found that bright animals tended to make use of spatial or interoceptive cues, while dulls preferred to use visual or exteroceptive cues. Forward going may be conceived of as more abstract or interoceptive than food pointing which is more exteroceptive or "stimulus-bound." As we shall indicate shortly, these findings of Tryon, Wherry, and Krechevsky are related in an interesting way to some recent work on the physiological basis of intelligence or maze-learning ability in rats. The whole question of factors in animal learning has been reviewed by Royce (1950).

Heron (1935) reported results on the selection of ability on the Minnesota automatic maze up to G_4. Unlike Tryon, he selected within

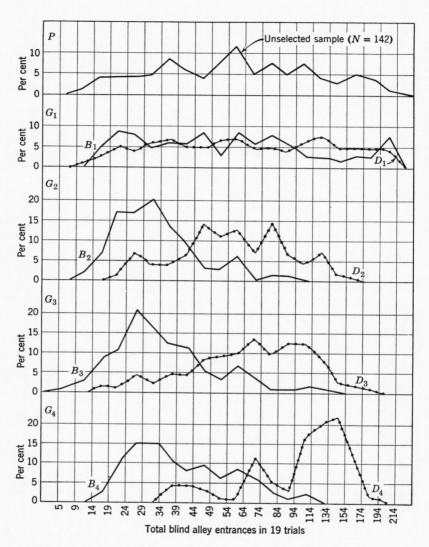

FIGURE 7-1. Selection for maze brightness and maze dullness in rats. (Tryon, 1942.)

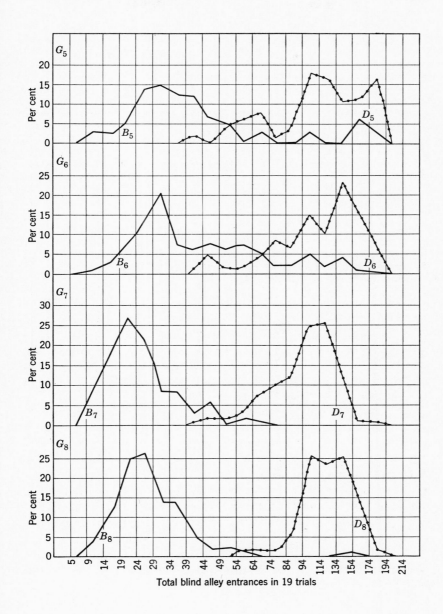

Total blind alley entrances in 19 trials

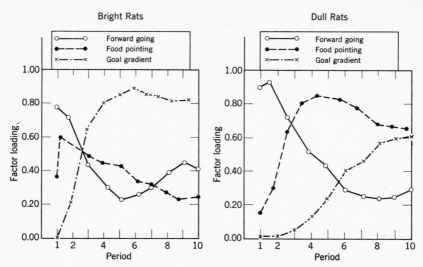

FIGURE 7-2. Changes in components of maze-learning ability during training shown by "bright" and "dull" rats. (Wherry, 1941.)

two lines, that is, genotypically rather than phenotypically. Good separation was obtained between brights and dulls. Later Heron (1941) presented data on generations G_5 up to G_{16}. His results are presented in Table 7-10. It will be seen that after G_4 separation is rather slow. In fact it is difficult to know whether the changes shown in the two lines are systematic or are merely random fluctuations. Possibly this difficulty is due to the genotypic method of selection. On the whole, however, dulls consistently showed a higher mean-error score than brights. They also ran more slowly, though this does not altogether account for their poorer learning ability (Heron, 1941).

A third experiment carried out by Thompson and Wrigley (Thompson, 1954) attempted to rectify some of the deficiencies involved in the studies already described. In particular, the experiment was designed to meet two requirements: first, that selection be made on the basis of operationally defined rat "intelligence," and that trait alone, unconfounded with other unknown traits; second, that a high degree of homozygosity be achieved in the two lines by means of inbreeding. To meet the first requirement the Hebb-Williams maze was used. It consists of a square enclosure with a removable wire-mesh top, a starting box in one corner, and a goal box diagonally opposite. Barriers of various lengths interposed in various ways between the starting box and the goal constitute the problems. Twenty-four such problems

TABLE 7-10

Selection for Maze-Learning Ability in Rats
(Heron, 1935, 1941)

	Bright		Dull	
	Mean Errors	S.D.	Mean Errors	S.D.
G_1	56.26	3.06	62.97	3.14
G_2	66.36	2.21	77.16	2.39
G_3	43.12	2.06	62.73	1.76
G_4	59.27	2.02	86.97	1.96
G_5	76.75	1.84	103.59	2.04
G_6	61.10	2.46	111.65	2.52
G_7	58.65	1.85	74.05	2.45
G_8	56.25	2.45	102.10	2.56
G_9	72.15	2.30	108.75	2.71
G_{10}	73.45	6.13	109.55	1.62
G_{11}	83.50	2.45	120.90	2.83
G_{12}	65.20	2.33	117.75	2.28
G_{13}	73.65	1.97	103.85	1.93
G_{14}	85.60	1.89	113.15	2.24
G_{15}	149.00	5.92	195.00	7.01
G_{16}	46.90	1.58	116.05	1.35

were used in the experiment, the second twelve being mirror images of the first twelve. Thus a fairly broad range of rat intelligence was sampled. The procedure involved a lengthy period of habituation for all animals on simple pretest problems until a certain criterion was reached. In this way, the influence of motivational and emotional differences was minimized. The Hebb-Williams maze, generally speaking, is analogous to human intelligence tests which involve a large number of short items usually administered only to subjects who have had previous preparation.

Results from G_1 to G_6 are shown in Figure 7-3. It can be seen that the mean scores of brights and dulls separate quite sharply after G_2 and are, in fact, significantly different in G_3. Very little overlap occurred in ensuing generations. The two lines are still being maintained by Zubek at the University of Manitoba.

The second objective (attainment of homozygosity) was handled less satisfactorily owing to the infertility of many of the brother-sister matings, particularly in later generations. However, it was noted that

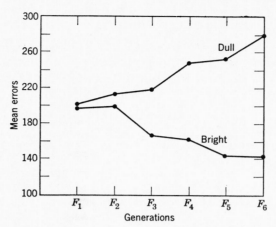

FIGURE 7-3. Mean error scores of "bright" and "dull" rats selectively bred for performance on the Hebb-Williams maze. (Thompson, 1954.)

selection based on genotype as well as phenotype was faster than that based on phenotype alone.

So far three cases of successful selection have been discussed. Two negative experiments should be mentioned at this point. One of these was designed to test a Lamarckian hypothesis (Rhine and McDougall, 1933). Although McDougall claimed to be able to produce rats that were superior learners through training their mothers, he was apparently unable to obtain any significant changes with selection. This negative result was intended as an answer to those critics who suggested that his so-called Lamarckian effect had been due merely to accidental selection. Some of his data are presented in modified form in Table 7-11. These are unusual results and, because of the results of other work, should be viewed with a great deal of caution.

Another negative case has been reported by Kuppasawny (1947). Using a simple water maze and breeding over ten generations, this investigator found no definite changes in his population due to selection. Since neither the experimental procedure nor the results are adequately described, it is not possible to draw any real conclusions from Kuppasawny's work.

On the whole, the total evidence favors the conclusion that brightness and dullness in rats as measured by the maze technique can be genetically selected and that, depending on the method of selection used, maximum separation between lines can be achieved in only a few generations.

TABLE 7-11

Negative Effects of Selection on Learning;
Seven Generations Favorably and Adversely Selected
for Errors on a Bright-Dark Discrimination Problem
(Rhine and McDougall, 1933)

	Favorably Selected		Adversely Selected	
	Mean Errors	No.	Mean Errors	No.
G_6	70	6	119	19
G_7	110	6	115	14
G_8	80	5	147	9
G_9	124	9	139	14
G_{10}	132	10	114	7
G_{11}	34	4	129	21
G_{12}	126	4	81	20

Strain-Difference Studies. One of the earliest studies in the field
—predating, in fact, the selection experiments—was carried out by
Bagg (1916, 1920). Bagg did not use genetically homozygous lines but
merely compared the performance of a number of coat-color breeds
of mice on a maze and on a multiple-choice apparatus. In view of
the extreme variability of performance, he was unable to make definite
statements about the genetic differences in his population. Nevertheless, he concluded that males were superior to females, and yellow
animals were duller than other breeds. He reported a sibling correlation of .50, but also stated that the resemblance between families was
almost as great.

Vicari (1929) compared reaction time in mice by means of a simple
three-unit maze. She used four stocks, Japanese Waltzers, DBA's,
BALB's, and Myelencephalic Blebs. These showed characteristic
differences in reaction time, the DBA's being fastest and the Waltzers
slowest. The slope of learning curves also differed. In crosses, Vicari
found that the low, flat learning curve of the DBA's was dominant
over the typical descending-ascending curve shown by the Waltzers.
Although the results were too complex to prove any simple genetic
hypothesis about reaction time, they did suggest some kind of multifactor inheritance.

A study of larger scope than the foregoing was carried on at the
Jackson Laboratory (Scott and Fuller, 1951). In general the program

was set up to meet a number of requirements (Fuller and Scott, 1954). These were (1) a constant environment so as to magnify possible genetic differences between the several dog breeds used, (2) a favorable social environment with emphasis placed on differences in social behavior, (3) testing of animals in a wide variety of situations, (4) testing carried out during the first year of life in order to control developmental changes, and (5) crossing and genetic study of those strains differing most in the traits under study. Although many more tests were given, we will concern ourselves here only with those relating to intellectual capacity. Altogether, seventeen of these were used. Detailed descriptions of these tests are available in the *Manual of Dog Testing Techniques* (Scott and Fuller, 1950). Five pure breeds and one type of hybrid were tested: basenjis, beagles, cocker spaniels, Shetland sheep dogs, wire-haired fox terriers and basenji-cocker crosses.

In one report, three tests of learning ability were used, leash control, discrimination and delayed response, and spatial orientation (Fuller and Scott, 1954). For leash control, the six breeds fall into three groups in terms of number of demerits, a high group including basenjis and Shetland sheep dogs, a middle group consisting of beagles and basenji-cocker hybrids, and a low group of cockers and wire-haired terriers. These data are presented in Table 7-12 and Figure

TABLE 7-12

Comparison of Five Dog Breeds and One Hybrid on Two Tests of Learning Ability (Fuller and Scott, 1954)

Breed	Leash Control (Deviant Score)	Discrimination and Delayed Response (Trials to Criterion)
Basenji	9.2 ± 0.3	68
Beagle	8.8 ± 0.4	24
Cocker spaniel	5.5 ± 0.4	53
Shetland sheep dog	10.3 ± 0.8	39
Wire-haired terrier	5.2 ± 0.3	37
Basenji-cocker cross	9.3 ± 0.4	87

7-4. In the test of discrimination, rank order of performance varied according to the measure used. On the whole, however, beagles and wire-haired terriers appeared to be consistently superior. Considerable overlap was found between the other groups. A relationship was found

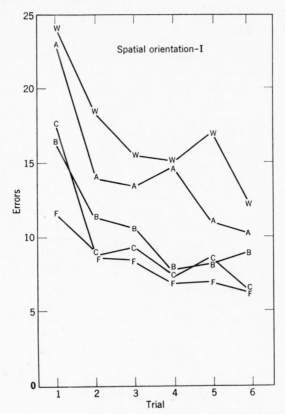

FIGURE 7-4. Comparison of five dog breeds on a test of spatial orientation. A, basenji; B, beagle; C, cocker spaniel; W, wire-haired fox terrier; F, basenji × cocker hybrid. (Fuller and Scott, 1954.)

between ability to discriminate cues and ability to delay responses, though it was felt that the two aspects of the test were still rather different. The final test, spatial orientation, involved the ability of the animal to choose on the basis of visual cues the correct path to food from two similar pathways which were incorrect. Figure 7-4 summarizes the main results. On a similar problem basenjis and wire-haired terriers continued to make more errors. The correlation between the two problems was .60. It is interesting that although reliability of the test increased over the six trials given, intraclass correlation, which directly reflects hereditary factors, did not. Thus, although the test became with time an increasingly good predictor of individual success, it reflected genetic differences as well initially as in later trials.

In 1955 a more intensive analysis was made of results for groups of tests that intercorrelate highly and reflect an underlying factor of ability. Using factor analysis, Anastasi, Fuller, Scott, and Schmitt (1955) found breed differences on each of five factors, activity and impulsiveness, docility or responsiveness to a human trainer, manipulation, visual observation, and persistence of positional habits. It should be noted in passing that the factorial composition of the test configuration was not constant but varied considerably with the stage of testing, a finding in line with Wherry's previously discussed work. On the whole, basenjis tended to be better in tasks requiring "independent action and visual observation of relations," but were especially deficient in tasks which depended on responsiveness to the human handler. They also did poorly on the discrimination-apparatus tests. Beagles tended to do very well on the three discrimination-apparatus tests and leash control, while cockers excelled in obedience training and leash control but not in stair climbing. Cockers were also poor in cue response and string pulling and below average on manipulation. Shetland sheep dogs appeared to be relatively poor on many variables, whereas wire-haired fox terriers were best on tests which seemed to call for confidence in strange situations. They also did well in the discrimination apparatus, but poorly on the maze. Basenji-cocker crosses showed behavior close to the total group mean on most measures.

Perhaps the most important aspect of this research lies in its illustration of the great complexity of so-called intelligent behavior and the necessity of isolating rational units before proceeding to genetic analysis. The work done is certainly a major step in this direction. One methodological criticism of the experiment is that the nature of the sample did not permit separation of the relative contributions of genic, chromosomal, and gametic communalities to the covariances (see page 340). Thus it was not possible to give a complete genetic interpretation to the factors isolated. Current research in this program is aimed at correcting these difficulties.

It may be concluded in general that the work on strain differences supports the conclusions reached by the method of selection. Both point definitely to heredity as an important determiner of intelligence and learning in animals.

PSYCHOLOGICAL AND PHYSIOLOGICAL CORRELATES
OF INTELLIGENCE

An important problem that the researcher in this area must face relates to the nature of the measures of intelligence that he uses. One way of attacking this problem is to attempt to find out what variables, both psychological and physiological, correlate with the measure used. This work we shall now examine briefly. Little has been done along these lines with human beings, at least from the standpoint of furthering our knowledge of the genetics of behavior. Consequently, we will confine ourselves to a discussion of the work on animals.

One of the earliest studies was by Krechevsky (1933). This investigator devised an ingenious apparatus in which the choice of path leading to food could be made by using either spatial or visual cues, both equally reinforced. Krechevsky found that Tryon's brights tended to use visual hypotheses, while the dulls used spatial hypotheses. These preferences became sharper over the 14-day testing period. Random-bred animals showed no consistent type of choice. As already mentioned, some writers have construed this difference as meaning that brights show more abstract behavior than dulls.

A study by Graves (1936) attempted to analyze further differences between Heron's bright and dull strains (G_5). Four measures were obtained with both groups, errors on a Stone multiple-T maze, activity in revolving cages, strength of drive on the Columbia obstruction apparatus, and reaction time to escape electric shock. A distinction in favor of the brights appeared on the maze test only. Correlations between tests were consistently low, a result in line with most other work. Intralitter correlation for drive turned out to be .31, a figure comparable to that obtained by Burlingame and Stone (1928). Another experiment dealing with Heron's strains was carried out by Heron and Skinner (1940). A significant difference in rate of bar pressing for periodic reinforcement was found, bright rats showing a higher response rate than the dulls. Similarly, brights also emitted more responses during the first three days of extinction. Skinner (1940) in a separate publication presented data corroborating the first of these findings on Heron's rats. The following year Kruse (1941) showed that bright animals (Heron strain) ate more when food was available for limited periods only. An interruption, however, caused more disturbance of the eating rate in bright rats than in dull ones. Kruse attributed this to higher level of emotionality among the brights.

One of the most thorough studies on the subject is that of Searle (1949) referred to above. It will be recalled that a large number of differences other than intellectual appeared between brights and dulls. Furthermore, the generality of the brights' superiority in learning was limited, showing up in some tests but not in others. Since we have already outlined Searle's main findings, we will not repeat them here. The main point they bring out is that Tryon's selection program resulted in a syndrome of differences rather than a single trait difference between his two strains. Animals within strains intercorrelate highly with each other for 30 variables but between strains they do not. This point is illustrated in Table 7-13. As will be indicated later, one effect of this phenomenon was to make any genetic analysis of strain crosses rather difficult.

TABLE 7-13

Intercorrelations within and between Tryon's "Maze-Bright" and "Maze-Dull" Rats with Respect to 30 Variables (Searle, 1949)

Group	No. of Rats	No. of Inter-r's	Ave. Inter-r
Bright vs. bright	10	45	.587
Dull vs. dull	10	45	.533
Bright vs. dull	20	100	−.188

Three studies were done to investigate the non-intellectual characteristics of the McGill bright and dull strains. In the first of these Thompson and Bindra (1952) found that brights and dulls were about equal in emotionality as measured by urination and defecation in a modified Hall open-field test and by latency of leaving a home cage to reach food at the end of an elevated open runway three feet away. Brights were somewhat more strongly motivated for food than dulls, though the difference was not statistically significant. In two other experiments, the exploratory activity of brights and dulls was compared. In the first of these, the two strains showed about the same amount of exploration on a simple elevated maze (Thompson, 1953a), but in the second, using an enclosed maze, dulls explored more (Thompson and Kahn, 1955).

On the physiological side, considerably less has been done. Heron and Yugend (1936) investigated the basal metabolism of Heron's brights and dulls (G_2). They found no significant difference in B.M.R. for the first group of brights and dulls they tested but a significant difference in the case of the second group, brights having the higher B.M.R. It is a curious fact that in group two the actual error difference between brights and dulls was smaller than in the first group of animals and, in fact, was non-significant. In addition, all group-two rats (both brights and dulls) had lower error scores than group-one animals. This is a puzzling result which cannot be easily explained but presumably must relate to some kind of threshold factor.

Silverman, Shapiro, and Heron (1940) examined the brain weights of Heron's two strains (G_{14}). They found that although brights had a slightly greater body- to brain-weight ratio than dulls, the difference was not significant. Four other measures of brain weight yielded no differences of any size, though in three of these the brains of brights were somewhat lighter. It should be mentioned that Bassett (1914) found much earlier that the animals of a small-brain-weight strain that he bred selectively learned more slowly than controls—a difference that increased in the three generations studied. Consquently the relation of brain size to genetically selected intelligence in rats is still ambiguous.

A more promising line of attack on the physiological correlates of learning ability in rats has come from biochemistry. Krech, Rosenzweig, and associates (1954) at the University of California at Berkeley have published an interesting set of observations relating cholinesterase (ChE) level in a number of cortical areas of rats to visual and spatial preferences in the Krech maze. Ten to 20 mg. of tissue from the visual, somesthetic, and motor areas of each hemisphere were assayed for ChE level in 19 rats. The relation of ChE level to visual and spatial preference is shown in Table 7-14. With the possible exception of motor areas, ChE level in visual and somesthetic cortex and the average of the two was directly and significantly related to strength of spatial preference. It will be recalled that spatial preference has also been shown to be significantly related to "maze-brightness." Consequently, we may infer that ChE level also influences intelligence. Krech, Rosenzweig, Bennett, and Kruekel (1954) advance two possibilities of theoretical explanation: (a) high ChE in one sensory region produces dominance of that area; (b) a generally high ChE level acts as a "general power factor" which underlies adaptivity. In a later publication Krech, Rosenzweig, and Bennett (1956) suggest that ChE level provides an index of readiness of nerve-impulse transmission in the central nervous system and that the relative ease of such transmission is related to capacity for adaptive behavior.

Along similar lines, Hughes and Zubek (1956), using the McGill brights and dulls bred by Thompson (1954), have shown that glutamic

TABLE 7-14

The Relation of Brain Cholinesterase Activity Level to Spatial and Visual Preference (and Brightness and Dullness) in Rats (Krech et al., 1954)

| | Mean Cholinesterase Activity Levels* in Different Cortical Areas | | | |
	Visual	Somesthetic	Motor	$\dfrac{V + S}{2}$
Spatial preference group (brights)	57.8	66.6	68.6	62.0
Visual preference group (dulls)	47.5	57.7	64.2	52.7
p value for differences	.01	.02	.30	.001

* Scores are based on rate of hydrolysis of acetylcholine perchlorate determined anaerobically with a pH meter at pH 7.95 and 37°C.

acid injections will exert differential effects depending on the genotype of the animal. Thus the injection produced a significant drop in error and time scores on the Hebb-Williams maze in dull rats but not in bright rats. A later publication indicates that the effect of glutamic acid lasts for several months (1957). The authors suggest that glutamic acid has an important relation to neural functioning and that it may compensate for certain metabolic defects present in dulls though not in brights. It is of great interest that both glutamic acid and ChE level relate to rate of acetylcholine metabolism. Consequently, the results of Hughes and Zubek gave indirect support to the data obtained by Krech et al. We may hope that more work along these interesting lines will be developed in the future.

THE GENETICS OF INTELLIGENCE

The final section of this chapter deals with the genetic basis of intelligence. This is a subject of great importance about which little at present is known. A good deal of rather interesting theoretical work was done by Fisher (1918), Hogben (1932a, 1933a, 1933b), Wright (1921) and others (see Chapters 3 and 4) relating correlational analysis to Mendelian genetics, but this has not been exploited so far to any noticeable extent by scientists doing empirical research in the area. There is a great need for fusion between theory and experiment. We will now consider some of the attempts that have been made to construct theories of how intelligence is transmitted genetically both in animals and in human beings.

Only two major attempts have been made up to now to build a theory of the genetics of human intelligence. The first of these was made by Hurst (1932, 1934), who based his model on two sets of data: (a) the Woods Royal Family data consisting of intelligence ratings of 212 European Royal families with 424 parents and 558 offspring; (b) Hurst's own Leicestershire data consisting of I.Q. scores of 194 families with 388 parents and 812 offspring. The Stanford-Binet and the Healy Picture Completion tests were used with the children and some lower-grade adults. Rating was used in the case of mediocre or higher-grade adults. His final scale of intelligence consisted of 11 grades, each grade being roughly the equivalent of 20 I.Q. points. Reliability of rating was checked whenever possible.

The total of 406 families appeared to fall into a number of different types. In the first place, they could be broken down into those which produced either all or half mediocre offspring and those which produced only a few mediocre offspring. There were 334 families which produced all or half mediocre offspring (incidence, about 75% or higher in the population), and of these families, 124, or one-third, produced all mediocre offspring. The remaining 210, or two-thirds, produced offspring of all grades, half being mediocre and half high or low grade. In other terms, of the type of family tending to produce an abundance of mediocre offspring, one-third are non-segregating, and two-thirds are segregating. The 72 families of the second main type tended to produce only about one-fourth mediocre and three-fourths high- or low-grade offspring. None of the parents in these families was rated as mediocre. Hurst's data are schematized in Table 7-15. From these results, Hurst concluded that mediocrity was a dominant character dependent on a single major gene, while high or low intelligence was recessive. Thus any individual having the gene either in homozygous or heterozygous form was mediocre or normal. Lacking it, he would be either high or low in intellectual level. At the same time, he noted that some offspring (about 26%) from matings between high- or low-grade parents were also mediocre. This being so, Hurst found it necessary to postulate the presence of five minor modifiers, Aa, Bb, Cc, Dd, Ee, which acted only when N was absent. In such a case, A, B, C, D, and E would act as unit increasers (10 I.Q. points), while a, b, c, d, and e would act as unit decreasers. Thus some individuals who carried the double recessive nn could also carry the modifiers in heterozygous form. These individuals would then also be mediocre.

TABLE 7-15

Summary of Hurst's Data on the Genetic Transmission
of Intelligence
(Hurst, 1934)

Intelligence of Parents	Number of Families	Intelligence of Offspring
Mediocre × mediocre	85	all mediocre
Mediocre × mediocre	77	½ mediocre, ½ high- or low-grade
Mediocre × high- or low-grade	39	all mediocre
Mediocre × high- or low-grade	133	½ mediocre, ½ high- or low-grade
High- or low-grade × high- or low-grade	72	¼ mediocre, ¾ high- or low-grade

This theory of genetics of intelligence is undoubtedly ingenious and also fits rather well the data on which it is based. However, it is difficult to explain why in the 77 families involving both mediocre parents half the offspring should be above or below normal. If a simple dominant is involved, non-normal children will appear only when both such mediocre parents are heterozygous for N, and in such a case the incidence of non-mediocrity should be only one-quarter at the very most. Allowing for the action of the minor modifiers which may also produce normality, the proportion presumably would be, in practice, less than this figure. In a broad way, the theory affords some explanation of the phenomenon of exceptional children appearing in otherwise quite homogeneous families. Furthermore, as Hurst points out, it explains a broad range of intellectual level, from idiot (nn, aa, bb, cc, dd, ee) to "illustrious" (AA, BB, CC, DD, EE). It does, of course, lack an independent test as Conrad and Jones (1940) have pointed out. An analysis of the G_2 or third generation, though perhaps beyond the resources of Hurst to obtain, would have been desirable as would the application of some of the statistical techniques suggested by Fisher and others.

A second theory has been proposed by Pickford (1949). This formulation rests on a simple multifactor hypothesis. According to Pickford, the distribution of Stanford-Binet I.Q. scores in the general population is such as to justify the action of ten equal and additive gene pairs. Since this model is backed by no facts other than the population distribution of I.Q., not a great deal can be said about it.

It is supported strongly by the work of Burt and Howard (1956). Some critics, however, have indicated (Conrad and Jones, 1940), that such a theory implies theoretical parent-child and sibling correlations in excess of those usually obtained empirically. This is not, of course, àn incisive criticism, since some workers, Cattell, for instance, have, in fact, obtained empirical correlations sufficiently high to fit such a multifactor hypothesis. Another deficiency suggested (Conrad and Jones, 1940) is the inability of the theory to account for regression of offspring means to the population mean, a phenomenon well documented by empirical studies (Outhit, 1933; Hurst, 1934; Cattell and Wilson, 1938). Regression can be explained statistically up to a point. Beyond this, a genetic explanation may be necessary. This cannot be afforded by a simple multifactorial theory.

Apart from the two theories described briefly above, little has been suggested in the way of genetic models for the transmission of human intelligence. Perhaps more empirical work is needed first. At the same time, a great deal has already been done to point up a number of basic facts that must be taken into account by future theorists and researchers. Some of these have already been reviewed (Conrad and Jones, 1940).

In the first place, we may regard intelligence as a quantitative character with a rather wide dispersion. How wide the dispersion is, however, and the kind of scale that best describes it are matters of debate. It is possible that with educational opportunities equalized the dispersion might not be as wide as it appears in most standardized tests. In addition it is entirely possible that a logarithmic scale might be a much more suitable way of representing intelligence than a normal probability scale. Whatever the case may be, multiple genes seem to be implied, though these may not necessarily be equal and additive. Second, there are many empirical observations, as we have already pointed out, to indicate that offspring regress below or above mid-parental means toward the population mean. Genetically speaking, this implies recessivity of extremes and dominance of normality. Third, variability of sibling intelligence appears to be greatest at the middle range of intelligence, according to the studies of Outhit (1933) and Conrad and Jones (1940). If true, this would militate against dominance of average level, as in Hurst's model. On the other hand, there is a slight suggestion from Carter's data (1932) discussed above that variability among offspring may be inversely proportionate to intellectual level of parents. Since Carter dealt with academic achievement rather than intellectual capacity and since the tendency is not marked, this possibility seems dubious. Fourth, parent-child correlations have been found by many workers (Pearson, 1904; Outhit, 1933; Cattell and Willson, 1938; Conrad and Jones, 1940) to be as great as, or greater than, sibling correlations. According to a dominance theory, the sibling should exceed the parental correlation. Fifth, homogamy must always be taken into account. In human beings, there is a tendency for like to mate with like in respect to intelligence (Jones, 1929; Richardson, 1939; Conrad and Jones, 1940). As Conrad and Jones have indicated (1940), homogamy may have considerable relevance to any genetic interpretations that are placed on correlational data. Even with complete dominance, for example, homogamy may equalize parent-child and sibling correlations. At the same time we may also mention a finding of Outhit's (1933) that difference between parents' I.Q.'s (that is, lack of homogamy) shows no correlation with variability of offspring.

Obviously, these basic data present a puzzling picture. Nonetheless, they have considerable theoretical importance. Any empirical work that aids in their clarification and elucidation will contribute greatly to the task of formulating adequate theoretical models of the genetics of human intelligence.

If little has been done at the human level, perhaps even less has been done with animals. One of the earliest lines of work bearing on the subject was begun by McDougall (1927) with the purpose of testing a Lamarckian hypothesis. Animals were trained to swim in a water maze from which they could escape by means of a dimly lighted route. They were forced to discriminate this side from another lighted side that involved shock. This was known as the "tank procedure." An additional method was also used by McDougall which he called the "bath procedure." It consisted of a simple water maze in which an animal was required merely to traverse a rather irregular path from start to finish as quickly as possible. In each of a number of successive generations rats were trained in these two mazes, and the scores of their offspring were compared with scores of control animals from untrained parents. Altogether, between 1927 and 1938, McDougall gathered information on 44 such generations. During the course of this period many small changes in procedure were introduced as well as various kinds of control experiments in order to measure the effects of environmental factors. A summary of his main results for the tank rats (McDougall, 1938) is reproduced in Table 7-16. It is of interest, as we mentioned earlier, that selection did not alter the results.

TABLE 7-16

Summary of McDougall's Data on the Transmission of Acquired Maze-Learning Ability
(McDougall, 1938)

Generations of Tank-rats in Groups of 8	No. of Rats	Mean Error per Rat	Range
G_{14}–G_{21}	130	56+	9–147
G_{22}–G_{29}	166	41	3–105
G_{30}–G_{37}	218	29	0–124
G_{38}–G_{44}	202	20	0–87

We shall not go into a detailed examination of McDougall's data. Needless to say, it met with considerable scepticism from all quarters. In addition, it was repeated with largely negative results by Crew (1932, 1936) and by Agar, Drummond, and Tiegs (1948, 1954). In a final publication, Agar et al. (1954) concluded that the changes over successive generations obtained both by McDougall and by themselves were due not to inheritance of acquired ability, but rather to long term fluctuations in strength and vigor in the colony. A graph of their results is shown in Figure 7-5. Whether their explanation is any more plausible than McDougall's, however, is doubtful. Another factor may also have been at work. The trained animals underwent quite severe stress (shock plus immersion in water) which may well have brought about drastic endocrine changes. These changes, in turn,

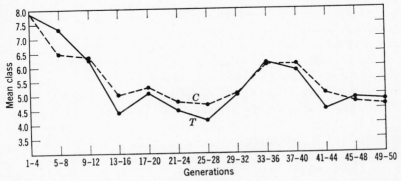

FIGURE 7-5. Learning ability in successive generations from trained (T) and untrained (C) parents. (Agar et al., 1954.)

might well have had some influence on the fetal development of the subsequent generations and their performance in the tank.

In summary, there would appear to be some possibility that McDougall's data had some genuine importance, though for reasons other than those he suggested. The inheritance of acquired characters is not taken as a serious hypothesis today, but further experimentation along the lines of effects of prenatal stress might prove interesting.

So far the method of selection has yielded little genetic information. Tryon (1940a) did attempt analyses of crosses between his bright and dull strains, but the results were ambiguous. As shown in Figure 7-6, variance of the F_1 was as great as variance of the F_2 cross. This made

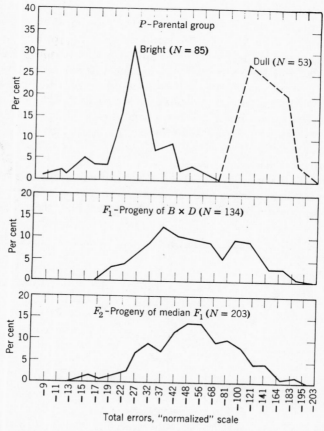

FIGURE 7-6. Results of crossing selectively bred "maze-bright" and "maze-dull" rats. (Tryon, 1940.)

genetic analysis virtually impossible. Conventionally speaking, such a result would mean that the two parent strains were not homozygous and that assortment occurred as much in the F_1 as in the F_2. Had Tryon been able to inbreed the two lines to a greater extent, he might have obtained more clean-cut data. On the other hand, it is also possible that the large variance of the F_1 was due not to chromosome assortment but to the effects of heterosis which masked genotypic homozygosity (Caspari, 1958). At present we do not know which interpretation is correct. Apart from this empirical ambiguity, Tryon (1942) has favored a simple polygenic theory of the inheritance of maze ability in rats involving genes with equal and additive effects sufficient in number to account for the normal distribution of ability shown by a random-bred population of rats. As he points out, some modification of this theory would have to be made to account for regression as well as other phenomena.

Pure-strain studies have likewise contributed very little so far to our knowledge of the inheritance of intelligence. However, it is likely that before long the previously described work from Bar Harbor and other laboratories will supply some answers. A number of interesting hypotheses have already been suggested by some of the investigators concerned, but since these apply to behavior in general rather than specifically to intelligence they will not be discussed in the present section.

In summary, it is clear that the available information on the inheritance of intelligence obtained with animal subjects agrees substantially with that obtained with human beings. In neither case, however, has much progress been made with respect to the genic mechanisms involved. It seems likely that before this can be accomplished a rather sharp reorientation will be necessary, possibly away from the standard models of Mendelian genetics. This possibility will be taken up later.

8

Personality and temperament

This chapter will summarize work relating to the inheritance of personality and temperament. As with the heredity of intelligence, evidence in this area has been accumulating for a long time and covers an astonishingly wide range of personality dimensions. Before examining this material we shall discuss briefly the various meanings of personality and temperament. Many of the problems which we shall consider have already been encountered in the chapter on intelligence.

Theories of personality have a long history (McClelland, 1951). All through the ages man has asked the question "What am I?" But it was not until the nineteenth century that the problem was attacked in an empirical manner. Freud and his followers were among the first to open up the field of inquiry, though it should be emphasized that Galton played an important role. Since this early work, a great deal has been written on the subject, more, in fact, than can be summarized here. A number of excellent source books are available that discuss thoroughly the various approaches that have been taken over the last fifty years (Allport, 1937; Cattell, 1946; Eysenck, 1947; Murphy, 1947; Brand, 1954; Hall and Lindzey, 1957). It is pertinent, however, to establish an orientation in this chapter by considering briefly the dimensions with which we shall deal. Personality tests range from verbal responses to Rorschach inkblots to finger-tapping rates. Any reaction may be looked upon as reflecting some aspect of personality and temperament, insofar as it relates to the emotional responsiveness of an individual. By "emotional" we refer not only to violent changes or disturbances in behavior, but also to the relatively mild states involved in dislikes or likes of particular objects or events. The words given by a subject in free-association experiments, the responses made to a Thematic Apperception Test card, or the way a questionnaire is answered, all may be regarded as relating to personality and temperament.

Obviously, this point of view is a very broad one. Nonetheless, since personality inheritance has been studied in so many ways, it is necessary to avoid settling at this point on any simple or narrow definition. In dealing with the empirical evidence gathered on the inheritance of personality, we shall discuss first the human, then the animal, experiments that bear on the subject.

HUMAN EXPERIMENTATION

As with other traits, the inheritance of personality traits in human beings has been studied by three main methods: pedigrees, familial correlations, and twin similarities.

Pedigrees. In his book *English Men of Science*, Galton (1874) managed to obtain letters from eminent scientists and their kin reporting on many characteristics that may be included under personality. Most relevant here are energy, perseverance, practical business habits, independence of character, religious bias, truthfulness, and taste for science. It is of interest to note that all these traits were studied by successors of Galton using more exact empirical tests and that the conclusions later reached were substantially the same, if somewhat more moderate. As we noted before, Galton was inclined to place great weight on heredity in the determination of eminence. In respect to personality, his views were no different. Thus he regarded even the taste for science as innate, though this might be suppressed by the bias of society against science. "A love of science might be largely extended by fostering and not thwarting innate tendencies. . ." (Galton, 1874, page 225).

Since Galton's time many more pedigree studies of temperament and personality traits have been made. Reference has already been made to the work of Gun (1930*a,b*) on hereditary traits in several lines of royal families. For example, "efficiency" is described as being the key characteristic of the Tudors, while "tactless obstinacy" is attributed to the Stuarts. These and other data (Finlayson, 1916; Davenport and Scudder, 1918; Gun, 1928) appear to indicate transmission of some kind. Whether this is social or genetic, however, is a problem that the pedigree method by itself cannot adequately solve. In view of this limitation which has been emphasized earlier we shall not discuss pedigrees further. This method is fallible when dealing with well-defined characters. With the complex subject of personality and temperament, it is even more so.

Family Correlations. The family-correlation method has yielded more exact data. A variety of tests have been used covering roughly three areas: personality traits, attitudes, and interests. Work on the general subject appears to start with Starch (1917). It has continued sporadically up to the 1950's. Good reviews of the literature have been made by Crook (1937), Roff (1950), Schwesinger (1933), and others (Sen Gupta, 1941; Eysenck and Prell, 1951).

Personality Tests. For the measurement of personality, one of the most popular tests has been the Bernreuter Personality Inventory (Anastasi, 1954). The test comprises scales to measure neuroticism, intraversion, dominance, and self-sufficiency. Although these dimensions are considered to be independent in the test, a critical study (Flanagan, 1935) has shown them to be correlated and probably reducible to two factors—confidence and sociability. In spite of this fact, familial correlations turn out to be rather different for the four scales. Hoffeditz (1934) found that in a sample of 100 fathers, 100 mothers, 111 sons, and 145 daughters, mean parent-child correlations were as follows: neuroticism, .278; self-sufficiency, .200; dominance, .294. It is interesting that daughters correlated higher with both parents, particularly the mother, than did sons. The similarity of mothers and sons was found to be slight, around .07. The size of correlations for the different scales varied considerably with the particular relationship. All, however, were consistently low, nor did they change appreciably with age. Crook and Thomas (1934) also obtained correlations for parents and children on the Bernreuter scale and correlations among sibs as well. On the whole their data agreed with those of Hoffeditz. Daughters tended to be more like parents (particularly mothers) than did sons. All parent-child correlations were low. Sibling correlations obtained were somewhat higher, especially those among sisters; these averaged about .32 for the three scales. The average for brothers, on the other hand, was only .12. There were no systematic differences in size of familial correlations between the scales. Sward and Friedman (1935) in their study of "Jewish temperament" also obtained consistently low correlations for the neuroticism scale of the Bernreuter. Mother-offspring correlations again tended to be somewhat higher than those between father and offspring. Perhaps the most complete study is that of Crook (1937) whose data for three of the Bernreuter scales are set out in Table 8-1. Only correlations corrected for attenuation are shown. Since age was found to have no effect on scores, no correction for this factor was used. It will be noted that as before all relationships involving a female (mother-daughter, sister-sister, father-daughter, mother-son) tend to be a little

TABLE 8-1

Family Correlations (Corrected for Attenuation) for Three of the Scales of the Bernreuter Personality Inventory (Crook, 1937)

	No. of Pairs	Scales		
		Neuroticism	Dominance	Self-sufficiency
Brother-brother	50	.25	.09	−.08
Brother-sister	56	.15	.10	.28
Sister-sister	51	.36	.33	.36
Father-son	62	.06	.05	−.03
Father-daughter	64	.24	.26	.39
Mother-son	68	.32	.22	.20
Mother-daughter	73	.62	.43	.13
Husband-wife	79	.07	−.06	.01

higher than those involving males only. Since the coefficients are all small, it is difficult to say whether this trend is significant. Nonetheless, the fact that it appears in all the four cited studies is worthy of mention. If actually significant, an interpretation in terms of family structure is more plausible than a hereditary one.

In summary, it would appear that the evidence for the inheritance of personality traits as measured by the Bernreuter test is not strong. Familial correlations are for the most part very low, and may well be caused by environmental rather than genetic factors.

In addition to the Bernreuter inventory, several miscellaneous tests of personality have been used. Starch (1917) used cancellation tests and tapping speed in order to measure mental ability. We have considered these measures in this chapter since they have low correlations with Binet-type intelligence tests and may well reflect temperament rather than intellectual skills. Cancellation of A's yielded a sibling correlation of .50, while cancellation of geometrical forms gave a correlation of .07. Sibs correlated .65 on tapping speed. Starch concluded that resemblance is no greater on tests affected by school work than on those not affected.

Koch and Stroud (1934) investigated familial correlations on three tests, the Thurstone personality schedule, the Woodworth psychometric inventory, and the Neymann-Kohlstedt test of introversion and extroversion. On a group of mixed sibs the correlation coefficient on the first two tests combined was .10, whereas it was .09 on the third test. Familial correlations of the same low order of magnitude have also been obtained for the Allport ascendance-submission scale (Crook and Thomas, 1934), on some general tests of personality (Pintner and Forlano, 1935), on an index of introversion and extroversion (Ushijima, 1935), and on the Minnesota Multiphasic Personality Inventory (Gjerde, 1949). In all these studies the highest correlation obtained was around .30, and most coefficients fell considerably below this.

Attitudes and Interests. Although personality traits as measured by the various schedules and inventories described above do not appear very similar among family members, attitudes apparently show more uniformity. Kulp and Davidson (1933), for example, have found sibling correlations for social attitudes ranging from .29 up to .60, with a mean of .40. Kirkpatrick and Stone (1935) find for religious attitude the following correlations: mother-daughter, .53; mother-son, .62; father-daughter, .53; father-son, .33. Children tended to be more similar in general to the mother than to the father. This tendency was found again by Kirkpatrick (1936) using an attitude-to-feminism scale, though all correlations were somewhat lower than for religious attitudes. Curiously enough, the author found that greater intimacy between a parent and a child actually tended to lower the correlation between them for the attitude-to-feminism scale. Correlations between mothers and children of .40 as opposed to parent-child correlations of around .30 have also been reported by Peterson (1936), using the Purdue Attitude Scales. Newcomb and Svehla (1937) with the Thurstone scales for attitude to the church, to war, and to communism obtained familial correlations as large as those usually obtained with intelligence tests. These data are shown in Table 8-2. Finally, Weltmann and Remmers (1946) found correlations between parents and children on political party choice, ranging from .80 to .94.

It is probably true to say that in respect to attitudes, similarity is determined almost completely by environmental factors. Basic inherited temperament may play some part in particular attitudes held, but this is probably of minimal importance. Since no foster controls appear to have been used by any of the writers mentioned, we cannot say definitely that this is so. As we shall see later, however, the twin data support this point of view.

Two studies have been done on family resemblances in interest patterns. One of these (Forster, 1931) used 25 scales given to 122 father-son pairs. The median correlation turned out to be .35 with a range of 0 to .49. The highest correlations were obtained on the scales for farmer, advertiser, real-estate salesman, physicist, chemist, and Y.M.C.A. secretary. Those for personnel manager, chartered ac-

TABLE 8-2

Family Correlations for Several Attitude Scales
(Newcomb and Svehla, 1937)

	Attitude to		
	Church	War	Communism
Parent-child	.63	.44	.56
Sibling	.60	.37	.48
Father-son	.59	.40	.40
Mother-son	.57	.44	.61
Father-daughter	.64	.44	.62
Mother-daughter	.71	.46	.51
Father-mother	.76	.43	.58

countant, artist, and city-school superintendent yielded the lowest coefficients. Strong's study (1943) obtained a range of correlations similar to Forster's, .11 to .48, with an average of .29 for 11 vocational interest scales.

It is likely as in the case of attitudes that heredity plays a minor role in the transmission of interests. The degree to which a son follows in his father's footsteps will be determined by a large number of environmental factors. Some of these will be sociological, such as the degree of vertical mobility in the society; others will be purely psychological, such as the kind of child-rearing practices extant in the home.

On the whole, the work done on inheritance of personality and temperament with the familial-correlations method yields a rather ambiguous picture. Although correlations of an appreciable size have been found for a number of traits and attitude and interest patterns, it is not at all certain that these depend at all on genetic factors. Controls have not been nearly as adequate in this area as in the corresponding work on inheritance of mental ability.

Twin Studies. *Personality Tests and Inventories.* Most of the ambiguities of the data obtained by the two methods outlined above are less serious in the twin studies of personality inheritance. Although the great diversity of the work makes any sort of rational classification of it difficult, we have attempted to group studies according to whether the authors were concerned primarily with tests, traits, interests, or personality deviations (e.g., social maturity, criminality, delinquency).

The Bernreuter inventory has also been popular in twin studies. Carter (1933, 1935) in two experiments tested 133 pairs of twins, including 55 MZ and 78 DZ pairs. His results for six scales of the Bernreuter test are shown in Table 8-3. Without exception, MZ pairs

TABLE 8-3

Twin Similarities in Scales of the Bernreuter
Personality Inventory
(Carter, 1935)

		No.	Bernreuter Scale					
			Neuroticism	Self-sufficiency	Introversion	Dominance	Self-confidence	Sociability
MZ		55	.63	.44	.50	.71	.58	.57
DZ								
	Like sex	44	.32	−.14	.40	.34	.20	.41
	Unlike sex	34	.18	.12	.18	.18	.07	.39

showed greater similarity than did the DZ pairs. This effect was largely independent of age according to the data. However, like-sexed DZ twins showed a great deal more similarity than unlike-sexed pairs. Correction for attenuation raised some of these correlations considerably. In the case of dominance, for example, the identical-twin correlation rose to .86. Portenier (1939), on the other hand, found rather different results. He compared 12 pairs of siblings with 12 pairs of twins, of which, however, only 2 pairs were monozygotic. His data, presented in Table 8-4 indicate that, on the whole, sibs are more similar than twins. This is perhaps surprising even from an environmentalist point of view. Fraternal twins are, of course, no more alike genetically than sibs, but there is no obvious reason why they should show less similarity on the Bernreuter scales. One can only suppose that family environment acted in Portenier's sample in such a way as to maximize differences between DZ twins as compared with ordinary sibs. Often, in the case of twins, parents deliberately attempt to vary treatment in order "to preserve the individuality" of each member of the pair. A comparison of Carter's data on his like-sexed twins with the corresponding data of Portenier also points up some discrepancies. For example, Carter found a fairly strong degree of similarity for introversion (.43, and .47 corrected), while Portenier re-

TABLE 8-4

A Comparison of Twins* and Siblings on Several Measures of Personality and Temperament
(Portenier, 1939)

Test	Correlation	
	Twin	Sibling
Bernreuter		
Neuroticism	.27	.54
Self-sufficiency	.67	.21
Introversion	−.02	.52
Dominance	.42	.58
Self-confidence	.21	.59
Sociability	.16	.53
Maller Character Sketches		
Habit pattern	.55	.23
Self-control	.08	.18
Social adjustment	−.03	.71
Personal adjustment	.38	.38
Mental health	−.07	.01
Readiness to confide	.37	.51
Total score	.04	.37
Allport Ascendance-Submission	.32	.50
Strong Masculinity-Femininity Index	.92	.67
Meier-Seashore Art Judgment	.51	.56

* Only two out of 12 pairs were monozygotic.

ported a coefficient for the same trait of only −.02. On the other hand, self-sufficiency gave a low correlation of −.14 for Carter's subjects but gave a correlation of .67 for Portenier's. It is possible that these discrepancies are due to differences in sample size and mainly to the small number of subjects used by Portenier. It should also be noted that the correlations reported for MZ twins by Carter are considerably higher than the corresponding coefficients of family resemblance described earlier. Consequently, the twin evidence for some genetic effect in Bernreuter test performance is fairly strong.

Other tests were used by Portenier. Results for these are also shown in Table 8-4. They included the Maller Character Sketches, the Allport Ascendance-Submission Scale, the Strong Masculinity-Femininity Index, and the Meier-Seashore Art Judgment Test. In all of these, sibling correlations turned out to be higher than DZ-twin correlations.

The major exception was Strong's test on which twins were more alike than siblings. In view of the lack of genetic variation in the experiment, no conclusion pertinent to our discussion can be reached. The chief value of the study is its demonstration that being a twin does have an important effect on an individual's relations with siblings. This may relate either to age factors or to culture.

Several investigators have used the Downey Will-Temperament Test. This scale measures mainly three groups of traits: (1) speed and fluidity of reaction; (2) forcefulness and decisiveness of action; (3) carefulness and persistence of reaction. Each of these traits is measured by several simple tests (Freeman, 1926). Newman, Freeman, and Holzinger (1937) and Tarcsay (1939) obtained no evidence for hereditary factors in will-temperament. However, both Koch (1927), who worked with a pair of Siamese twins, and Bakwin (1931) found a suggestion of twin similarity.

Another aspect of personality inheritance that has been studied concerns occupational-interest patterns. As in the case of the family-correlation method, the twin method has tended to indicate that hereditary factors may play some part. Carter (1940), in a study of 43 monozygotic and 77 dizygotic pairs, found a correlation of .50 for MZ and .28 for DZ pairs on the Strong Occupational Interest Inventory. As with so many of the studies described here, it is difficult in this one to rule out categorically the influence of environment in producing likenesses. Even if heredity were not a factor, however, it would still be of considerable interest to know that identicals are more alike than fraternals, since this would have important implications for child-rearing practices.

Response Mode and Tempo. In this connection it is worth referring to the extensive twin literature on the heritability of handwriting. Although many studies have been published on this topic, there has been disagreement in regard to the importance of genetic determinants of this trait. At present no definite conclusions can be stated. It is clear that results must depend in large measure on the particular handwriting dimension being studied. Thus Carmena (1935) and Miguel (1935) have stressed genetic factors in the pressure component of handwriting, though von Bracken (1940a,b) has disagreed. von Bracken (1940a,b) has favored inheritance of speed, on the other hand, whereas writing angle has been stressed by Nicolay (1939) and Hermann (1939).

The question of speed or tempo of reaction is an interesting one and has been studied by a number of investigators with reference to heredity. Frischeisen-Köhler (1933a,b) found it was definitely conditioned by genetic factors. Tests included tapping with finger, foot, and hand at a rate "most agreeable to the subject," and, second, choosing a preferred metronome speed. Results are shown in Table 8-5.

TABLE 8-5

Similarity of MZ and DZ Twins in Personal Tempo as Measured by Several Tests (Frischeisen-Köhler, 1933)

Test	Mean % Intrapair Deviations	
	MZ	DZ
Speed of tapping	11.1	17.5
Metronome speed preference	7.8	15.5
Tapping and metronome combined	7.8	15.0

MZ cotwins are much more alike than DZ pairs. Siblings showed a mean deviation for both tests of 15.4 and that for unrelated individuals was 20.6. Other familial resemblance data obtained by Frischeisen-Köhler supported the twin evidence. If both parents were quick, 4% of the children were rated as slow, 56% quick as, and 40% as moderate. If both were slow, 71% of the children were also slow, none quick, and 29% moderate. With both moderate, 17% of the children were slow, 17% quick, and 66% moderate. Frischeisen-Köhler concluded strongly in favor of hereditary determinants of tempo and suggested a genetic model to account for the results obtained.

Confirmation of these results was attempted several years later by Newman, Freeman, and Holzinger (1937). Their procedure differed insofar as they instructed their subjects to tap as rapidly as possible, rather than at an agreeable rate. Hence their scores probably reflected physiological capacity rather than temperament. Mean-percent differences in tapping rate were as follows: for 50 monozygotic pairs, 19.3 ($r = .814$); for 51 dizygotic pairs, 29.0 ($r = .689$). Although these differences were in the right direction for a genetic hypothesis, they were not statistically significant.

Along similar lines but at the verbal rather than at the motor level, Carter (1939) found evidence of concordance for speed of word association. Using a highly reliable measure, he obtained for MZ pairs a correlation coefficient of .53 compared with .44 for DZ pairs. Carter (1935) also showed that this greater MZ resemblance held more for association to pleasant than to unpleasant or indifferent words. Using the most reliable of several measures, Sorensen and Carter (1940) subsequently obtained a corrected correlation of .52 for 38 pairs of MZ twins, and .30 for 34 DZ pairs. Burke (cited by Sorensen and Carter, 1940) also obtained generally greater similarity within a free-association test. Cattell and Malteno (1940) studying association fluency obtained a correlation of .66 for 31 monozygotic pairs, .59 for 53 dizygotic pairs. Correction for attenuation yielded correlations of .78 and .70, respectively.

Somewhat related to the traits of tempo and association fluency is perseveration. This refers to the tendency of individuals to continue in some repetitive performance. Usually, simple motor tasks are used such as writing letters or numbers in a prescribed order which is changed from time to time by the experimenter. Perseverative tendencies are usually measured by the degree to which a preceding task interferes with a subsequent one. The greater the lag resulting from the first task, the higher the perseveration score. Yule (1935) obtained perseveration scores for 115 pairs of twins from Hermann and Hogben's group (1933). He used a reliable index which was not correlated with age. The resulting correlations were as follows: monozygotic pairs, .65; dizygotic, like-sex, .36; dizygotic, unlike-sex, .14. Concordance for the trait was fairly clear. Later, however, Cattell and Malteno (1940) found a correlation of .10 for their monozygotic pairs, .47 for their dizygotic pairs. In contradiction to Yule, these figures obviously do not support a genetic hypothesis for perseveration. It is impossible at present to explain the discrepancy between the two studies. A replication would be most desirable.

The final paper to be considered here—one of considerable importance—is by Eysenck (1956). This writer extracted by factorial analysis of a number of tests of personality and intelligence, an *introversion-extroversion* factor. Intraclass correlations showed that this factor was influenced by heredity at least as much as intelligence. Eysenck went on to relate theoretically introversion-extroversion dimensions to reactive inhibition. Reactive inhibition is a technical term in learning theory (Hull, 1943) and roughly refers to a fatigue factor that tends to inhibit repetition of the same response. In this respect, it is the inverse of perseveration. He argued that introverts show very little, extroverts a great deal, of reactive inhibition. Proof of this contention was supplied by comparing performance of extreme individuals of the introvert and extrovert types (dysthenics and hysterics, respectively) on two learning tasks and a figural after-effects experiment. On all these tests, dysthenics showed evidence of less reactive inhibition (i.e., more perseveration) than hysterics, thus supporting Eysenck's hypothesis. If his conclusions generally are valid, they are of great importance. Here is a clearcut case of a basic variable of temperament, relating to both personality and learning ability, that is strongly dependent on genetic factors. More work along these lines will undoubtedly be of great value.

Projective Tests. Another area of genetic investigation has been concerned with hereditary determination of projective-test scores, primarily responses to Rorschach inkblots. The Rorschach Test aims at analysis of personality by means of a subject's responses to ten standardized inkblots, some of which are black and white, others colored. A number of scoring categories are used, which vary somewhat with different investigators (see Anastasi, 1954). Three broad categories are most commonly used: location, or the part of the blot to which the subject responds; determinant, whether the response involves form, color, shading, or "movement"; and content, what the response is about. On the whole, the Rorschach is one of the most popular projective tests, especially among clinicians. For these reasons, it is not surprising that its relationship to genetic factors has been studied. Bleuler (1929) examined 75 pairs of siblings and 610 pairs of unrelated persons. Resemblance in Rorschach psychograms occurred in 69.7% of sibs, but in only 50% of non-siblings. In a later work the same author (1933), reviewing some of his own and other researches, reached the conclusion that, even with good controls for environmental conditions, the influence of heredity was about four times as strong as the influence of environment on determination of Rorschach Test score similarities. Marinescu, Kreindler, and Copelman (1934) also obtained positive results in twin studies. Kerr (1936), however, working in Britain, came to more moderate conclusions. Her main results on similarities between MZ and DZ twins with respect to Rorschach's personality types are presented in Table 8-6. Coarctative responses are defined as those indicating "ego-limitation."

Clearly, whereas MZ pairs are alike in a larger percentage of cases, this trend is only slight. Distribution of "banal" responses and of identical responses over the two groups gave no indication of hereditary factors. Later Eckle and Ostermeyer (1939) claimed to have obtained moderately positive results on twin similarities in Rorschach responses, but, on the whole, the evidence is ambiguous.

Two studies (Szondi, 1939; Rabin, 1952) have also been done on the inheritance of responses to the Szondi pictures. This test, involv-

TABLE 8-6

Similarity of MZ and DZ Twins on Rorschach Response Types
(Kerr, 1936)

% Agreement

	Both Coarctative	Both Introversive	Both Extroversive
MZ twins	33.30	18.50	0.00
DZ twins, like sex	21.07	23.60	0.00
DZ twins, unlike sex	30.60	16.30	2.04
Unrelated individuals	19.20	18.40	0.00
Random expectancy	22.80	18.90	0.84

ing a number of photographs of mental patients in different psychiatric categories, operates on the assumption that a person having a propensity to a certain type of abnormality will express a preference for the appearance of persons actually having this abnormality. Hence if asked to rank the photographs in order of preference, he will do so in a way that has diagnostic value. Whatever one may think of the test and its rationale, both studies referred to above have found some suggestion of similarity in members of identical-twin pairs. Whether this is genetically conditioned or not, however, is another question that cannot be settled at present.

Perceptual and Sensory Capacities. A final group of behavioral studies may be mentioned here briefly inasmuch as the traits involved have some bearing on personality inheritance. This group is concerned with differences in perceptual and sensory capacities. It has been found that identical twins are similar in production of after-images (von Bracken, 1939), eidetic imagery (Smith, 1949), imaginal and motor functions (Zilian, 1938), accommodative convergence (Hofstetter, 1948), and spatial orientation (Malan, 1940). The authors of these studies have all suggested that heredity plays a role in determining these variables. However, in spite of the case that has been made by such writers as Smith (1947), it is doubtful whether these factors have much to do with personality, and we have chosen to treat them separately (Chapter 5).

In summary of the twin studies just discussed, it may be said that they generally support the view that a number of testable dimensions of personality depend on inheritance. However, the conclusions to be drawn from the data are by no means as clear as they are in the case of intelligence. Obviously, much remains to be done, particularly in the matter of obtaining a rational and parsimonious description of personality.

ANIMAL EXPERIMENTATION

As in the chapter on intelligence, we shall consider experimentation with animals in the study of temperament and personality inheritance under two methodological headings: first, selection studies, and second, studies of strain differences. Before going on to these, we find it worth noting that personality is as difficult to define in animals as it is in human beings. Although a number of excellent studies and surveys of the area have been made (Hall, 1941; Moss, 1946; Munn, 1950; Stone, 1951), our knowledge and techniques are still very far from complete. The terms personality and temperament as used here will cover roughly three main areas: (*a*) activity level; (*b*) emotionality, including wildness, aggression, and timidity; (*c*) social behavior, including dominance-submission and competition relations.

Selection Studies. Only two major studies have been done on the inheritance of traits of temperament using the method of selection. The first dealt with the trait of motor activity (Rundquist, 1933). It may be noted here, parenthetically, that the character does in fact relate to temperament, as shown in a number of studies, especially those by Richter and others, to be discussed later. Rundquist used Richter-type activity wheels, basing selection on the number of revolutions in the last fifteen days of a twenty-one-day testing period. Up to the fifth generation, selection was purely phenotypic. After that point, the strains were separated from each other and selection carried out only within the active and inactive strains. The main results up to G_{12} are set out in Table 8-7. Inbreeding was utilized only sporadically. To hasten the accumulation of new generations, the earliest maturing animals were chosen as parents in each generation. It will be seen from the table that selection for inactivity was much more effective than for high activity. This applies both to males and females, though somewhat more for males. The sex difference may well be due to the influence of the estrus cycle, which tends to raise activity level in females.

Several points should be noted in connection with this investigation. First, conditions of maintenance were not uniform during the first part of the experiment, and the increased performance of the active animals as compared with the parental strain may have been largely an environmental effect. Second, it is also possible that the

TABLE 8-7

Selection for Activity and Inactivity in Rats
(Rundquist, 1933)

	Males						Females					
	Active			Inactive			Active			Inactive		
	No.	Mean	S.D.	No.	Mean	S.D.	No.	Mean	S.D.	No.	Mean	S.D.
G_1	17	141	78	14	72	89	10	115	65	9	104	83
G_2	10	138	72	15	84	65	9	142	39	18	90	48
G_3	7	153	92	13	65	66	7	200	67	7	129	65
G_4	24	143	96	25	129	104	31	181	122	20	173	89
G_5	19	141	96	16	31	27	22	198	61	20	60	52
G_6	30	178	90	23	22	25	23	255	69	25	68	55
G_7	28	131	80	18	10	17	27	205	97	28	50	45
G_8	29	136	70	11	15	19	29	234	70	19	39	49
G_9	32	168	41	21	22	45	20	237	53	25	46	47
G_{10}	26	150	75	25	4	5	26	257	77	23	24	34
G_{11}	26	151	66	21	6	9	25	267	104	29	23	28
G_{12}	26	123	53	29	6	5	23	172	66	23	20	24

Revolutions in thousands for 15 days.

parents represented previous and inadvertent selection for docility in separate lines and that mixing these up produced genotypes with greater capacity for response. Rundquist (1933) and Brody (1942) have argued that the inactive strain was less variable than the active, and hence was more homozygous. This is not a sound deduction, however, since one cannot assume that the genetic determiners involved affect activity-level in a linear manner or that the environmental variance is independent of the genotype. It might have been desirable to rescale the data using the logarithms of number of revolutions. Under such a transformation the inactive strain would be considerably more variable, since many inactive animals had zero or near-zero scores. Offspring of very lethargic parents in the inactive strain were not different, however, from those of more active parents in the same strain. Hence the extreme inactives were apparently not genetically unique, but were animals which, for some reason or other, failed to receive a strong enough environmental push.

There are, however, other grounds for supposing that the inactives were more homozygous. Their fertility was generally lower, and the stock could not be propagated beyond G_{25}. Since then, another inactive strain has been bred by selection within active × inactive hybrids. It is doubtful that inactivity is a by-product of homozygosity, in view of the fact that inactivity appeared much more quickly than fixation of alleles could have occurred. In addition, high activity does not appear to be altogether incompatible with inbreeding (Thompson, 1953b). Consequently, in view of all these difficulties, not much can be stated definitively regarding the relative homozygosity of the two strains. This fact places limitations on Brody's (1942) genetic analyses, which we will consider separately.

The second major selection study was by Hall (1938) on emotionality in rats. The measure used by Hall was frequency of urination and defecation over 12 daily two-minute trials in a fairly large, brightly lit' open field. Scores varied from 0 to 12, that is to say, from no defecation or urination on any day to elimination on all days. While Hall (1934) and Broadhurst (1957, 1958) have both regarded this method of measuring general emotionality in rats as valid and useful, others (Bindra and Thompson, 1953; Hunt and Otis, 1953) have found it rather limited and specific. A full discussion of this point is beyond the scope of the present chapter. We may accept, temporarily, Hall's measure as being a valid indication of emotionality and proceed to look at his selection data. The parental generation, consisting of 145 rats, was divided on the basis of open-field scores into high and low scorers. Selection was then carried out within each of these strains, breeding from the most emotional animals of the emotional group and the least emotional of the non-emotional group. Selection on this basis was carried on to G_{12}. Means and standard deviations for parents in the two strains up to this point are shown in Table 8-8. It is clear that the emotional strain increased in emotionality up to G_9, at which point it appeared to stabilize. Variation in this line decreased on the whole. Selection for non-emotionality, on the other hand, was much less successful, and the last three generations are hardly less emotional than the first three. In other words, maximum effects appear very quickly. This contrasts rather sharply with the larger time taken to reach a maximum of high emotionality. Subsequent crosses between the two strains indicated that in all probability neither was fully homozygous. However, Hall's evidence for inheritance of some aspect of emotionality is quite convincing.

No other systematic selection studies dealing with temperament have been done. Such selection, however, regularly occurs in dogs though not in a controlled way (Humphrey and Warner, 1934). Similarly, the process of domestication in animals is essentially selection

TABLE 8-8

Selection for Emotionality and Non-emotionality in Rats as Measured by Defecation and Urination in an Open-Field Situation (Hall, 1938, 1951)

Number of days defecation or urination
Parental generation

No.	Mean	S.D.
145	3.86	3.54

	Emotional Strain			Nonemotional Strain		
	No.	Mean	S.D.	No.	Mean	S.D.
G_1	40	3.07	3.36	35	0.46	0.77
G_2	18	4.72	4.12	18	1.94	2.28
G_3	65	3.92	3.64	50	1.02	1.30
G_4	84	4.69	3.89	52	1.40	1.43
G_5	75	4.96	3.85	59	0.41	1.18
G_6	48	6.87	3.28	51	0.51	1.13
G_7	72	7.82	3.18	53	0.17	0.47
G_8	77	8.37	2.94	40	1.07	2.46
G_9	85	10.31	2.09	32	1.68	3.25
G_{10}	66	10.41	2.08	22	1.45	3.13
G_{11}	57	10.11	2.39	42	1.05	2.01
G_{12}	47	10.40	2.18	31	1.65	2.53

for docility (Richter, 1950). Some outcomes of these kinds of selection are discussed in the next section.

Studies of Strain Differences. A number of studies have investigated activity level in different strains within various species. Utsurikawa (1917), one of the earliest experimenters in this area, measured among other things speed of reaction to a bell in two strains of rats, one inbred, the other outbred. The inbred reacted more quickly and more intensely than the outbred. On the other hand, on a rating scale of free activity involving walking, climbing, running, washing, sniffing, seeking for food, and lifting the lid of the cage, the outbred animals had much higher scores. Given auditory stimulation, outbred rats were slightly more active when the sound was continuous, less so when it was intermittent. For inbred rats, the reverse was true. In agreement with a previous experiment by Ada Yerkes (1916), the data as a whole suggested that inbreeding had produced an animal that was fast and hyper-responsive to stimuli, but one with a lowered level of activity under normal conditions. Evidently this finding has some bearing on emotionality, a dimension that Utsurikawa also considered and to which we shall return in a moment. A number of years later, another study of activity and temperament was made by Sadovnikova-Koltzova (1926), who observed the behavior of progeny of white rats and wild-gray hybrids on a Hampton Court maze. Her results led her to conclude in favor of three groups of genes, determining activity level, emotion, and seeking tendencies, respectively.

Vicari (1929) experimented with four pure mouse strains, comparing their running speed in a simple maze over a number of trials. The strains used were an inbred line of Japanese Waltzers (JW), a strain with abnormal eyes (ABN), and two inbred strains of normal phenotype, BALB and DBA. Mean running times over the series of fourteen trials and for the first and fourteenth trial alone are shown in Table 8-9. The poor showing of the waltzers was probably related

TABLE 8-9

Running Time of Four Mouse Stocks on a Simple Maze (Vicari, 1929)

Strain	No.	Time in Seconds			
		Mean, Trials 1–14	Standard Error	Mean, Trial 1 only	Mean, Trial 14 only
JW	86–28	73.1	8.6	115.3	75.0
BALB	93–78	50.1	4.4	94.6	28.6
ABN	28–26	27.0	2.9	24.5	22.7
DBA	28–27	12.5	1.8	10.3	7.9

to their sensori-motor defect which resulted in excessive non-goal directed activity. Eye defects *per se* did not impair running speed, since the ABN's were slightly superior to the BALB's. The effects of learning upon heritable variation are evident from a comparison of the mean times for the first and fourteenth trials. The order is unchanged, but the relative distance between ranks is altered.

A number of experimenters have considered the inheritance of one rather special aspect of activity, namely, exploration. This particular kind of behavior has considerable significance to the psychology of motivation. Typically, it is measured in terms of number of arms traversed by an animal in a simple T- or Y-maze, no incentive being offered other than the exploration itself (Montgomery, 1952). Orderliness of exploratory activity is also sometimes recorded by analyzing the temporal sequence of arm choices. A similar method of measuring exploratory activity is by use of an open field divided either by barriers or by a grid on the floor into a number of sections. The number of sections traversed in a certain time period can be used as a measure of exploration.

Both methods, a Y-maze and an open field, were used by Thompson (1953b, 1956) in a systematic analysis of the activity of a number of inbred strains from the Jackson Laboratory. In the first of these studies, differences in open-field activity were found between fourteen inbred and one hybrid strain. Results are set out in Table 8-10. A highly significant between-strain variance was found, indicating the operation of genetic factors. It is interesting to compare these results

TABLE 8-10

Exploratory Activity in Fifteen Mouse Strains
(Thompson, 1953)

Rank	Strain	Mean Number Crossings	Probability of a Significant Difference*	
			.05	.01
1	C57BR/a	459	>3	>5
2	C57BL/6	361	>7	>10
3	C57BL/10	359	>7	>10
4	DBA/1	334	>8	>12
5	ND	308	>8	>12
6	BDP	286	>10	>13
7	DBA/2	253	>11	>14
8	LP	194	>13	
9	AKR	188	>13	
10	C3H	177	>13	
11	Obese	149	>15	
12	TC3H	117		
13	BALB/c	74		
14	AK/e	60		
15	A/Jax	20		

* This column is read as follows: the probability that the difference between rank 3(C57BL/10) and rank 7(DBA/2) and lower is due to chance is less than .05. The probability that the differences between C57BL/10 and strains of rank 10 and lower is due to chance is less than .01.

with Heston's (1949) chart showing the origin of some of the strains used by Thompson. The three C57 strains have a common origin from Lathrop's colony, and they rank together at the top of the distribution. The two DBA strains, though isolated for many years, do not differ significantly. BALB/c's and A's have some common ancestry, and both have scores near the bottom. C3H, derived from a cross between the ancestral DBA and BALB/c lines, is intermediate between the two in activity. Strain TC3H is descended from C3H through an ovum transferred to another strain to free the line from mammary-tumor milk agent. The difference in exploratory behavior between these strains, though fairly large, does not reach the .05 level of significance. This constancy of behavioral results with genetic events occurring as much as 100 generations removed is most interesting, though other comparisons might not turn out as well.

The second study by Thompson (1956) extended the analysis of activity in 5 of the 15 strains used before. In addition to open-field activity, a Y-maze was used. Results on the open field, as far as rank order of scores for the five strains, was exactly as in the earlier experiment. The same rank order, with one exception, held up on the Y-maze test. The results are shown in Table 8-11 and Figure 8-1.

TABLE 8-11

Means and Variances in Activity Level Shown by Five Inbred Mouse Strains in Two Test Situations (Thompson, 1956)

Strain	Open Field			Y-maze		
	No.	Mean	Variance	No.	Mean	Variance
C57BR/a	40	532.2	22274.46	20	284.8	2480.04
C57BL/6	40	338.2	10887.14	20	181.0	416.16
AKR	40	185.0	27924.95	20	231.8	3014.01
BALB/c	40	37.4	6752.64	20	137.0	1239.04
A/Jax	40	11.4	1072.94	20	79.6	852.64

Genetic differences in activity between stock and inbred albino rats have been shown by Williams (1956) and between different inbred strains by Carr and Williams (1957). Results from three inbred strains, hooded, blacks, and albinos, on a Y-maze are shown in Figure 8-2. Over five days of testing, significant differences were obtained between hooded and black, and hooded and albino, though not be-

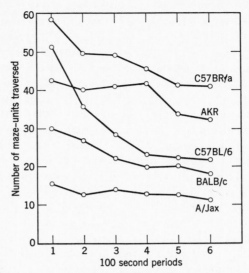

FIGURE 8-1. Activity levels of five inbred mouse strains as functions of time. (Thompson, 1956.)

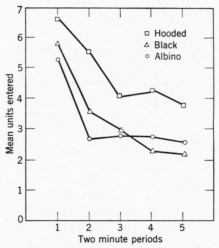

FIGURE 8-2. Exploratory activities in a Y-maze of three rat strains. (Carr and Williams, 1957.)

tween black and albino. Blacks were found to explore in a significantly more orderly fashion than hooded, though this difference was not very large in absolute terms.

Broadhurst (1958*a,b*) obtained slightly different results from those of Carr and Williams. Open-field ambulation scores of albinos were found by Broadhurst to be higher than those of hooded animals. Although the testing procedures were different, Thompson (1956) has shown that two tests very similar to Broadhurst's open field and Carr and Williams' Y-maze, correlated around .6. The hooded line was the same in both cases (August line 35322). Consequently the difference must be attributed to the albinos used by each, in Broadhurst's experiment, a Wistar stock, and in the Carr and Williams study, a Fischer line. It would be of considerable interest to compare these two lines directly on the same test.

Anderson (1939) reported on activity in dogs. Using an automatic recording device to study differences between six breeds, he found that German shepherds and cocker spaniels shared a generally high level of activity, which tended to remain constant over a 24-hour period of testing. British bulldogs, dachshunds, and Pekingese showed a medium activity level with a diurnal cycle. Basset hounds were low in activity and particularly inactive at night. These results seem to agree well with general observation. Further data along the same lines were reported by Scott (1950) dealing with "non-adaptive activity" in four dog breeds caged for short periods. These were basenjis, beagles, cocker spaniels, and wire-haired fox terriers. The fox terrier showed a good deal of trembling in the situation and also more pacing and stereotyped movements than beagles or cockers. Basenjis showed the most pacing. Since the numbers were very small, however, not much weight can be given to these data. Furthermore, the behavior of the four breeds was probably fairly specific to the situation.

In a different test situation involving a learning element, Scott and Charles (1954) have obtained other results. Arguing that small genetic differences may be magnified by special environmental circumstances, they gathered data on activity differences in four breeds as influenced by habit formation. The subjects were rated for activity on a three-point scale while being trained to stand still during weighing. Results were based on a period between 5 and 18 weeks of age during which this training was carried on. As shown in Figures 8-3 and 8-4, small initial differences between basenjis, beagles, cockers, and wire-haired terriers tended to increase with respect both to ratings of quietness and activity. The rank order for activity level, however, is different from the one obtained in the cage situation with adults. This effectively underlines not only the importance of habit on the degree of genetic differences in activity but also the importance of the general environmental situation in which activity is observed.

In summary, there is little doubt that activity level as measured in

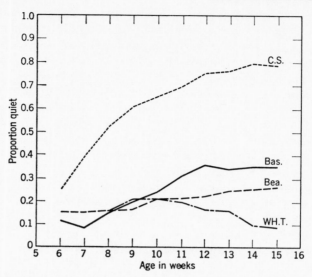

FIGURE 8-3. Proportions of animals rated as "quiet" in four dog breeds as a function of age. Bas., basenji; Bea, beagle; C.S., cocker spaniel; WH.T., wire-haired terrier. (Scott and Charles, 1954.)

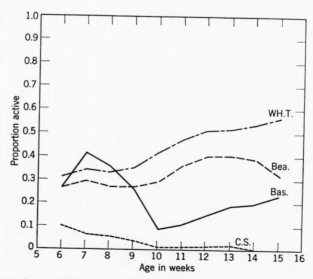

FIGURE 8-4. Proportions of animals rated as "active" in four dog breeds as function of age. Abbreviations as in Figure 8-3. (Scott and Charles, 1954.)

a number of species, including rats, mice, and dogs, is strongly dependent on genetic factors. The next step should involve an analysis of the components of activity. It is probably not a unitary trait and should not be treated as such in any genetic analysis.

Emotional Behavior. Studies of emotional behavior were certainly among the earliest in the field of behavior genetics. The work perhaps starts with an observation by Phillips (1912) on wildness in mallard and black ducks and their hybrids. On the basis of general observation, he concluded that wildness, as observed in blacks, is inherited as a dominant character. In the following year Robert M. Yerkes (1913) published a study of the inheritance of wildness, savageness, and timidity in rats. Four five-point rating scales were used. The subjects were captured wild rats and tame hooded animals from the Harvard colony. The contrast between the two parent lines, Yerkes pointed out, was extremely marked and could definitely be attributed to genetic factors. In the tame strain, females were less gentle and tame than males. Coburn (1922) reported work that was essentially a continuation of Yerkes' study but used mice instead of rats. Wild gray and tame strains were rated for wildness and savageness, timidity being omitted. There was a striking difference between the wild and tame strains in these traits, and, as before, females were found to be wilder than males. Both Yerkes and Coburn tested hybrids, and these results are considered later.

Dawson (1932) also studied the inheritance of wildness and tameness in mice, but instead of a rating scale, he used an objective measure, the average time taken to traverse a 22-foot runway in three trials. A barrier was moved along behind the subjects to prevent retracing. Reliability of the measure over the whole population was .92. The subjects were laboratory-raised offspring of wild mice (*Mus musculus*) and three strains of tame mice. Again, marked behavioral differences between the genotypes were found, indicating the influence of hereditary factors. Stone (1932) reached the same conclusion using rats.

Several further studies on rats and on mice give additional indications of the inheritance of emotionality. One of these, by Hall and Klein (1942), dealt with aggressiveness in two strains of rats—those previously bred by Hall for emotionality and non-emotionality on the basis of the elimination test. A six-point scale was constructed by the author to describe the aggressive behavior of one animal toward another. The scale ranged from a zero score if a rat showed no interest in the other animal to a score of 6 when fierce wrestling and severe biting were involved. A large difference between the two strains was found. The non-emotional animals initiated 326 attacks as against

68 initiated by the emotional animals. The aggressiveness score of the average non-emotional rat was about twice as great as that of the average emotional subject. These results indicated that aggressiveness was inherited and, at least to some degree, was negatively correlated with emotionality as measured by Hall. Some support was given to this conclusion by the work of Scott (1942) on the social behavior of three inbred strains of mice, C57BL/10, A albinos, and C3H agoutis. Neither study, however, was designed to separate the three types of genetic correlation. Hence the nature of the relationship between emotionality and aggressiveness cannot be defined.

In a careful study, Farris and Yeakel (1945) examined the emotionality of gray Norway and Wistar albino rats. By Hall's defecation measure, Norways turned out to be somewhat more emotional than Wistars, though the difference does not quite reach the .05 level of confidence. Another measure, however, yielded a significant difference between the two strains, the Norways being more emotional. Unlike Hall and Klein, Farris and Yeakel found a high *positive* correlation between aggressiveness and emotionality. Though a somewhat different method was used to assess aggressiveness, the contradiction appears to be real. In view of these results, Farris and Yeakel suggested that the term "fearful" be used for rats with high elimination scores, rather than "timid" as used by Hall (1941). A rat that is fearful in the open-field situation is not necessarily timid, but may be very wild and savage. Obviously the relationship between these different aspects of emotionality and temperament are extremely complex and should be carefully sorted out before much in the way of genetic analysis is attempted.

A study by Lindzey (1951) examined emotionality in five inbred mouse strains, DBA/2, C57BL, C3H, BALB/c, and A. Significant differences in open-field defecation and urination between the strains were found. The BALB/c's proved to be the most fearful or timid, followed by C3H, DBA/2, A, and C57BL in that order. The strain rank order found by Lindzey was partly verified by Fredericson (1953) using a different method, namely, the degree to which mice would stay close to or leave the walls of any open field. It was assumed that more fearless animals would more readily traverse the central areas of the maze. Average number of center-field contacts were found to be as follows for the three inbred strains used: C57BL/10, 9.16; C3H, 0.83; BALB/c, 0.00.

A similar study of emotional behavior and food drive in mice, on a larger scale, was done by Thompson (1953b). Samples from 15 different strains were observed in an open-field eating situation under conditions of moderate food deprivation. Amount of food eaten and frequency of defecation were recorded during six consecutive daily 10-minute trials. Results for the two measures are shown in Tables 8-12 and 8-13. Significances between strain differences were found for

TABLE 8-12

Hunger Drive in Fifteen Mouse Strains Measured by Mean Grams of Food Eaten in 10-Minute Testing Periods on Six Consecutive Days
(Thompson, 1953b)

No.	Strain	Mean Grams Eaten	p Values of Differences*	
			.05–.01	.01–.001
1	TC3H	204	>6	7
2	AKR	199	>6	7
3	C3H	183	>7	8
4	DBA/1	176	>7	10
5	ND	171	>7	11
6	C57BL/6	162	>11	12
7	AK/e	131	>13	
8	C57BR/a	128	>13	
9	LP	124	>13	
10	DBA/2	121	>13	
11	C57BL/10	116		
12	BALB/c	99		
13	Obese	82		
14	BDP	82		
15	A/Jax	80		

* This column is read as follows: the probability that the difference between rank 3(C3H) and rank 7(AK/e) and lower is due to chance is less than .05. The probability that the difference between C3H and strains of rank 8 and lower is due to chance is less than .01.

each test. The two measures correlated —.796. The more fearful animals ate less. It may be noted that there is some discrepancy between the results obtained here and those obtained previously by Lindzey (1951). This discrepancy is probably due largely to different testing procedures.

Broadhurst (1958b) in the course of an intensive investigation of the nature of rat emotionality has presented data on five homozygous strains, albino, brown, brown-hooded, black-hooded I, and black-hooded II. We have already presented his results on activity in an

TABLE 8-13

Emotionality in Fifteen Mouse Strains Measured
by Percentage of Mice in Each Strain Defecating
During Six 10-Minute Testing Periods
(Thompson, 1953b)

Strain	%	Strain	%	Strain	%
AK/e	96	A/Jax	78	C3H	52
BDP	85	DBA/2	70	C57BL/6	40
Obese	83	C57BR/a	66	AKR	34
LP	82	C57BL/10	58	ND	27
BALB/c	82	DBA/2	57	TC3H	11

open field. In addition, he found strain differences in amount of emotional defecation, measured over four days. Two groupings appeared, a so-called non-reactive group of strains consisting of black-hooded I, brown, and brown-hooded, and a reactive group consisting of black-hooded II and albinos. It will be noted that, as far as strains are concerned, there appears to be a somewhat positive relationship between defecation and ambulation. Albinos score highest on both, while black-hooded I animals score lowest on both. It is of some interest that Hall (1936) in a previous study found a small negative correlation between defecation and ambulatory activity which increased, however, with exposure to the open field. Obviously, the relation between the two measures is extremely complex and needs to be analyzed further. Although there may be a genetic basis for frequency and amount of defecation in a mildly stressful situation, this is not to say that defecation is the best measure of emotionality.

Thorne (1940) initiated work at the Cornell Morphological Station on the inheritance of emotionality in a larger mammal, the dog. He observed 178 subjects, representing 14 different pure breeds and 19 types of hybrids. Three tests of approach-avoidance behavior were used. In the first, the experimenter would offer food through the fence of the animal enclosure. In the second, he would enter the runway and squat while offering food. In the third, he would enter the enclosure on the run and stand while offering food. The dog's reactions were noted in each case. On the basis of data so obtained, he concluded that although most dogs became friendly during the testing period, about 25% of the subjects showed unfriendliness which was not easily modifiable. The use of a special forced handling method resulted in some of the unfriendly group becoming friendly. Most of these animals, however, fell into two types, an excitable type which became increasingly refractory and difficult to handle and another type which appeared to be paralyzed by fear and submitted passively to handling. As it turned out, a great many of the unfriendly group were second, third, and fourth generation descendants of a single bitch who was known to be a fear-biter. Thorne concluded that the fear response underlying unfriendliness was hereditary.

The last study to be considered in this section is an analysis of emotional behavior in ten dog breeds by Mahut (1958). Six main dimensions of emotionality were observed, no response, avoidance, teasing, approach-avoidance, wariness, and curiosity. Significant breed differences were found in four of these categories as shown in Table 8-14. Mahut divided the subjects into two main groups, "fearful" and

TABLE 8-14

Emotional Differences on Four Variables in Ten Dog Breeds (Mahut, 1958)

Breed	No.	Avoidance		Teasing		Approach-Avoidance		Wariness	
		Mean	S.D.	Mean	S.D.	Mean	S.D.	Mean	S.D.
Collie	16	2.69	1.65	0.37	0.70	0.50	0.71	0.75	0.66
Ger. shepherd	11	2.63	1.07	0.36	0.88	0.18	0.39	0.81	1.00
Corgi	15	2.40	1.23	0.06	0.25	0.20	0.54	1.33	0.94
Stand. poodle	24	2.29	1.40	0.33	0.83	0.71	1.00	0.96	1.00
Dachshund	30	2.10	1.25	0.36	0.71	0.33	0.70	1.20	1.16
Minit. poodle	28	1.53	1.35	0.25	0.51	0.35	0.35	1.93	1.31
Bedlington	14	1.00	1.36	1.28	1.33	0.50	0.98	0.50	0.63
Boston terrier	20	0.40	0.49	1.40	1.15	1.05	1.11	0.65	0.96
Boxer	30	0.36	0.71	2.43	1.52	0.43	0.80	0.66	1.13
Scottie	14	0.21	0.41	1.42	1.11	1.85	1.13	1.00	1.14

"fearless" animals. These categories were defined somewhat arbitrarily in terms of high scores on avoidance and wariness as opposed to high scores on teasing and approach-avoidance and curiosity responses respectively. The first group included, rather paradoxically, working and hunting dogs, collies, German shepherds, miniature and standard poodles, corgies, and dachshunds. The fearless group included boxers, Boston terriers, Bedlingtons, and Scottish terriers. Since the observations were made mainly in homes (most of the animals were pets) and in rather loosely defined situations (e.g., response to opening umbrella, toy snake, etc.), it is rather difficult to relate this work to previous experiments in the field. The experiment mainly points up the great need for more comprehensive theory in the field of emotional behavior. An incisive point made in the study, however, was that many of the genetic differences were obliterated by experiential factors. Rearing in a restricted environment thus tended to increase fearfulness irrespective of genetic constitution. Two final studies dealing with different species may be mentioned. Guhl and Eaton (1948) found evidence for inheritance of aggressiveness in poultry, and Leopold (1944) concluded that wildness had a genetic basis in turkeys.

Social Behavior. It must be recognized that the separation of social behavior from emotionality and activity is arbitrary and made merely for the sake of convenience. Much of the work done on the inheritance of social behavior deals, for example, with dominance and submission, two traits that relate intimately to aggressiveness and fearfulness. The way individuals interact in a group, at least at the level of genetic inquiry, is always reducible to individual characteristics of temperament and personality.

Although a great deal has been done on comparative social behavior in animals (see Allee et al., 1949; Crawford, 1939; Smith and Ross, 1952; Hebb and Thompson, 1954; Thompson, 1958; Scott, 1958), relatively little has been done from the standpoint of its heritability. Ginsburg and Allee (1942) studied dominance and submissiveness in three inbred mouse strains, C57BL, C3H, and BALB/c. They found clear strain differences in fighting tendencies, the blacks being the most aggressive, followed by the agouti C3H and BALB/c. These differences were not affected by cross-fostering. However, they noted that individual animals could be conditioned by experiencing many victories or defeats to be more or less aggressive. It appeared to be easier to train a socially dominant mouse downward than to condition an inferior one upward. Intermediate mice were more readily conditioned in either direction. Some support was given to this work by Scott (1942) using the same strains, and also an additional strain, A. Although no attempt at quantification was made in this study, the relative aggressiveness displayed by the first three strains was similar to that found in the Ginsburg and Allee study. Mice of strain A turned out to have a lower threshold for attacking an intruder than any of the other strains. Fredericson and Birnbaum (1954) studied fighting behavior in two mouse strains, C57BL and BALB/c/Sc. While C57BL's were usually more competitive, BALB's would often become so if the motivation was high enough. Because of this fact, the authors suggested a concept of behavioral dominance according to which an organism inherits a repertory of behaviors, each with different probabilities of elicitation. In an encounter between animals of different strains, the stock with the more vigorous behavior pattern exerts a dominant influence upon the nature of the social relationship which ordinarily develops.

A case for the inheritance of social behavior has also been made in a different species, gamecocks. Fennell (1945) found not only dominance tendencies but also specific modes of attack varied from breed to breed. Breed differences in dominance of hens have also been found by Potter (1949) and others (see Allee et al., 1949; Smith and Ross, 1952). Similarly, James (1949) studied dominance order of groups of puppies as indicated by food intake. The more aggressive pups were also the more dominant, and both traits appeared together early in life. Shifts in dominance commonly occurred, however, around 115 days of age. Alcohol often had the effect of increasing aggressiveness. Later James (1951) found breed differences in dominance order, fox terriers being more dominant than beagles. An interesting relationship was found between dominance and territoriality. The more dominant the animal, the larger the territory it controlled. Another study, also dealing with dogs, was done by King (1954) using basenjis and cocker spaniels. Basenjis showed a much more rigid hierarchical structure than did cockers and were also more rejecting of and aggressive to animals which were strange. These aspects of social behavior also varied with the breed and sex of the stranger. King concluded that aggression was genetically determined and underlay the kind of social organization which developed in a breed of dog.

King's work has been largely corroborated and extended by Pawlowski and Scott (1956) using, in addition to basenjis and cockers, beagles and wire-haired fox terriers. Breed differences were found which related in a complex way to motivational level. Thus the four breeds did not differ greatly in social hierarchy until between the eleventh and fifteenth week. Around this time terriers showed strong dominance relationships as compared to basenjis, beagles, and cockers. By one year basenjis had increased in percent of dominance relations almost to the level of terriers. Beagles and cockers both showed rather less dominance at this age than they did at fifteen weeks. Males tended to be more dominating than females.

In summary, the evidence clearly indicates that social behavior and group organization is influenced by the genetic make-up of the individuals comprising the group. Such traits are even further from primary actions of genes than are individual traits such as emotionality and fearfulness. Hence, their inheritance may be expected to be complex.

Comparison of Human and Animal Studies. We have now covered the main body of work, both at the human and animal levels, dealing with the inheritance of personality and temperament. The evidence is strong that heredity plays a large part in the determination of a great many kinds of traits in a wide range of species. Studies in many kinds of behavior such as projective test responses, interest patterns, tempo, aggressiveness, fearfulness, and timidity all point to this general conclusion. This is not to say, of course, that environmental effects are negligible. On the contrary, it is likely that these are often much more important sources of individual differences than the variance due to genes. In many of the studies we have reviewed, especially those using human subjects, the contributions made by the two sets of factors have not been clearly isolated by use of appropriate control. Better experiments can be done. The extension of the animal data to man is not unreasonable for emotional traits closely related to physiology. The parallels are not very close when dealing with interest patterns or Rorschach responses.

We now turn to the two final sections of this chapter, one dealing with work on the physiological basis of these characters, the other with work on the genetic transmission of personality and temperament.

PSYCHOLOGICAL AND PHYSIOLOGICAL CORRELATES OF TEMPERAMENT

As with intelligence, one of the more promising lines of attack on the genetics of personality and temperament involves the discovery of more parsimonious ways of describing the domain. This can be done by attempting to find basic psychological factors that underlie clusters of correlated traits or, perhaps even better, by looking for physiological or anatomical substrates of these traits.

Developing a unified concept of temperament from psychological data is not simple. The degree of association between personality traits depends a great deal on the species in which they are assessed, the manner of measuring and analyzing their relationships, the age and experience of the subjects, and other variables. Several investigators have made a start, however, in creating order out of confusion. We may mention Anderson's (1937, 1938a,b) analysis of the interrelationships between drives in the rat, Royce's (1955) factorial study on emotionality in the dog, and Willingham's (1956) factor analysis of 20 variables of emotionality in mice. Royce isolated ten factors: timidity, heart reactivity, aggressiveness, activity level, audiogenc reactivity, timidity II, plus four unidentifiable and underdetermined factors. Willingham found six factors: elimination, freezing, grooming, reactivity to experimenter, reactivity to light, and emotional maturity. As Willingham points out, Wenger (1948) previously was able to isolate two factors in human beings, muscle tension and autonomic balance, that appear to correspond quite closely with the freezing and elimination factors in the mouse. It seems very likely that other convergences will be found.

Future work on the genetics of temperament might very well proceed along the lines demarcated by these studies. Experiments based on well-standardized unitary traits would certainly be applicable to a wider range of behavior. Such traits may, of course, still prove to be complex genetically.

Turning to physiological approaches, we find a number of studies which have attempted to relate activity level, wildness, and emotionality to various structural and physiological variables. Rundquist and Bellis (1933) measured the basal metabolic rates of male and female rats from Rundquist's active (A) and inactive (I) strains. Readings were made two days after removing the subjects from the activity wheels and after 12 hours of fasting. Male A's averaged 8.25 cal./ gm./hr. Corresponding values for the I strain were 6.28 for males and 6.45 for females. The strain differences were definitely significant. Data were presented to prove that the effects were not caused by differences in age, weight, respiratory quotient, or amount of previous exercise. Similarly, Hall and Lindsay (1938) also found positive correlation in rats between activity level and basal metabolic rate (B.M.R.) which was disturbed only slightly by thyroidectomy. Schopbach, Keeler, and Greenberg (1943) showed that wild gray Norway rats operate at a lower B.M.R. than do Wistar albinos and that low B.M.R. appeared to be transmitted as a dominant character dependent on multiple factors. They concluded that B.M.R. was lowered by the gene for piebald coat color. Since it now appears that wild rats differ from tame animals in activity level, mainly under conditions of fasting which raises the activity of wilds (Richter and Rice, 1954), the matter is obviously rather complex.

A good deal of work has also been done on the endocrine systems of wild and domesticated strains of rats. Yeakel and Rhoades (1941) weighed adrenal, thyroid, and pituitary glands from Hall's emotional and non-emotional strains. Emotional males had larger adrenals and thyroids than non-emotional males, whereas emotional females had larger pituitaries and thyroids than non-emotional females. Rogers and Richter (1948) found striking differences in the size of adrenal glands in two wild strains of rats (Norways and Alexandrines) and a tame strain (domesticated Norways). Most of the difference was in the cortical portion of the gland, rather than the medulla. F_1 hybrids resembled the tame parent in adrenal size. Evidently wild animals depend heavily on adrenal function for survival, the cortex of this gland playing an important adaptive role in response to stress. It is significant that domestic rats survived adrenalectomy, but wild ones tended not to survive it.

Further endocrine differences have also been found. Wild rats have a great deal more adrenal cholesterol than tame animals. Capture causes temporary loss of cholesterol with a return to normal in 24 hours (Nichols, 1950). Richter, Rogers, and Hall (1950) showed that salt replacement failed to compensate for adrenalectomy in wild but did so in tame rats, and Woods (1954) found that fighting caused a decrease in adrenal ascorbic acid content in domesticated but not in wild rats. Finally, Richter and Uhlenhuth (1954) demonstrated that gonadectomy had little effect on the activity of wild Norways, but a very marked reducing effect on that of domesticated Norway animals. The authors suggested that running activity is controlled in wild rats largely by the adrenals, in tame animals by the gonads, and that during the process of domestication, there occurs a gradual shift from adrenal to gonadal control of many bodily functions. This interesting hypothesis deserves to be followed up to determine whether it is a peculiarity of the rat or a general phenomenon. Certainly endocrine differences are implicated in many instances of heritable variation of behavior. (See also Chapter 10.)

A final line of work bearing on the present topic concerns the linkage between temperamental and morphological characters. It has been the thesis of Kretschmer (1936) and Sheldon and Stevens (1942) among others that there is a correlation between morphological characters, particularly body build, and temperament. Thus, an endomorphic build is associated with a rather phlegmatic, underreactive personality; a mesomorphic build with an impulsive, adventurous spirit; and an ectomorphic build with an introverted, thoughtful, cautious temperament. Although these ideas do find some useful applications in different contexts (see Chapter 9), they do not stand up too well empirically (Child, 1950).

Similarly, with lower animals, Keeler (Keeler, 1942, 1947, 1948; Keeler and King, 1942) has suggested that correlations can be shown in a variety of species between coat color and such behavioral traits as wildness, docility, and activity. Presumably these represent pleiotropic effects of the coat-color genes. However, Thompson (1953*b*) with mice and Broadhurst (1958*b*) with rats found no correlation between color and temperament. The observations made do not permit generalization. Some coat-color genes may have pleiotropic effects upon physiological processes which affect behavior, and others may not. Linkage may explain other observations. Until more and better-controlled experiments are done, the issue must remain open.

In summary, the work on psychological and physiological correlates of personality and temperament has opened some useful leads, particularly with respect to the part played by endocrines in determining strain differences. Since the immediate effects of genes are biochemical, it seems that further research along these lines should help our understanding of the inheritance of personality.

MECHANISMS OF GENETIC TRANSMISSION

Genetic mechanisms for transmission of personality are less well studied than those for intelligence. This is particularly true with human subjects, and even at the level of the lower animals information is scanty. About the only genetic model that has been suggested for humans is that of Frischeisen-Köhler (1933*a,b*) in her study of personal tempo. She hypothesized on the basis of her data that this trait was determined either by multiple genes occurring in two allelic series with dominance of quick tempo or by a single allelic series with intermediate inheritance. She regarded both interpretations as being compatible with her data. The evidence Frischeisen-Köhler has on this trait is rather limited and therefore we cannot fairly assess the value of the model she suggests. Since there is very little else in the way of theory at the human level, we will turn to animal studies.

As has been already pointed out, two generations of Rundquist's active and inactive rats (G_{21} Series 1, G_{22} Series 2) were crossed by Brody (1942) to investigate the mode of transmission of activity level. Means and standard deviations of activity scores in thousands of revolutions are presented in Table 8-15. A comparison of the means of each group with those of its parents gives a clear indication of heritability, as in each case the offspring are intermediate. Otherwise the pattern is inconsistent. The F_1 is sometimes closer to the A parent, sometimes to the I parent. In the crosses of Series 1 both F_2's were lower in activity than the F_1 and had larger standard deviations as would be expected if "activity genes" were segregating. In the Series 2 crosses, the F_2 was more active than the F_1, and the larger standard

TABLE 8-15

Spontaneous Activity in Crosses between Rundquist's Active (A) and Inactive (I) Strains of Rats in Units of Thousands of Revolutions Per Fifteen Days
(Brody, 1942)

Generation	F_{21} Crosses (Series 1)			F_{22} Crosses (Series 2)		
	No.	Mean	S.D.	No.	Mean	S.D.
Females						
$P(A)$	13	125	36.5	21	169	54.0
$P(I)$	56	14	20.1	24	17	24.0
F_1	54	116	56.2	62	81	59.8
F_2	99	68	66.0	30	142	79.8
$F_1 \times A$	42	129	69.2	23	182	43.2
$F_1 \times I$	22	41	66.6	23	53	52.2
Males						
$P(A)$	14	140	53.8	19	110	50.7
$P(I)$	48	10	13.9	14	11	19.4
F_1	28	75	43.1	49	22	27.9
F_2	96	32	44.0	35	42	46.9
$F_1 \times A$	45	55	57.2	26	95	61.2
$F_1 \times I$	20	2	3.7	14	11	12.8

deviations may be here merely a function of the particular scaling system used. It is interesting to compare the proportions of very inactive (under 1000 revolutions in 15 days) and very active (over 200,000 revolutions in 15 days) individuals in the cross-bred groups as shown in Table 8-16. The divergence between Series 1 and Series 2 data is quite marked. If extreme inactivity were the result of homozygosis, one would not expect so much of it in hybrid animals.

Brody concluded that the two strains differed primarily at one locus, the allele for low activity being dominant in males and the allele for high activity being dominant in females. This argument she based on the abrupt separation of A and I animals during selection as well as the results of the crosses. The F_1 matings of Series 1 did produce males of low activity and females whose activity score varied somewhat more. Also in the $F_1 \times A$ backcrosses, the females were about as active as the parents, whereas the males could be divided into a high and a low class. The inconsistency between the two series, however, as well as the fact that F_1's of both sexes tested (Series 1 for

TABLE 8-16

Percentage of Very Inactive (Under 1000 Rev./15 Days) and Very Active (Over 200,000 Rev./15 Days) Rats in Crosses between A and I Strains (Brody, 1942)

Generation	F_{21} Crosses (Series 1)		F_{22} Crosses (Series 2)	
	Very low	Very high	Very low	Very high
Females				
*P(A)	(0.0–6.5)	(18–70)		
*P(I)	(0.0–26.1)	(<1)		
F_1	0.0	7.0	16.7	4.0
F_2	32.3	8.0	10.0	20.0
$F_1 \times A$	12.8	15.0	0.0	30.0
$F_1 \times I$	50.0	6.0	8.7	2.0
Males				
*P(A)	(0.0–14.3)	c. 20%		
*P(I)	(0.0–50.0)	0.0		
F_1	0.0	0.0	49.0	0.0
F_2	45.3	0.0	11.4	0.0
$F_1 \times A$	28.6	2.0	4.0	3.0
$F_1 \times I$	70.0	0.0	5.0	0.0

* Range of the means for separate generations of the parental strains.

males and Series 2 for females) tended to show an intermediate level of activity, argues against such a model. Probably a polygenic system acting upon a behavioral trait highly sensitive to environmental factors and to some aspects of sexuality could be fitted to the data with less difficulty. In a later publication (1950) Brody adhered in the main to the single locus hypothesis, but stated, "this alone would not wholly account for the effects of selection in the inactive strain." Although the specific genetic hypothesis set up is perhaps not acceptable, the experiment stands as one of the most thorough and well-controlled investigations in behavioral genetics.

Hall (1951) also made crosses between his emotional and non-emotional strains of rats. The results are presented in Table 8-17, which may be compared with Table 8-8. It can be seen that the F_1 means tend to resemble the non-emotional rather than the emotional parents. Standard deviations are close to those of each parent. Unfortunately

TABLE 8-17

Crosses between Emotional and Non-Emotional Strains of Rats
(Hall, 1951)

Generation	Defecation-Urination Scores		
Emotional × Non-emotional	No.	Mean	S.D.
$G_{10} \times G_{10}$	32	4.53	3.84
$G_{11} \times G_{11}$	22	2.81	2.15
$G_{12} \times G_{12}$	27	3.00	2.55

Hall did not obtain F_2 crosses. He says, "Had the two strains been pure, the variability of the hybrids would have been smaller than that found. . . . It was deemed unfruitful to make further crosses with impure strains" (Hall, 1951, page 324). In point of fact, the F_1 hybrids were not much more variable than either parent. Hall would perhaps have been justified in making further crosses, and it seems possible that he would have obtained segregation in his F_2's.

Of the experimenters using pure strains, only four have attempted any genetic analysis. Vicari (1929) in her study of running speed in four mouse strains made three crosses. In each, the F_1 was similar to the more active parent in speed. In the BALB × DBA and BALB × ABN crosses, the F_2 did not differ significantly from the F_1. The F_2 of the JW × BALB cross regressed toward the JW stock. It was not possible from the data to draw any definite conclusions about the genetic mode of transmission of running activity.

Coburn (1922) suggested that the traits of wildness and savageness in mice were carried by multiple factors. Although some of the crosses made seemed to suggest dominance of wildness and savageness and others recessivity, Coburn concluded that additivity of effects was the most probable relationship between alleles. The traits tended to decrease in intensity with continued testing and both responded to selection.

Dawson (1932), as we noted above, measured wildness in mice in terms of time taken to traverse a 22-foot runway. Most of the genetic analysis done by him is based on crosses between the wild (W) and the tame albino (T) stock. He concluded on the basis of F_2 and backcross means and variances that only two or three gene pairs with major effects were involved. Wildness was strongly dominant. No evidence was found for linkage between wildness and physical make-up.

We have recalculated Dawson's data using the logarithm of the time in seconds as a score. The results are shown in Table 8-18. The

TABLE 8-18

Genetics of Activity with Dawson's (1932) Data Recalculated Using a Logarithmic Transformation

Strain or Cross	Mean	Variance
Wild	.795	.0147
Tame	1.380	.0156
F_1(W $\times$ T)	.864	.0184
$F_1 \times$ W	.830	.0116
$F_1 \times$ T	1.276	.0656
F_2	1.059	.0283

$\bar{x}$ = Mean log time in seconds.

F_1 is much more like the W parent, as Dawson found before, but is still significantly slower ($t = 4.05$, $p < .01$). The F_2 is more variable and spans almost the entire range of the parental generation. The backcross to W consists entirely of fast runners, while the backcross to T has a wide range and includes a small number of individuals much slower than any of the original T stock. The best fit to these data is a two-locus system, with factors for high activity dominant at both loci. By applying the formulae of Wright and Castle (Wright, 1952) to the rescaled data, a minimum estimate of four gene differences between W and T is obtained. The potency ratio (Mather, 1949) is 0.80 and heritability in the F_2 is about 35%. Thus, a polygenic model fits reasonably well. It was clearly recognized by Dawson that the absence of distinct modes in the backcross and the response to selection in the T stock proved that although relatively few genes fixed "fast" responses, many others had a minor influence on the general range of speed. It would be interesting to know how wild mice would respond to selection in the presence of "active" alleles as well as "inactive" alleles.

The final study done by Thompson and Fuller (1957) dealt with exploratory activity in two test situations, an open field with barriers, and a Y-maze. Crosses were made between the high activity (C57BR) and low activity (A) strains in order to test the applicability of a polygenic model to the inheritance of a quantitative behavioral character. Square-root transformations were used to normalize the distributions for open-field activity. The data from this test were used as an example in a previous chapter and have been set out in Table 3-9 (page 85). For convenience, they are reproduced here with the data for the Y-maze in Table 8-19, and 8-20. In both tests the means fell into a systematic order in which the higher scores are obtained by the groups with more BR genes. In the open-field test there is clear segregation in the F_2 and heritability is estimated at about 60%.

TABLE 8-19

Genetics of Activity; Crosses between Two Inbred Mouse Strains, One High-, the Other Low-Scoring in Two Tests of Activity (Thompson and Fuller, 1957)

	Open Field		Y-maze	
	Mean	Variance	Mean	Variance
C57BR/a	532.26	22,274.46	284.80	2,480.04
A/Jax	11.40	1,074.94	79.62	852.64
F_1	302.97	10,420.10	160.63	1,097.78
F_2	287.87	23,613.46	164.89	1,787.81
$F_1 \times BR$	395.99	22,259.62	206.18	477.86
$F_1 \times A$	148.34	11,816.92	131.53	800.48

Raw scores are shown.

TABLE 8-20

Genetics of Activity; Crosses between Two Inbred Mouse Strains, One High-, the Other Low-Scoring on Open-Field Activity, Using a Log Transformation (Thompson and Fuller, 1957)

	Units of Open-Field Traversal	
	Mean	Variance
C57BR/a	22.89	9.74
A/Jax	1.91	16.48
F_1	16.98	12.23
F_2	16.09	29.60
$F_1 \times BR$	18.92	30.15
$F_1 \times A$	11.04	27.58

Both with raw and with transformed scores, the F_1 mean is closer to the BR than to the A mean, indicating the presence of some dominant genes for high activity. The minimum number of gene differences is estimated at four, using Wright's formulae on the transformed scores (three pairs with raw scores), and there are indications that these estimates may be low. Most puzzling is the fact that with transformed scores, both backcrosses have variances as high as that of the F_2. Sampling error, a deficiency in the scaling technique, or some kind of complex gene interaction are possible causes. The fact that the transformation used results in approximately equal variances between the two parent strains and the F_1 (as intended) seems to point to the last of these possibilities. Just what this is, is not altogether certain at present.

The Y-maze results are similar. Means again fall in order as before, but there is little suggestion of dominance of high activity. F_1 and F_2 means are slightly smaller than the average between the parents. Heritability is estimated at 31% using raw scores. The minimum number of gene pairs operating is about seven pairs. Unlike the results in the open-field test, backcross variances here are smaller than those of the parents or of any other cross.

These results point up sharply the dependence of genetic models on the situation used. Although the two activity tests are ostensibly similar, and, in fact, correlate significantly (.60), they yield results that are not congruent with a single model. This applies not only to the question of dominance, but also to degree of heritability and number of genes involved. More extensive data are badly needed, although fault may well lie in the models rather than in the experimental procedures.

9

Mental disorders

In this chapter we shall cover genetic work bearing on the major classes of mental illness, namely, schizophrenia, manic-depression, melancholia, senile dementia, and psychoneurosis. We shall also touch on investigations of the role of heredity in such disorders as criminality, suicide, homosexuality, mental defect, and epilepsy.

Definitions and descriptions of mental illness present complex problems. One of the most obvious criteria separating the normal from the abnormal person is that the latter, whether voluntarily or involuntarily, is undergoing some form of hospital treatment or in some other way is on a psychiatrist's records. We cannot assume, however, that persons having no contact with a hospital or with psychiatrists are all normal. Many mentally ill individuals, for one reason or another, live their lives in the outside world. Thus hospitalization or case-record criteria are useful only as starting points. They tell us that most individuals in hospitals are abnormal; they do not tell us that all those outside hospitals are normal. Because of this difficulty, genetic surveys of mental illness should always include precautions against the biased selection that can arise from relying on these criteria too rigidly.

More exact ways of diagnosing the abnormal have been described in many text books. One schema, adopted by The American Psychiatric Association (Noyes and Kolb, 1958), divides mental illness into three major categories as follows: (I) Disorders caused by or associated with impairment of brain tissue function. These may be due to various agents such as trauma, toxins, pre- or peri-natal accidents, infections, and a number of others. (II) Mental deficiency, both endogenous and exogenous. (III) Psychogenic disorders without any clearly defined physical causes or structural brain changes. This last group includes involutional psychoses, the various types of schizophrenia, manic-depression, paranoid reactions, undefined psychotic reactions, psychoneuroses, and personality disorders. We shall be concerned primarily with this last group, though we shall also deal briefly with other categories. It should be noted that the specific types of disorders within the broad classes are delimited both nosologically and etiologically. The difference between schizophrenia and manic-depression, for example, is defined largely by the characteristic symptoms involved in each entity. On the other hand, a disease like alcoholism, grouped under "personality disorders," is defined in terms of the causative agent producing abnormal symptoms. It is likely that as knowledge of mental illness increases, classification will tend to become more and more etiological. In fact it is quite possible, as several writers (Kallman, 1947; Silveira, 1952) have suggested, that genetics may eventually contribute a great deal in this direction. At present, however, we must be content with a somewhat loose classificatory scheme based on several different dimensions. As with the realm of personality and intelligence, rational phenotypic description is again a central problem. It will be discussed in the course of the chapter.

The methods which have been used in studying the inheritance of mental illness are essentially similar to those already described in connection with other aspects of behavior. They are the familial resemblance or proband method, the twin concordance method, and a combination of the two, the twin-family method developed by Kallman (1946). Insofar as mental disorders represent discrete phenotypic categories rather than regions on a continuous scale, these methods are somewhat different from those reviewed in the two previous chapters. Since the various methods which have been used were presented in Chapter 4, they will not be reviewed here at length. We shall consider only their development in the history of psychiatry and their applications to the study of mental illness.

The twin method, as noted earlier, traces to Galton and was used in the field of psychiatry by a number of authors after him. Most of these early reports, however, dealt with isolated instances of twins, both of whom showed mental illness of some kind. Siemens (1924) and Luxenburger (1928, 1930) rightly pointed out that such cases could not be combined to make an unbiased statistical sample. Luxenburger proposed instead the use of a so-called uninterrupted series in which all twins in a sequence of hospital admissions were located and concordance rates computed for the resulting sample. This procedure would give a truer estimate of the importance of hereditary factors, since there would be no selection operating in favor of describing concordant pairs only, as there was in the early case-report publications. An anti-heredity bias will, of course, locate more cases of discordance. Subsequently most workers in the field have been careful to follow Luxenburger's suggestions. Their samples are chosen so as to include not only both concordant and discordant pairs, but also representative proportions of male and female pairs and of identical and fraternal pairs.

The second method, the proband method, may be attributed to the Munich school (Planansky, 1955). It has been used since 1929 by investigators in the field in many parts of the world, particularly in Scandinavia and the United States. Essentially, this method involves the selection of a random sample of cases (probands or propositi) in a particular psychiatric category. All available relatives of these cases are then located for study. When these have been diagnosed, expectancy rates for incidence of mental illness among them are computed and these rates compared with those for a randomly chosen control sample which is taken from the general population. Various special problems such as changes in risk with age, the inclusion or exclusion of the probands themselves in the expectancy rates, and others have been handled by variations of the basic methodology (see Chapter 4). The final technique, the twin-family method, simply involves a comparison of expectancy rates for all degrees of genotypic similarity ranging from remote, as among probands and grandparents or cousins, to identical, as between identical twins. Concordance rates for fraternal twins are generally used as a means of controlling for environmental effects, since the individuals in such pairs, although genetically no more similar than sibs, may be assumed to develop in as similar environments as do the partners of an identical-twin pair. We have already discussed the validity of this assumption in several chapters.

In broad outline, these are the main methods employed in the field of psychiatric genetics. Their exact usage and specific details involve many more problems than can be dealt with adequately here. We shall concentrate on evaluating the main conclusions of various studies, ignoring, for the most part, technical flaws or difficulties when they do not seem to detract much from the major results. Good reviews of the work to be discussed have been made by Rudin (1923), Slater (1944, 1953b), Barahal (1945), Kallman (1953, 1954a), Penrose (1953), and Planansky (1955), to mention only a few. These may be consulted by readers who wish to go further into psychiatric genetics.

SCHIZOPHRENIA

The term schizophrenia refers to a broad array of abnormal symptoms which have as their central core a disorganization of basic personality. This disorganization may involve hallucinations, a retreat from reality, delusions, dreaminess, confabulation, a dissociation between ideas and emotional response, and other such symptoms. Historically, the syndrome was first delineated by Connolly in England and later designated by Morel in 1800 as *dementia praecox,* because of its common onset in adolescence. Morel felt it was mainly determined by heredity. Kraeplin in 1896 extended but also specified the definition of the category to include several other disease entities which he felt had basically the same common denominator. Finally, the term dementia praecox was replaced by Bleuler in 1911 by the designation schizophrenia. Today, four main types of schizophrenia are widely recognized (Noyes and Kolb, 1958); simple, hebephrenic, catatonic, and paranoid. Though the first of these is somewhat of a "waste-basket" category, the others refer to fairly definite symptomatologies which overlie the common disorientation or "splitting" of the personality. Hebephrenia is usually characterized by silliness, incongruous smiling and laughter, and early age of onset; catatonia by phases of stupor (often catalepsy) and excitement; and paranoid schizophrenia by delusions with persecutory or megalomaniac content. However, this division is an idealized picture, and many schizophrenics do not fit at all clearly into a single category. For the most part, the genetic work presented in this chapter deals with the schizophrenic syndrome as a whole, though a few workers have attempted to analyze the subcategories separately.

We shall now examine evidence on the inheritance of schizophrenia as a general syndrome, presenting both proband and twin studies. In all instances, comparisons must be made with frequency of schizophrenia in the general population which has been estimated to be between 0.5 and 1.0% (Kallman, 1938; Pollock and Malzberg, 1940; Fremming, 1947; Slater, 1953b). Expectancy rates vary slightly when corrections are made for inbreeding, mortality rates, and age. Although a few estimates have been higher, 3% by Böök (1953), for example, the range mentioned appears to be typical of a wide variety of different populations in America, Germany, and Scandinavia and may consequently be regarded as reasonably accurate (Kallman, 1953). In mental hospitals schizophrenia has a high frequency among first admissions. Its somewhat lower frequency among readmissions, however, indicates its tendency to be a chronic disease (Noyes and Kolb, 1958). Among relatives of proband cases in both lineal and collateral lines, expectancy rates are very much higher. Some of the evidence, as summarized by Kallman in several publications, is set out in Table 9-1. It is obvious that these figures are a great deal higher than the

TABLE 9-1

Expectancy of Schizophrenia in Relatives of Proband Cases
(Kallman, 1946; Kallman and Barrera, 1942)

Relationship to Proband	% Expectancy*
Step-sibs	1.8
Half-sibs	7.0–7.6
Full sibs	11.5–14.3
Children,	
one parent affected	16.4
both parents affected	68.1
Parents	9.3–10.3
Grandparents	3.9
Grandchildren	4.3
Nephews and nieces	3.9

* Ranges are shown where different figures were obtained.

general expectancy rate and generally correlate with degree of kinship. Such a correlation is a strong indication of hereditary factors. Kallman's data have been generally confirmed by a number of other investigators. Elsasser (1939) has calculated the expectancy for children of two schizophrenic probands at 50%, whereas Schulz (1939) obtained 31% (41% if both had the typical form) and Luxenburger (1928) 68% for the same relationship.

It should be noted that Kallman's figures represent the risk for persons of both sexes who survive the manifestation period of the disease, a period estimated to extend from 15 to 44 years of age. Within this age range there are no differences between the sexes in expectancy rates.

Although Kallman's data have been criticized on a number of technical grounds (Pastore, 1949b, 1952), the general conclusion to which they point is probably sound, as Hurst (1951, 1952) has indicated. At the same time, some work done in the field is in notable disagreement. Pollock and Malzberg (1940) studied the families of 175 proband cases. Among their relatives, only a few cases of schizophrenia were diagnosed, giving hardly more than chance expectancy. It is difficult to know why there is such a discrepancy between these results and those obtained by other workers. Possibly one reason for it is the rather small sample used by Pollock and Malzberg. Since those studied by Kallman are considerably larger, perhaps it is fair to place more confidence in his conclusions. His conclusions are also supported by a greater number of studies.

Kallman (1946) considers that the expectancy rates obtained in his proband families are probably underestimates, owing mainly to the fact that celibacy is considerably higher and fertility lower in schizophrenics than in normal individuals. Table 9-2 shows this quite clearly.

TABLE 9-2

Marriage and Birth Rates in Normal and Schizophrenic Populations (Kallman, 1946)

	% Marriage Rate	% Birth Rate
General population	71	3.3
Schizophrenics		
Nuclear Group	39.1	1.4
Peripheral Group	70.1	3.1
All	50.3	1.9

In view of these facts, we might expect that proband data, particularly in the direct lines, will be obtained from the less deteriorated cases of schizophrenia, since only the more mildly afflicted individuals mate and have children. Hence expectancy rates will probably be lower than predicted from simple genetic hypotheses. The same factors that permit a schizophrenic to marry and propagate probably also provide his children with a certain resistance to the psychotic process.

Twin studies lend direct support to the conclusions drawn from proband data. Almost without exception, investigators in psychiatric genetics have shown high concordance rates for schizophrenia in twins. Some sample studies are presented in Table 9-3. Although some of the concordance rates that have been found for MZ twins are low, notably those of Luxenburger (1930) and Rosanoff et al. (1934c), the general picture presented strongly supports the hereditary point of view. It is important to note that the degree of concordance found depends a great deal on the method and care of the diagnosis. Very often diagnoses differ from hospital to hospital or even in the same hospital from time to time. It is difficult to tell whether such differences relate only to superficial aspects of the disease entity or whether they are basic. The best way of meeting this difficulty is to use only cases that have been personally interviewed by the investiga-

TABLE 9-3

Expectancy Rates in MZ and DZ Cotwins
of Schizophrenics, as Found
in Several Studies
(Kallman, 1953)

Author	DZ		MZ	
	No.	% Expectancy	No.	% Expectancy
Luxenburger (1928, 1930)	60*	3.3	21	66.6
Rosanoff et al. (1934c)	101	14.9	41	68.3
Essen-Möller (1941)	24	16.7	7	71.4
Slater (1951)	115	14.0	41	76.0
Kallman (1938–1953)	685	14.5	268	86.2

* These include 23 cases of twins whose zygosity was not definitely ascertained.

tor himself, using reliable diagnostic procedures. This procedure was followed by Slater (1953a,c) in a careful study of 67 MZ and over 200 DZ twins. Since the concordance rates found by him (see Table 9-3) were not very different from those found by other investigators, we can assume that most of the data have not been seriously biased by inconsistent diagnostic procedures. Rosanoff et al. (1934c) dealt with the problem of consistent diagnosis in a similar way but also attempted to get gradations of similarity between members of the twin pairs. Where both individuals in MZ pairs were affected, they found that 43.9% showed similar affections, 17.1% showed a quantitative dissimilarity, and 7.3% showed qualitative dissimilarity. Corresponding figures for DZ twins are 5% for each of the three categories. It has been claimed by Rosenberg (1944) that the figure of 43.9% represents the most accurate assessment of concordance and, as such, is too low to support a genetic hypothesis. Rosenberg apparently feels that when concordance is not perfect in monozygotic twins, we must hold to an environmentalist viewpoint on the causation of schizophrenia. In the light of modern genetic theory which does not postulate a one-to-one relation between genotype and phenotypic expression, this criticism does not have much cogency.

Recently in psychiatric literature a great amount of work has been devoted to so-called childhood or preadolescent schizophrenia (Hoch and Zubin, 1954, 1955). Unlike the classical syndrome which usually has its onset during or after puberty, the childhood variety may begin very early, often in the first few years of life. According to Kallman and Roth (1956), about 1.9% of all schizophrenias have the onset before age fifteen, and these represent 0.6% of all first admissions in mental hospitals. While there is no question that this disease entity, like its adult counterpart, is strongly influenced by a variety of environmental factors, there is also strong evidence that genetic causation plays a part. Kallman and Roth (1956) studied 35 DZ and 17 MZ pairs of twins reared apart. Cotwin expectancy rates were 17.1% and 70.0%, respectively. These figures do not deviate much from those for the total schizophrenic population of 22.9% and 88.2%, respectively (with age corrections). Sometimes schizophrenia in co-twins of child schizophrenics occurs before, sometimes after, adolescence. Consequently, the authors conclude that preadolescent schizophrenia is determined genetically to the same extent and apparently by the same genotype as the adult form. They suggest that the difference between the two forms lies in the number of secondary factors which lower constitutional resistance or interfere with the containability of early cases. Expectancy rates calculated on relatives of singleton cases of childhood schizophrenia were as follows: for parents, 8.8%; for sibs, 9.0%; or 9.2% and 12.2%, respectively, with corrections for age. These figures approximate those obtained for adult schizophrenia and therefore support the main conclusions based on the proband and twin data that we have just presented above.

A second set of experimental data bearing on childhood schizophrenia has been obtained by Bender and Gruggett (1956). Their genetic findings are set out in Table 9-4. Although the sample size is small, the figures shown do generally support those of Kallman and Roth, both as to the genetic basis of the syndrome in question and as to its close relation to the adult form. Kanner (1954), on the other

TABLE 9-4

Expectancy of Schizophrenia in Relatives of Childhood Schizophrenic Proband Cases (Bender and Gruggett, 1956)

% Affected

	Mother	Father	Sibs	Paternal Collaterals	Maternal Collaterals
Schizophrenic child	14	12	3	11	11
Normal child	3	1	1	0	0

hand, has had reservations both in respect to its genetic determination and its relation to adult schizophrenia.

Before leaving this general section on the inheritance of schizophrenia, we should discuss one more question. This concerns the general transmission of schizoid personality or what Kallman has called *schizoidia*. As the name suggests, the personality syndrome involves the main characteristics of schizophrenia but in lesser degree. Because the disturbance is less acute, it is considerably harder to diagnose accurately. Nevertheless, some investigators have attempted genetic studies. Hoffman (1926) suggested that so-called schizoid personality which might manifest itself in acute psychosis was not a unitary clinical entity, but rather a collection of traits that should be investigated separately. Kallman (1946), however, presented empirical data on the subject along with his expectancy rates for schizophrenia. These are reproduced for a number of degrees of kinship in Table 9-5.

TABLE 9-5

**Expectancy of Schizoid Personality in Relatives
of Schizophrenic Proband Cases
(Kallman, 1946)**

	% Expectancy*
Step-sibs	2.7
Half-sibs	12.5
Sibs	31.5
DZ cotwins	23.0
MZ cotwins	20.7
Parents	34.8

* Only definite cases included.

The data do not appear to be consistent. The twin cases suggest that schizoidia depends rather less on hereditary factors than the psychosis it presumably underlies. The proband cases, however, support a hereditary hypothesis. Kallman (1953) considered it to represent either heterozygous expression of the schizophrenic genotype coupled with weak resistance or homozygous expression with strong resistance. However, the evidence for this idea is by no means decisive as yet. It is a rather interesting hypothesis that certainly justifies further study.

The Specificity of Schizophrenia. The specificity of the schizophrenic genotype is a problem that has been widely discussed and one on which complete agreement has not yet been reached. Concretely, the question has at least two parts: First, is the schizophrenic genotype inherited as a simple unit underlying the diverse phenotypic forms the syndrome may take? Second, does the genotype underlying schizophrenia also underlie other forms of mental illness such as manic-depression, mental deficiency, and others? Since the second of these questions can be examined better after the presentation of material on other mental diseases, we shall consider only the first at this point.

We must recognize that schizophrenia as a syndrome covers not only the four classical subtypes, namely, simple, paranoid, catatonic, and hebephrenic, but also a great variety of unclassifiable symptoms that make even the most elementary subdivision difficult. The relevant question here concerns the genetic dependence or independence of these different aspects of the schizophrenic phenotype. Is there evidence for a nuclear schizophrenic genotype underlying all varieties and phases of the syndrome, or are the facts better explained in terms of a number of distinct genotypes which may or may not relate to each other? This question has been widely debated and presently opinions are held on both sides of the issue. Kallman (1946, 1953, 1954a), for example, with many others (Luxenburger, 1937; Zehnder, 1941; Elsasser, 1952; Slater, 1953a), supports the view that there is a unitary genotype for schizophrenia which may express itself in different ways depending mainly on the environmental pressures. It is quite characteristic for the disease to take many clinical forms in the same families, as many workers have pointed out. Kallman (1938) has further shown that the subtypes of schizophrenia differ somewhat in the expectancy rates they show. In children of probands these rates are as follows: for hebephrenic, 20.7%; for catatonic, 21.6%; for simple schizophrenia 10.4%; and for paranoid schizophrenia, 11.6%. Kallman argues from these figures that the first two were more closely related to the nuclear genotype than the last two. He suggests that the different symptomatology in each of these subdivisions is due to the action of genetic modifiers superimposed on the major genotype.

In contrast to Kallman's point of view, Rosanoff et al. (1934a), Weinberg and Lobstein (1943), and Essen-Möller (1941, 1952) have stressed the variations in the symptoms and suggested that different genetic mechanisms may be necessary to account for such differences as are found. Obviously, the conflict between these points of view is not serious and represents simply a difference in emphasis. It is quite likely that there is a nuclear genotype for basic schizophrenic psychosis, and it is equally possible that the variations in the symptoms which are manifested by individuals in this broad category are also dependent on particular genetic mechanisms. Any decision regarding these possibilities, however, must be delayed until a firmer liaison has been established between diagnosis of phenotype and genetic analysis. Still different views have been offered by other writers. Leonhard (1936) has distinguished between so-called typical and atypical schizophrenics. The former have strongly distinct subtypes and are deteriorative; the latter are characterized by a cyclical course with generally favorable prognosis. According to Leonhard, the typical cases show less hereditary causation than those in the atypical group. Bleuler (1930) has similarly attempted to distinguish between two groups of schizophrenias, one with and the other without hereditary causation. He concludes that although schizoid traits are probably caused by a specific genotype, a trend to actual dementia is not. This appears to be rather similar to the suggestion of Essen-Möller (1952) that the manifestation of the schizophrenic genotype depends on the presence of a basic schizoid personality which is more common in relatives of probands than actual schizophrenia. Witterman (1926) and Wildermuth (1927) found evidence that the psychotic syndrome is composed of a number of inherited symptom complexes which are transmitted separately and may be traced in family lines.

Obviously a considerable degree of confusion still surrounds the problem of the schizophrenic genotype. There are evidently a number of possibilities, different ones having support from different investigators. A carefully planned program of research done on a large scale could perhaps settle the matter and make a basic contribution to our understanding of the genetics of schizophrenia.

The final question that will concern us in this section relates to the genetic mechanisms by which schizophrenia is transmitted. In discussing these we shall also examine briefly the part played by constitution in determination of the schizophrenic syndrome.

Genetic Transmission of Schizophrenia. Perhaps more studies have been done on the genetics of schizophrenia than on any other behavioral trait. In spite of the value of this work, however, the picture is still by no means clear. Two main possibilities are open. In the first place, one or a few Mendelian unit factors may be involved. These may be either dominants, recessives, or both in some combination. On the other hand, polygenic systems may be operating on an essentially continuously distributed trait.

It is fair to say that most of the work done in the area has favored the first of these two alternatives. This is probably due partly to historical factors in the development of psychiatric genetics in Munich and elsewhere and in part to the fact that schizophrenia is usually defined in an all-or-none way. Unlike personality characteristics or intelligence, schizophrenia is present or not, operationally speaking, and hence can be treated in much the same way as traits such as "taste blindness" or phenylketonuria. At the same time it must be stressed that the categorical definition of schizophrenia is somewhat arbitrary and is mostly a matter of convenience. Individuals who have deteriorated beyond a certain point can no longer function properly in society and must then be hospitalized for treatment. This does not mean, however, that there is no gradation of symptoms from normal to acutely deteriorated. Some workers, Eysenck (1958), for example, have gathered evidence favoring this view, though it has been criticized by others (Pearson and Kley, 1958). Consequently, we must be very cautious about jumping to any conclusions regarding the mode of transmission of schizophrenia. From what we know about the nature of the behavioral trait alone, there are no strong grounds for favoring either the simple Mendelian model or the polygenic model.

As already stated, however, most workers in the field have tried to explain their data in terms of a few unit dominants or recessives. Planansky (1955) has pointed out, in fact, that no investigator has directly argued for a multiple-gene model. Consequently we shall turn directly to models along the more classical Mendelian lines.

In this category a division may be made between workers favoring primarily recessivity theories and those favoring dominance theories. One of the foremost proponents of the former view has been Kallman (1953). He has suggested that schizophrenia is carried by a major mutant recessive gene whose effect is probably to produce some enzyme deficiency. The metabolic deficiency in turn affects general behavioral adjustment rather than specific symptoms, since different types of symptoms may be observed not only in monozygotic twin pairs and in different members of the same family, but even in the same affected individuals at different times.

The recessivity hypothesis has been presented in various forms by a number of other workers, including many from the Munich School (Rüdin, 1916; Luxenburger, 1935; Weinberg and Lobstein, 1943). It has been clearly recognized by workers holding this position, however, that the data are not fully in agreement with such a hypothesis in any simple form. Usually the disease does not reach the 25% expectancy rate in siblings of schizophrenic probands. Furthermore, theoretically, all children of two schizophrenic probands should turn out to be schizophrenic, but, empirically, the figures obtained are usually between 40% and 66%. One solution to this problem, suggested by Rüdin (1916), is to postulate that more than one pair of genes are operating. Initially he favored the idea of a double recessive. Later (1923) he hypothesized a trifactorial mode for the inheritance of psychoses in general, involving two recessives and a dominant.

Neither of these models fully explains the low incidence of the disease in children of twin probands nor have such complex hypotheses proved useful in physiological analyses. Perhaps the more common and, in our opinion, the more cogent point of view involves the assumption of varying degree of penetrance of the schizophrenic genotype. Kallman (1948a, 1953, 1954a) suggested that expressivity is determined by a genetically non-specific constitutional defense mechanism which he regards as "unquestionably polygenic." This mechanism relates to the effect of certain mesodermal tissue elements which inhibit expression of the disease. It will be recognized that this suggestion is almost identical with the early theories of Kretschmer (1951) and others of the Munich school (Luxenburger, 1939) who related aesthenic physique to schizophrenia. The relationship is expressed in Table 9-6.

TABLE 9-6

Relationship between Physique and Degree of Deterioration in Schizophrenics (Kallman and Barrera, 1942)

Degree of Deterioration	Body Type (Mean Rating)		
	Pyknic	Athletic	Aesthenic
Extreme	3.01	2.82	4.41
Moderate	3.01	3.17	4.20
Slight	3.16	3.76	3.72

As things stand now, Kallman's view of this relationship is probably more accurate than the rather simple theory originally proposed. A study by Kline and Tenney (1951), for example, appears to indicate that whereas the aesthenic or in Sheldon's terms the ectomorphic physique shows little correlation with schizophrenia, strong presence of athletic or mesomorphic components is usually an indication of good prognosis for surgical therapy among those affected. This finding clearly supports Kallman's thesis. Kallman further suggests (1953) that under certain circumstances, a heterozygote with low resistance may break down under stress such as mescalin or lysergic acid (Kallman, 1954b), for example, as easily as a homozygote with strong resistance.

Evidently a theory such as this has enough flexibility to give it wide explanatory value. But for the same reason, it is a rather difficult theory to test. The data at present certainly do not contradict it, but, on the other hand, they do not definitely support it in preference to other theories.

A contrary dominance theory of schizophrenia has been supported by such workers as Patzig (1938), Böök (1953b), Koller (1939), and Schulz (1940a,b). This hypothesis, also, must assume lowered penetrance to account for the empirical expectancy rates in relatives of probands. Slater (1958) has shown that a number of surveys give results in accordance with monogenic inheritance with a manifestation rate of 26% in heterozygotes and 100% in homozygotes.

At the present time, the empirical data are too scanty to allow definitive choice between the various views presented. On the whole, a recessivity hypothesis appears to have a slight edge, mainly in view of the low frequency of schizophrenia in the population. To interpret this according to the dominance model would perhaps put undue strain on the concept of penetrance, a construct that is a little too elastic to be very useful empirically. On the other hand, a dominance theory is able to explain much of the data, especially the relatively low expectancy rates in offspring of two schizophrenic parents (Slater, 1958). Each theory has its strong points and its weak points. Until a model can be specified so precisely that it, and it alone, predicts the occurrence of schizophrenia in relatives of index cases, judgment between the present alternatives must be withheld.

Success in relating schizophrenia to one or several metabolic defects would be of great value in clarifying the genetics of this condition (see Kety, 1959). Research in this area is active, and the eventual outcome may well provide the kind of decisive evidence which is needed. In the meantime the case for heritability of schizophrenia must stand on the genetic evidence alone. Experience with the so-called psychomimetic drugs has indicated that extremely minute amounts of certain chemical configurations can seriously disturb brain function. The organic basis for schizophrenia may likewise be a minor disturbance in terms of overall metabolism, though of critical importance for behavior.

MANIC-DEPRESSION

The syndrome of manic-depression was designated in 1896 by Kraepelin. He suggested that its two main symptoms, depression and mania, were merely different phases in a single disease entity which depended primarily on some organic substrate. The general frequency in the population has usually been estimated at between 0.4 and 0.5% (Slater, 1938, 1953c; Kallman, 1953, 1954a) though some estimates in particular locales have been as high as 7% (Tomasson, 1941). Statistics relating to its occurrence in mental hospitals vary widely from as high as 30% to as low as 5% of admissions. It appears to occur more commonly in females than males and is relatively more frequent in higher socio-economic classes (Noyes and Kolb, 1958).

The specific symptomatology of the manic-depressive syndrome may best be described by considering its two phases separately. The manic phase consists in general of exaggerated self-confidence and aggressiveness, emotional instability, boisterousness and lack of constraint. Frequently there are rapid alterations in mood from extreme affability to violent temper. Thought processes are characterized by very rapid flow, an appearance of illogicality, and often an egocentric tone. Motor activity is likewise commensurate with affect and cognition and is likely to be abnormal in intensity and form. The depressive phase, on the other hand, follows an almost exactly opposite course, ranging in degree from mild to stuporous depression which involves affective level, thought, and activity.

The two phases alternate cyclically in some patients, but in others only one appears. Because of its cyclical nature and because the phases often involve symptoms similar to those seen in schizophrenia and in certain psychoneuroses, manic-depression is a difficult entity to classify except in very clear-cut cases. This means that genetic studies, if they are to pin down hereditary influences, must be very careful to define diagnostic criteria as precisely as possible.

Inheritance of Manic-Depression. Until the 1920's little was done on the inheritance of manic-depression, though a few studies (Koller, 1895; Jolly, 1913; Sünner, 1922) did find some evidence of abnormalities in ancestors of psychotic patients whose illnesses had cyclical features. As with schizophrenia, really fruitful work did not commence until the innovation by the Munich School of the proband method. Since this time a number of surveys have been made, the majority of which favor a strong influence of genetic factors.

As we have already pointed out, the incidence of manic-depression in the general population is probably less than 1.0% and, according to Kallman (1954b), most likely about 0.4%. Almost all studies of relatives of index cases have obtained much higher incidence rates. Thus they indicate that heredity may play an important role in the etiology of manic-depression psychosis. Some studies summarized by Kallman (1953) are shown in Figure 9-1 and may serve as examples.

These series agree fairly well and represent positive evidence for hereditary factors in manic-depression. In addition Slater (1936), summarizing work in the field up to 1936, has set expectancy rates for uncles and aunts of probands at about 5% and for cousins around 2.5%. In all cases, incidence among proband relatives is much higher than in the general population. Furthermore, there is a definite increase in expectancy rate with increase in degree of genetic relationship. According to Kallman (1954b), in fact, monozygotic twins show perfect coincidence, although this may be artificially high owing to the fact that non-hospitalized subjects were not included. It will be noted from Table 9-7 that some of the expectancy rates found, notably those

TABLE 9-7

**Summary of Studies on Expectancy Rates
for Manic-Depression among Relatives
and Cotwins of Probands
(Kallman, 1954b)**

		Relatives of Manic-Depressive Probands				
Investigator	General Population	Parents	Children	Sibs	DZ Cotwins	MZ Cotwins
Luxenburger (1927–36)	0.4	10.6–24.4	30.6–38.7	12.7		75.0
Banse (1929)		11.8		18.1		
Schulz, Rudin (1931–51)	0.4	15.7		13.3–29.1		
Slater (1938–51)	0.5–0.8	10.2–15.5	12.8–22.2	11.7	23.3	66.7
Tomasson (1941)		2.0		7.1		
Strömgren (1938)	0.2–0.4	7.0		4.0		
Sjögren (1948)	0.6–0.8	7.4		4.1		
Pollock, et al. (1939)		3.7		4.2		
Kallman (1950)		23.4		23.0	23.6	92.6
Rosanoff et al. (1935)				1.5	16.4	69.6

Rates were computed on heterogeneous samples and are not strictly comparable between studies.

by Tomasson (1941), Strömgren (1938), Sjögren (1948), and Pollock and Malzberg (1940), are quite low. In the studies by Pollock, Malzberg, and Fuller (1939), for example, among all relatives of over 100 manic-depressive probands, only 11 were found to be affected with the psychosis. This amounted to about 0.8% expectancy, a figure only slightly higher than the incidence in the general population and even lower than the figure of 1.5% obtained by the same investigators (1934) in an earlier study.

It is difficult to evaluate the validity of such findings. Since the rates are lower than those found in any of the other studies listed, they must be viewed with scepticism. They may have been due to a number of possible factors such as too narrow a diagnosis of the manic-depressive syndrome or insufficient correction for age-specific expectancies among the proband-relatives considered. Slater (1944) has criticized the study rather severely on methodological grounds and does not regard the conclusions to be justified. Taking the evidence as a whole, it is highly probable that manic-depression depends on heritable factors.

At this point it is of interest to consider the inheritance of cyclical tendencies, less marked than the psychotic syndrome, which are analogous to schizoidia. As with the latter personality syndrome, cycloid deviations are not easily diagnosed, owing to the fact that persons in this group tend to move around a good deal and may also be unwilling to discuss previous states of depression or hyperactivity in their own life histories (Kallman, 1954b). However, such work as has been done indicates some genetic determination. Table 9-8, taken from Kallman (1954b), shows expectancy rates for cycloid personality in relatives of manic-depressive probands.

TABLE 9-8

Summary of Studies on Expectancy Rates for Cycloid Personality among Relatives of Manic-Depressive Proband Cases (Kallman, 1954b)

Investigator	General Population	Relatives of Manic-Depressives			
		Parents	Children	Sibs	Dizygotic cotwins
Banse (1929)		5.0	14.4	2.7	
Luxenburger (1933)	0.8	12.2	13.4	18.8	
Röll and Entres (1936)	0.7	1.8	6.1		
Slater (1938)			13.4		
Kallman (1953)	0.7	14.5		12.9	30.9

It may seem curious that in MZ twins coincidence is less than in DZ twins. The reason for this is that the cotwin of a MZ proband manic-depressive is very likely to be psychotic also. This largely precludes the possibility of a diagnosis of cycloid personality in the usual sense. There is much more leeway for its occurrence in the cotwin of a DZ proband; hence the seemingly paradoxical figures.

Genetics of Manic-Depressive Psychosis. At the present time, the consensus of workers in the field is that manic-depression is dependent on a single autosomal dominant. Kallman (1954b) has claimed that nearly 60% of cyclic index cases come from the mating of one normal to one manic-depressive or cycloid parent. This figure is probably somewhat higher than is warranted by most data (Merrell, 1951), but if accurate, it would indicate a tendency for the trait to be expressed if a gene for it is present even in heterozygous condition. In addition, the ratio of affected to unaffected sibs in such families is found to be around 0.9:1 when unclassified persons are omitted and cycloid individuals added to clearly manic-depressive cases. This approximates the ideal 1:1 ratio required by a theory of single-factor dominance, assuming heterozygosity in the affected parent.

Another argument used by proponents of this theory (Kallman, 1954b; Slater, 1936; Merrell, 1951) has been that if an autosomal dominant is operating, incidence should be about equal in the three groups, sibs, parents, and children of probands. Recessivity should result in a higher proportion of cases in the sib group. In fact, expectancy rates in the three groups are about equal, although different investigators have set all of them at various levels, ranging from as low as 2% up to and even above 25%. Certainly, it seldom seems to happen that sibling rates turn out to be higher than parental or offspring rates (see Figure 9-1). A third line of evidence has been presented by Slater (1936). He noted that expectancy rates in the three groups, parents, uncles and aunts, and cousins, have been found to be 10 to 12%, 5%, and 2.5% respectively, that is, in a 4:2:1 ratio. These ratios indicate the operation of single-factor inheritance and, together with the other lines already discussed above, suggest a single dominant autosomal gene.

For this hypothesis to accord properly with the data however, as Slater (1936), Kallman (1953, 1954a, 1954b), and Merrell (1951) have pointed out, an explanation must be offered to account for the low absolute-expectancy rates found in relatives of probands (about one-fifth that required by the theory) and also for the sex differences that exist with respect to the disease. Several hypotheses have been sug-

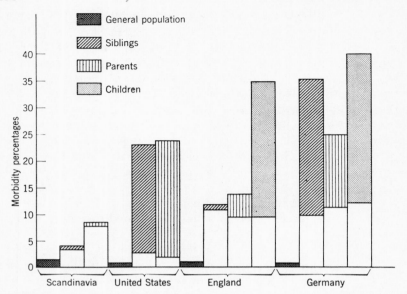

FIGURE 9-1. Summary of studies of expectancy rates for manic-depression in families of proband cases. (Kallman, 1953.)

gested concerning the first point. In the first place, manic-depressives have a higher rate of celibacy and produce fewer children than normal people. This comparison is shown in Figure 9-2 from Kallman (1953). Lower fertility could conceivably result in a lower expectancy rate among proband relatives if (and this is a big if) it were caused by selection against the manic-depressive genotype. Such a hypothesis is possible, but has no factual support at present. A second viewpoint, the more common one, is that the autosomal dominant gene in manic-depression has a relatively low penetrance. This penetrance in turn, as suggested for schizophrenia, might depend on inherited biochemical dispositions whose behavioral expression requires special physiological or genetic circumstances. A third related view is that special environmental influences are required for expression of the syndrome (Slater, 1936). This effect is inferred from the usual lack of perfect concordance in monozygotic twins.

Possibly normal social living is arranged in such a way as to minimize the occurrence of stresses that will set off extreme behavior in potentially abnormal individuals. Such a buffering effect of environment would tend to lower general incidence of psychosis as well as kinship expectancy rates. The genotype may be viewed as a necessary but not a sufficient condition for manic-depression. It would be in-

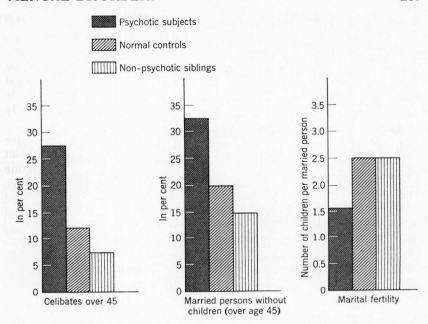

■ Psychotic subjects

▨ Normal controls

▥ Non–psychotic siblings

FIGURE 9-2. Marriage and birth rates in normal and manic-depressive populations. (Kallman, 1953.)

teresting to compare population rates under normal conditions with those during periods of long-term social stress, such as economic depressions or rapid social revolution. Finally, the use of too limited criteria for manic-depression may give artificially low expectancy values (Slater, 1936). It is obvious that the addition of cycloid cases increases rates considerably above those computed from hospital admissions alone.

In view of these factors, a theory of dominance can be plausibly maintained in spite of the empirically low expectancy rates. The second problem, that of sex differences, has suggested the hypothesis of a sex-linked inheritance. Rosanoff et al. (1935) have supported this notion with a genetic theory whose details we will examine in a moment. This view has been rejected by others (Slater, 1936; Merrell, 1951; Kallman, 1953) in favor of the hypotheses either that degree of penetrance varies with sex or that the difference in incidence between sexes is actually artificial due to a higher incidence of suicide among male manic-depressives. Since observed kinship expectancy rates are not easily explicable by a sex-linkage theory, these alternative possibilities appear more plausible. To determine exactly how they apply more research will be needed.

Two other possibilities to account for the sex difference may also be suggested. First, it may be due to partial sex limitation. Female-hormone output, especially those hormones associated with the menstrual cycle, contribute to cyclical disorder. Second, cultural values may be such as to tolerate extreme shifts in mood more readily in women than in men. This may result in special patterns of early rearing whose effect may show up in cycloid tendencies.

An interesting variation to the theory of autosomal dominance outlined above has been suggested by Rosanoff, Handy, and Plesset (1935). On the basis of their data (though perhaps they have gone beyond them) they have postulated the operation of two genetic factors. The first, an autosomal dominant, is a gene for cyclothymia, labeled C. This is assumed to have wide distribution in the population and to function in all phases of emotional behavior as well as in severely pathological conditions. It does not give rise to psychosis, however, unless a second gene is present. This is a sex-linked activation factor, A, which may also relate to normal emotional life. By itself it cannot give rise to manic-depression. Only the combination of the two genes does this. Thus there are two possible male genotypes in which psychotic manifestations can occur, $CCAY, CcAY$. In females, correspondingly, there are four vulnerable genotypes, $CCAA, CcAA, CCAa, CcAa$. Between all possible male and female genotypes, 54 different kinds of mating are possible. While this theory is an interesting one and has considerable flexibility, it is also relatively untested and perhaps untestable. As set forth in the following chapter, congruence between specific genes and specific factors of behavior is inherently unlikely.

Whichever of these genetic models is correct, the problem of physiological channels by which the disease comes to expression still faces us. On the whole, manic-depression and cycloid-personality type tend to be associated with a mesomorphic or endomorphic physique and obesity (Kallman, 1953, 1954a,b). Furthermore, whereas schizophrenia is often associated with tuberculosis, manic-depression is often linked to a strong tendency to cardiovascular disease, gout, and diabetes. Kallman (1953) has noted, for example, that in the case of discordant two-egg twins, wherever one member of the pair was found to be obese, it was always the psychotic one, and that degree of obesity correlated with severity of symptoms. Sometimes recession of weight accompanied a diminution in number of attacks. Consequently, there is reason to believe that this constellation of disorders is related to a group of metabolic disturbances which are genetically associated. It is likely that biochemistry will eventually provide effective assistance in the problems not only of manic-depression in particular, but also of psychosis in general.

The Relationship of Schizophrenia and Manic-Depression. We have already indicated that many workers in the field favor the view that schizophrenia is carried by a unitary genotype and is distinct, for the most part, from other forms of mental illness. The same has been said of manic-depression. Since these are the two major psychoses, it is of great importance to determine exactly the extent to which they are related. The proof or disproof of some degree of relationship between them should influence heavily the direction which research on prophylaxis and therapy will take.

To date, there is no definite agreement on the point under discussion. The Munich School, starting with Rüdin, has tended to regard the two forms of illness as distinct, basing this conclusion on their relative lack of occurrence in the same kinship groups. Manic-depressives, on the whole, tend not to have schizophrenic relatives and vice versa. Luxenburger (1937, 1939), Slater (1936, 1953b), and Kallman (1948b, 1953, 1954a,b) have all inclined to this viewpoint. Certainly there is much evidence that supports this view, showing that the expectancy rates for occurrence of schizophrenia among relatives of manic-depressive probands are not much greater than chance. At the same time, other studies have pointed to the opposite conclusion. Kant (1942) in a study of 100 schizophrenics found that manic-depression tended to occur more frequently in families of the less deteriorated probands than in those of acute cases. Similarly, Schulz (1939) found that manic-depression occurs fairly frequently in children of two schizophrenic parents, though, in the reverse relationship, schizophrenia does not appear as often in children of two manic-depressives. Marriages between schizophrenics and manic-depressives produce about the same proportion of children affected by each disease (approximately 15%). Schulz inferred from these data that the two types of psychoses probably have a common genotype. It will be recalled that Pollock and Malzberg (1940) in their study came essentially to this conclusion. Wildermuth (1927) apparently observed schizophrenic relatives of manic-depressive patients who actually showed periodicity in their symptoms; likewise, he found manic-depressive relatives of schizophrenic probands who developed atypical symptoms with schizoid features. He concluded with Witterman (1926) that symptom complexes, rather than classically defined disease entities, are inherited. Lewis (1957) also presented data supporting the single genotype theory of Schulz, though he clearly recognized that this conclusion is somewhat vitiated by the lack of well-defined diagnostic criteria. Likewise,

Mitsuda (1956) showed that schizophrenic probands did have manic-depressive relatives and manic-depressive probands had schizophrenic relatives, provided that the probands were not classified as typical.

In summary, we may state that there are not yet adequate grounds for arriving at a definite conclusion regarding the relationship between schizophrenia and manic-depression. The conflicting results that have been obtained are difficult to compare and assess, especially in view of the flexibility of diagnostic procedures.

Involutional Psychosis. According to Noyes and Kolb (1958), the involutional psychoses fall into two categories, one characterized largely by depression, the other by paranoid ideas. Since no genetic work has been done on the second of these, we will deal only with the first. Nosologically, it has been considered doubtful by many psychiatrists whether involutional depression should be treated as a distinct disease entity or whether it should be included under some other category, for example, manic-depressive psychosis or schizophrenia. As we shall see shortly, genetic studies have a good deal to contribute to the solution of this problem.

The most outstanding clinical feature of involutional depression is its dependence on age. Although there is some variation, it occurs for the most part in men during the late fifties and in women during the late forties. These are the periods of life during which the endocrine and especially the reproductive glands begin to show a decline in functional activity, that is to say, the involutional periods. The main symptoms include profound depression, hypochondriasis, instability, delusions of sin, feeling of impending death, regrets regarding the past, and a general sense of failure. Prognosis is fairly good (around 50% recovery), especially with the use of electric-shock therapy. Incidence of the disease in the general population has been set by different investigators (Brockhausen, 1937; Sjögren, 1948) at between 0.3 and 0.8%.

Like schizophrenia and manic-depression, involutional depression seems to be dependent on genetic factors. Data indicating this conclusion are summarized in Table 9-9. Expectancy rates in relatives of probands turn out to be considerably higher than incidence found for the general population. The difference is not as marked, however, as it is in schizophrenia and manic-depression. The little which has been done on the problem using twins (Kallman, 1952c) supports the above conclusion. Monozygotic twins show a coincidence of around 61% as compared with 6% for dizygotics. Brockhausen (1939) in a study of over 200 propositi suffering from involutional depression found that the syndrome could be divided into two types, one with

TABLE 9-9

Summary of Studies on Expectancy Rates for Involutional Psychosis among Relatives of Index Cases
(Kallman, 1954)

Investigator	General Population	Relatives of Index Cases with Involutional Psychosis					
		Parents	Chil- dren	Half Sibs	Sibs	Dizygotic Cotwins	Monozygotic Cotwins
Brockhausen (1939)	0.3–0.8	1.1–5.3	2.7		1.4–3.3		
Sjögren (1948)	0.3–0.7				6.0		
Kallman (1952c)		6.4		4.5	6.0*	6.0*	60.9

* The corresponding percentages for the siblings and cotwins of manic-depressive index cases are 2.5 and 3.1, respectively.

phasic and the other with recurrent symptoms. Relatives of the first of these groups turned out to contain a large number of manic-depressives, about as many as might be expected in relatives of manic-depressive propositi. In the second group, schizophrenia often occurred in relatives of those propositi whose non-phasic psychoses showed paranoid features. Whether such symptoms were associated or not, however, the recurrent cases had very few manic-depressive relatives. Brockhausen concluded that involutional psychosis does not relate to manic-depression but, at least in paranoid cases, rather to schizophrenia. His conclusion in this respect has been strongly supported by Kallman (1953, 1954a,b) and also by Slater (1953a). All of these investigators have found that the expectancy of schizophrenia in relatives of involutional depressive probands is slightly higher than in the general population. Thus it is possible that the syndrome in question is at least partly a schizophrenic-like response to age-specific factors arising during the onset of the involutional period. Behavior genetics has done a real service to psychiatry in developing these relationships between the three major classes of psychoses.

Somewhat related to involutional depression, inasmuch as it is a syndrome closely associated with age, is senility or so-called senile dementia. In view of the fact that since the turn of the century the number of persons over 65 has at least doubled, the incidence of senile psychosis has also increased enormously. According to Noyes (1953), persons with this syndrome comprise about 17% of first admissions to mental hospitals in New York State.

The immediate cause of senility appears to depend on the degenerative features of the aging processes, which include gradual loss of energy, narrowing of interest, decline in alertness and intellectual ability, and often loss of intimate social relationships. In general, these deficits are usually both psychological and organic. There is no doubt that the social-psychological changes that accompany aging can be a great source of anxiety to the old person. At the same time, it is also true that many anatomical changes occur, whose seriousness may vary with the individual concerned. Deficiencies associated with circulation and metabolism, for example, may be important causal factors in senile dementia.

The symptoms of the syndrome usually involves depression, lack of adaptability, diminished mental capacity, hostility, and generally regressive changes in personality structure. Delusions and hallucinations may also occur. Physical alterations usually go with psychological changes. There is often loss of weight, uncertainty of gait, tremor, and slowing of speech. Sclerosis, if present, may produce headaches, dizziness, and other disorders.

The heritability of senile dementia unfortunately has not been widely studied. However, it is thought that the three special types of brain atrophy associated with later maturity are dependent on genetic factors and that these are probably simple dominants or recessives rather than polygenic systems (Kallman, 1953). Meggendorfer (1926, 1939) suggested that all senile dementias are referable to two dominant genes of low penetrance, one carrying longevity, the other the pathological changes occurring in senility. Weinberger (1926) similarly postulated only one specific factor for the syndrome. Kallman and his associates (1948, 1949, 1951, 1952c, 1953), on the other hand, found no single entity on the basis of studies of senescent-twin family units, but rather found a complex of minor deficiencies intensified by age. Kallman considered these to represent age-susceptible personality traits dependent on many genes rather than on a few. No relationship was found to exist between schizoidia and senile dementia. Consequently, the latter is probably quite differently determined than involutional melancholia.

NEUROTIC DISORDERS

The large group of maladjustments falling under this category are regarded as far less malignant than the psychotic disorders. Some workers (Noyes and Kolb, 1958) consider them as intermediate between psychosis and normality whereas others, on the other hand, take them to represent an entirely different dimension from the psychotic diseases (Eysenck, 1947). Although the general group includes a great variety of subtypes, such as hysteria, psychasthenia, obsessive-compulsive symptoms, and others, many clinicians feel that the basic problem in all of them is defense by the patient against anxiety. The causes of the anxiety and types of defense against it serve as a means of more exact and particularized classification. Although we shall not deal with all of them individually, one classification system of psychoneuroses adopted by the American Psychiatric Association recognizes the following categories: anxiety reactions, dissociative reactions, conversion reactions, phobic reactions, obsessive-compulsive reactions, and depressive reactions (Noyes and Kolb, 1958). It will be noted that this categorization has a slant toward behavior symptomatology rather than etiology. From the standpoint of objectivity this classification may make more sense than an etiological one, though it does not, of course, solve the perennial problem of specificity versus generality of neurotic disorders.

Brown (1942) examined the incidence of neurosis among parents and sibs of three groups of neurotic probands: anxiety neurotics, hysterics, and obsessionals. His results are set out in Table 9-10. It will be

TABLE 9-10

Expectancy Rates for Various Kinds of Neurotic Disorders in Parents and Sibs of Proband Cases
(Brown, 1942)

Types of Proband Cases	Percent of Affected Relatives					
	Anxiety Neurotics		Hysterics		Obsessionals	
	Parents	Sibs	Parents	Sibs	Parents	Sibs
Anxiety neurotics	21.4	12.3	1.6	2.2	0	0.9
Hysterics	9.5	4.6	19.0	6.2	0	0
Obsessionals	0	5.4	0	0	7.5	7.1

noted that not only is there some evidence of a hereditary factor, if we assume on the basis of Fremming's survey (1947) that normal expectancy is around 2%, but that the different categories have a good deal of genetic specificity. Incidence of anxiety neurosis, for example, is considerably higher among parents and sibs of probands with this form of illness than is incidence of the other two types of disorder. Since from these data no correlation can be made between expectancy rate and closeness of kinship and since there is no control for environment, the results cannot be regarded as very decisive evidence for the operation of genetic factors. At least, however, they are compatible with the hypothesis that neuroses are heritable. Data in agreement with those of Brown, but perhaps even less definite, have been presented by Rüdin (1953) for compulsive symptoms. Parents, sibs, and children of compulsive probands were found to show the respective expectancy rates of 4.6%, 2.3%, and 1.3%. These figures are somewhat lower than Brown's and are probably not much greater than chance expectancy, though no exact figures are available on incidence of this particular disorder in the general population.

More convincing evidence is available from the several twin studies of Eysenck (1951), Eysenck and Prell (1951), and Shields (1954). Eysenck suggested that neuroticism is a unitary dimension of personality definable in terms of a test battery. By his method of criterion analysis he was able, in fact, to extract empirically a neuroticism factor in addition to one for intelligence. With Prell, he then administered the tests to 20 MZ, 24 DZ, and 6 pairs of twins whose zygosity was doubtful. His results are summarized in condensed form in Table 9-11. On the basis of Holzinger's H' statistic, neuroticism as defined here proved to be strongly dependent on hereditary factors. In other terms, 80% of individual differences on this factor could be attributed to genotype. Results for particular tests in the battery showing the highest hereditary loading are also included in the table. It should be noted that only three tests of those listed in the table, static ataxia, body sway suggestibility, and autokinetic movement, have high loadings (over .40) for the neuroticism factor. The conclusion drawn by Eysenck, that neuroticism is inherited as a biological unit, must therefore be viewed with some caution.

A later study by Shields (1954) used a sample of 62 like-sexed twins, 36 MZ and 20 DZ between 12 and 15 years of age. Two aspects of concordance for psychiatric maladjustment were studied, quantitative (degree of concordance for neuroticism) and qualitative (concordance or discordance for neuroticism). Results for these two parameters in-

TABLE 9-11

The Hereditary Determination of Neuroticism: MZ and DZ Twin Pair Correlations on Individual Tests and on a Neuroticism factor (Eysenck and Prell, 1951)

Trait	MZ Pairs		DZ Pairs		Hereditary Determination, H'
	Raw Corre-lation	Corre-lation Corr. for Age	Raw Corre-lation	Corre-lation Corr. for Age	
1. Intelligence	.905	.890	.670	.660	.676
2. Tapping area	.193	.164	−.148	−.144	.269
3. Tapping speed	.557	.552	.266	.011	.547
4. Level of aspiration	.320	.272	.084	.038	.243
5. Motor-speed test	.700	.643	.296	.243	.528
6. Speed of decision	.340	.339	−.122	−.122	.193
7. Static ataxia	.857	.856	.537	.532	.692
8. Body-sway suggestibility	.737	.734	.128	.110	.701
9. Strength of grip	.850	.774	.468	.392	.628
10. Word dislikes	.512	.510	.394	.380	.210
11. Personality inventory	.369	.365	.273	.257	.145
12. Lie scale	.485	.481	.167	.109	.418
13. Flicker fusion	.709	.705	.229	.209	.627
14. Autokinetic movement	.734	.722	.228	.210	.648
15. Autokinetic suggestibility	.534	.534	.141	.135	.461
16. Backward "S"	.711	.708	.491	.477	.423
17. Fluency	.357	.353	.118	.114	.270
Neuroticism factor	.851		.217		.810

dicated that concordance was much higher in the MZ than in the DZ pairs both qualitatively and quantitatively. Over twice as many individuals of MZ pairs belonged in the same degree of concordance group as did individuals for DZ pairs. A check on the influence of closeness of social relationship was also made. It was found that members of MZ pairs were in fact much closer to each other socially than members of DZ pairs. Shields, however, found that similarity of psychiatric symptoms was not dependent on degree of attachment. Consequently, the data appear to give some support to a genetic hypothesis.

Another common form of behavior that may be considered symptomatic of neurosis or emotional maladjustment is enuresis or bed wetting. This has been studied in great detail by many investigators both from a clinical and a genetic point of view. On the whole, most of the evidence indicates that hereditary factors are important in the etiology of enuresis. These reports since the beginning of the twentieth century have been well reviewed by Hallgren (1957). Expectancy rates computed by many authors for parents and children of propositi varied from 1% to over 30%. Although any computation of general incidence in the population varies a good deal with the age and sex of the cases on which it is taken, the most typical figures appear to vary around 10% (Hallgren, 1957). Genetic analyses for modes of transmission have favored both recessive (Frary, 1935; Petrovsky, 1934) and dominance (Oransky, 1928) hypotheses. Hallgren, however, considered none of these ideas fully justified by the data on which they were based.

His own analysis yielded results summarized in Table 9-12. It is

TABLE 9-12

Incidence of Enuresis among Relatives of 215 Propositi (Hallgren, 1957)

	Parents		Siblings	
	Affected	Not Affected	Affected	Not Affected
Male	64	144	40	89
Female	38	177	25	108
Totals	102	321	65	197

clear, in the first place, that expectancy is much higher in males than in females. The difference is in fact statistically significant. Second, expectancy is about 25% for both parent and sibling groups. Excluding families in which determination appeared to be clearly nongenetic, Hallgren arrived at the following estimates: 38.5% for fathers, 23.4% for mothers of propositi; 38.5% for male and 20.5% for female sibs. Rates for uncles and aunts were found to be 8.0% and for grandparents, 2%. These last two values were no higher than the chance expectation value used by Hallgren of 9.5%. He went on to test eight different genetic hypotheses, but found that the data were so complex as to make any definite conclusion very difficult. However, there was a suggestion that either of the following two models were most likely: determination by a dominant major gene whose expression was controlled by the action of the external environment and polygenes; or determination solely by the interaction of polygenes and the external environment. It is of interest that in spite of sex differences existing for enuresis, genetic analyses failed to support either complete or partial sex-linkage, though they did not definitely disprove these possibilities. In general, we may remark by way of conclusion that Hallgren's monograph is a model of careful analysis and scholarly interpretation which should be consulted directly by any reader wishing to pursue any problem in psychiatric genetics.

The general evidence, then, favors the view that some psychoneuroses (and allied disorders) depend on hereditary factors, though more work is needed to make this conclusion completely convincing. In effect, nothing is known regarding the mode of genetic transmission of neurotic disorders.

DEVIANT FORMS OF BEHAVIOR

Criminality. According to a number of investigators, criminality, delinquency, and psychopathic personality also depend on hereditary factors. The relevant papers on the subject have been summarized by Shields (1954) in a table reproduced here (Table 9-13). It is clear from these eleven studies that concordance is more marked in MZ than in DZ twins. On the average, criminality and delinquency occur in both members of an MZ pair about three times as frequently as in only one member, whereas almost exactly the opposite holds true for fraternal twins. Since environmental factors are relatively constant in this comparison, a good deal of weight may be attributed to genetic factors. As Kranz (1936) has pointed out, however, it is true that some of the studies listed in Shields's summary have used rather loose criteria for diagnosis of zygosity. Kranz, in contradiction to other experimenters, has found relatively small differences in concordance between identicals and dizygotics of the same sex. For this reason Kranz has tended to emphasize environmental factors almost as much as genetic factors. His findings must be weighed against Borgström's (1939) report of higher concordance in MZ (75%) than DZ twins (40%) with respect to a very strict criterion of similarity, namely, conviction for the same crime. In such matters, of course, it cannot be doubted that environment is important. Probably genotype determines par-

TABLE 9-13

Summary of Researches Done on Hereditary Factors in the Determination of Criminality and Delinquency (Shields, 1954)

Condition Studied	Author	Country	Year	MZ		DZ Like Sex		DZ Unlike Sex	
				Con-cordant	Dis-cordant	Con-cordant	Dis-cordant	Con-cordant	Dis-cordant
Adult crime	Lang	Germany	1929	10	3	3	15	—	—
Adult crime	Stumpfl	Germany	1936	11	7	7	12	2	26
Adult crime	Kranz	Germany	1936	20	11	23	20	7	43
Adult crime	Borgström	Finland	1939	3	1	2	3	2	8
Adult crime	Rosanoff et al.	U.S.A.	1934	25	12	5	23	1	31
Juvenile delinquency	Rosanoff et al.	U.S.A.	1934	39	3	20	5	8	32
Behavior disorder	Rosanoff et al.	U.S.A.	1934	41	6	20	34	8	21
Juveniles with personality disorder	Kranz	Germany	1937	7	4	0	3	2	6
Child maladjustment	Kent	U.S.A.	1949	7	0	4	2	2	1
Hysteria	Stumpfl	Germany	1937	3	6	0	9	—	—
Psychopathy and neurosis	Slater	England	1953	2	6	4	25	1	13
Totals				168	59	94	161	33	181

ticular physical and psychological characteristics that predispose individuals toward similar types of asocial behavior given the right set of circumstances. This moderate point of view has some cogency if we consider that the mental illness known as psychopathy (a syndrome often involving criminal acts) appears to have some hereditary as well as environmental determination. This is quite different from saying that the criminal tendencies *per se* are inherited. So also in the case of the non-neurotic criminal, it is not criminality that depends on genes but traits such as aggressiveness and physical strength that may result in the commission of crime. Such constitutional factors may play an important role here, as Rosanoff, Handy and Rosanoff (1934*a*) suggested, though the evidence on this point is limited. In this connection, Hill and Watterson (1942) have found that psychopaths, particularly of the aggressive type, tend to have abnormal EEG's.

Suicide is a symptomatic reaction to environmental stress. It occurs more frequently in males than in females (Weinberg, 1920; Kallman, 1953; Noyes and Kolb, 1958) and more commonly in certain geographical areas than others (Sorokin, 1947). Genetic studies on suicide, however, indicate that it has little relation to genotype. Kallman, Deporte, Deporte and Feingold (1949) found in 18 pairs of MZ and 21 pairs of DZ twins only one case of concordance for suicide. This discordance was true even though many of the pairs were remarkably alike with respect to such factors as choice of occupation, economic status, and marital difficulties. Kallman (1953) concluded that suicide is definitely not dependent on hereditary factors.

Homosexuality. Another type of deviant behavior, commonly regarded in our society as having serious importance, is homosexuality. Some interesting work has been done on the hereditary aspects of this deviation. Lang (1940) attempted to adapt Goldschmidt's theory of intersexes (see page 18) to human male homosexuality. If some homosexuals are transformed females, the sex ratio in their sibs should deviate from the usual 106 males to 100 females. Lang had access to the confidential records of the police departments of Munich and Hamburg, and reported that the sex ratio in the sibs of 1015 known homosexual men was 121.1:100 (chi-square = 13.54, $p = .001$). Among sibs of married homosexual males, who were less likely in Lang's opinion to be biological intersexes, the sex ratio was more nearly normal.

Darke (1948) attempted to confirm these findings by determining the sex ratio of the sibs, half-sibs, and offspring of 100 known homosexuals in an American federal prison. He found some evidence for a predominance of males among the siblings of the younger probands, but interpreted this in environmental rather than genetic terms. Rather than considering homosexuality to be caused by chromosomal imbalance (with excess of male sibs as a necessary outcome), Darke attributed homosexual tendencies to association with male siblings in the home.

Kallman (1952a,b) has summarized the results of Lang and Darke and has compared them with data which he has collected on the sibling sex ratio of 145 index cases. He stresses the difficulty of obtaining genetic information on a trait which bears so great a social stigma and is so often hidden. The deviant sex ratios in siblings of male homosexuals reported by Lang were not found in Kallman's sample. The scale of all three investigations was large enough so that sampling errors probably do not explain the discrepancy. Lang's results might be the expression of some systematic bias in the reporting of the sibling sex or, alternatively, a predominance of male siblings may in certain cultural settings predispose males toward homosexuality. The whole attempt to compare human homosexuals with Lepidopteran intersexes stems from the concept of a direct effect of the chromosomal content of the body cells upon the direction of sexual affections. On general principles this is an unlikely premise, and we shall see below that direct evidence from cases of human hermaphroditism contradicts it.

The major part of Kallman's study on genetic factors in homosexuality was an investigation of twins. Thirty-seven MZ pairs and 26 DZ pairs were found in which the degree of homosexuality was evaluated on the Kinsey index system (Kinsey et al. 1948). The results given in Table 9-14 show high concordance among the MZ pairs and low concordance in the DZ pairs. The proportion of male homosexuality in the DZ cotwins is somewhat higher than that reported by Kinsey for the general male population, but the significance of this is questionable in view of the small size of the sample.

A study of the detailed case histories led Kallman to make the following comments: "Index pairs have developed sexual tendencies independently and often far apart from each other. All deny any history of mutuality in sex relations." Overt homosexuality has multiple causation, but the discordance of DZ pairs compared with the concordance of MZ pairs weakens arguments overstressing such factors as social ostracism and parental incompetence.

Kallman's results need not be interpreted as proof that homosexuality has a specific hereditary basis. Six of the MZ cases were concordant for schizophrenia as well as homosexuality. These individuals would have difficulty in heterosexual adjustment and might

TABLE 9-14

**Gradations of Overt Homosexuality in the Cotwins
of 85 Male Homosexuals
(Kallman, 1952)**

Monozygotic Cotwin Rating

Index Case Rating	6	5	4	3	2, 1, 0	Sum
6	16	3	0	0	0	19
5	3	3	1	2	0	9
4	0	1	2	2	0	5
3	0	2	2	0	0	4
Total	19	9	5	4	0	37

Dizygotic Cotwin Rating

Index Case Rating	6, 5	4, 3	2	1	0	Sum
6	0	1	1	5	5	12
5	0	0	0	1	5	6
4	1	1	0	0	2	4
3	0	0	0	1	3	4
Total	1	2	1	7	15	26

secondarily adopt homosexual practices. Twenty-two additional cases were diagnosed as schizoid personality, obsessive-compulsive, or excessively alcoholic. Given a common family environment during youth and assuming that some aspects of personality are heritable, the concordance of MZ twins in sexual orientation becomes attributable to similar patterns of experience operating on similar substrates. This interpretation requires that heritable constitutional factors play some role, for the family environments of discordant DZ pairs must also have been very much alike. There is no need to assume that the constitutional factor is specifically sexual. In fact, studies of sex hormone physiology in male homosexuals have failed to uncover any specific dysfunction which might provide a link between gene action and deviations in sexual behavior (Witschi and Mengert, 1942).

An extreme case of contradiction between morphological sex and gender orientation is found in transvestism. Transvestites adopt the clothing, hair style, and behavior patterns of the opposite sex. The hypothesis that these individuals are high-level intersexes has been advanced. Techniques have been developed for the reliable diagnosis of chromosomal sex by means of skin biopsy (Moore and Barr, 1954). Barr and Hobbs (1954) studied the nuclear morphology of five male transvestites. In each case the cytological picture was typically masculine.

Other Sexual Deviations. Another approach to the problem of the nature of genetic determination of sexual orientation is the study of hermaphroditism. Money, Hampson, and Hampson (1955b) have examined some of the basic concepts of human sexual differentiation. Incongruities may exist between sex classification based upon any pair of seven types of criteria: (1) sex of rearing; (2) external genital morphology; (3) internal reproductive accessory organs; (4) hormonal sex and secondary sexual characteristics; (5) gonadal sex, if gonads are present; (6) chromosomal sex; and (7) gender role, or the orientation of an individual as male or female in social relationships.

In a survey of 76 patients Money et al. (1955b) found contradictions between sex of rearing and chromosomes (19 cases), gonads (20 cases), hormones (27 cases), internal accessory organs (17 cases), and external genital organs (23 cases). Many cases involved multiple incongruities, but in the majority there was no ambiguity in gender orientation. The individual assumed a role as male or female, depending upon the sex of rearing. In none of the cases of contradiction between chromosomes and assigned sex had any behavior problems occurred. When the discordance was more overt, a small percentage sought to change their gender role or became practicing homosexuals. The authors interpreted their material to mean that psychological masculinity or femininity in its most intense aspect of gender role is not attributable to chromosomal, gonadal, or hormonal agencies or to morphological differences of the internal or external reproductive organs. "Sexual behavior and orientation as male or female does not have an innate instinctive basis. Though gender imprinting begins by the first birthday, the critical period is reached by about eighteen months. By two and a half years gender role is well established."

This conclusion does not mean that the physical substratum has no importance in sexual behavior. Money et al. (1955b) emphasize that overt incongruities caused much distress and anguish in their patients. When corrective plastic surgery was possible, beneficial results were always obtained. The point is that conflict over sexual orientation does not occur at the chromosomal level of organization, but at a psychological level. It is dangerous to apply theories derived from one species to a quite different one. The genetic mechanism may be similar, but the organization of behavior may be extremely divergent in form.

In concluding this section we shall consider the inheritance of sexual precocity. Some cases are apparently the result of developmental accidents with no clear relationship to the genotype, but familial occurrence has been recorded by a number of investigators (Witschi, 1939; Jacobsen and Macklin, 1952). The problem of social adjustment is the same whether the condition is familial or whether no hereditary basis can be demonstrated. Case histories of afflicted individuals (Jacobsen and Macklin, 1952) show that the age of development of heterosexual interests is affected in the hereditary conditions. If this is true in extreme cases, genes affecting the rate of physical development within the normal range probably have some effect upon psychosexual development. These effects are likely to be on the intensive and durational dimensions of behavior rather than upon its direction and specific patterning.

MENTAL DEFICIENCY

The category of mental deficiency is very broad. It includes a great many different types of syndromes, many more, in fact, than can be treated here in detail. Because the term is rather a loose one, the term "feeble-mindedness" has sometimes been preferred. Borrowing a definition of the American Association on Mental Deficiency, we may include under mental deficiency or feeble-mindedness "all degrees of mental defect due to arrested or imperfect mental development, as a result of which the person so afflicted is incapable of competing on equal terms with his normal fellows or of managing himself or his affairs with ordinary prudence" (Noyes and Kolb, 1958). Incidence of feeble-mindedness in the general population is estimated at about 1%, though, if cases of less severe deficiency are added, expectancy rates are higher. Obviously, at the upper end of its range (I.Q.'s above 45), mental defect may be considered as an arbitrarily cut-off portion of the lower end of the normal I.Q. distribution. However, as Roberts et al. (1935, 1937b) and Roberts (1950) have indicated, the incidence of intellectual defectives below this level is too high to be fitted to the normal curve. Consequently, expectancy rates vary a good deal depending on the breadth of the category being used. This means that a crucial problem here is classification of subtypes of mental deficiency. Doing this is in some ways even more difficult than with mental illnesses, since some types of mental deficiency vary from normality in degree rather than in kind. Again, expectancy rates for feeble-mindedness will differ considerably, depending on the cultural norm against which it is judged. Even the means of making such a judgment may present difficulties except in extreme cases. Most intelligence tests are certainly not culture-free and have limited value for groups very different from the one on which they were standardized. For these reasons, most workers in the field have preferred to start, at least, with an etiological classification of types of mental deficiency. A combination of several of the schemata suggested will be used here.

In the first place (Strecker, 1947; Tredgold, 1947), mental deficiency may be divided into primary and secondary types, depending on whether the intellectual deficit can or cannot be referred to some definite insult, trauma, or disease. Since primary mental retardation may eventually be found to relate to some organic change, this division is a provisional one that separates cases of deficiency with obvious organic involvement from those cases with less obvious organic involvement. In the secondary group, two main kinds may be further distinguished, those due to exogenous and those due to endogenous causes. The former class includes those cases of mental impairment clearly due to external agents such as toxins, traumas, infections, and the like. The endogenous class takes in all cases of intellectual deficiency dependent on neurological or morphological changes associated with genotype. Within the endogenous grouping, a distinction may be made between disorders caused by morphological and neurological changes and disorders related to inborn errors of metabolism. The complete scheme is summarized in Table 9-15 together with the probable genetic mechanisms involved where applicable. Cutting across the etiological classification is another relating to type of genetic mechanism involved and an additional one involving measurable degree of impairment from idiot (I.Q. under 20) and imbecile (I.Q. 21–50) to the various grades of moron (I.Q. 50–70). In the following discussion of mental deficiency the schema outlined above will be used as a main framework, though reference will also be made to the other divisions as well. Since the treatment here is not intended to be exhaustive, only samples from each category will be examined.

Primary Mental Deficiency. As indicated above, primary mental defect probably involves those individuals at the lower end of the normal curve of intelligence. The division point between this group and the pathological variants to be discussed shortly is thought to occur around 45 in the I.Q. scale (Roberts, Norman, and Griffiths, 1937b). That is to say, these defectives may be accommodated within the frequency curve for normal intelligence. The etiology of the defect is, then, to be sought in those same factors that determine

TABLE 9-15

Classification of Types of Mental Deficiency with Examples and Probable Genetic Mechanisms Involved

Type	Cause	Example	Probable Genetic Mechanisms
Primary	Heredity. May be correlated physical changes.	Moron	Polygenes
Secondary Exogenous	Traumas, infections, toxins, environmental agents. Heredity may determine a predisposition to occurrence and form of some organic diseases.	Cerebral palsy	None known
Secondary Endogenous	Heredity where main effect is to produce severe morphological or neurological changes.	Neurofibromatosis	Dominant
		Tuberous sclerosis	Dominant
		Naevoid amentia	Dominant
		Huntington's chorea	Dominant
		Primary microcephaly	Recessive
		Macrocephaly	Recessive
	Heredity whose main effect is to produce some metabolic error in:		
	a. Lipids	Amaurotic idiocy	Recessive
	b. Amino acids	Phenylpyruvic oligophrenia	Recessive
	c. Carbohydrates	Galactosuria	Recessive
	d. Pigment	Hallervorden-Spatz disease	Recessive

general intelligence, which most likely are multifactorial (Slater, 1944; Roberts, 1950; Allen, 1958). Such a point of view is supported not only by the incidence of this class in the general population, but also by work of Roberts (1940), which shows a sib to sib correlation for uncomplicated mental defect of .535. This figure fits a multiple-factor hypothesis quite adequately. Southwick's work (1939) with 488 children of institutionalized defectives points essentially to the same conclusion.

Though no gross lesions may be present in primary mental defectives, minor abnormalities apparently often occur. Damon (1941), using anthropometric measurements, showed that morons differ significantly from normals in a number of physical characteristics. They show relatively smaller size, more linearity, lower foreheads and narrower temporals, more asymmetry, thicker lips, and other such differences. It is likely, however, that these physical symptoms are correlated features of a general syndrome rather than causative agents influencing intelligence level.

As with general intelligence, it is important to know the extent to which primary mental defect can be broken down into smaller, more convenient classes or whether it is a genetically uniform entity. Brugger (1939, 1940) concluded, from an examination of research findings, that the second conclusion is correct. He further proposed that mental deficiency without marked physical signs is recessively determined. Most workers, however, appear to favor a polygenic theory. Kallman (1953) has set out correlational data from a number of sources to support this point of view, as Slater (1944) has also. Certainly, if Brugger's theory is correct, it might raise difficulties in considering primary mental defect to be part of the curve of normal intelligence.

Obviously the problem of handling primary mental deficiency is a difficult one. It is a category that includes a large proportion of all defectives, and at least some, if not all, of those in the higher grades can be fitted to the bottom end of the I.Q. distribution. Low-grade defectives are too numerous to be treated in the same way and, in addition, usually show stigmata of organic defects.

Secondary Mental Deficiency. Included in this class are those conditions in which lowered intellectual level is directly caused by some external or exogenous agent. These may be toxins, infections, traumata, endocrine disorders, emotional stresses, or birth injuries. Good reviews on which we shall draw heavily have been made by Jervis (1952), Kallman (1953), Allen (1958), and Fraser (1958a,b).

We shall not be concerned with conditions such as cerebral palsy which have no demonstrated relationship to heredity. It is not always easy, however, to determine the role of genetics even for rather common syndromes. The example of Mongolism will serve to illustrate the difficulty.

Mongolism. Mongolism or Mongoloid idiocy accounts for 5% to 10% of all institutionalized defectives. The syndrome is characterized by a number of physical abnormalities, in particular, slanted palpebral tissues with epicanthic folds, slanting eyes, and flatness of the face, all of which produce a superficial resemblance to members of the Mongolian race. Benda (1946) has argued that all these features are sequelae of impaired pituitary function and has proposed the name *acromicria* for the condition. The term is analogous to *acromegaly*, pituitary hyperfunction resulting in gigantism. The intellectual deficit is reflected by an I.Q. between 15 and 40.

For many years Mongolism was a puzzle to geneticists. On the one hand there was abundant evidence that prenatal factors, operating presumably through the mother, were involved. Penrose (1934) showed definitely that older mothers had an excessive proportion of Mongoloid offspring. Øster (1953) reported that the oldest mothers in his group were thirty times as likely as the youngest to produce Mongoloids. A high incidence of disturbances of pregnancy during its early stages was reported by Benda (1946) who postulated some metabolic insufficiency of the mother as a contributing cause. Since maternal physiology cannot be expected to regulate the distribution of genes, the correlation between age of mother and incidence of Mongolism contradicts a hypothesis of genetic etiology.

Despite the strength of the evidence for environmental causation, there have been indications that heredity does play an important role. Kallman (1953) and Allen (1958) have noted several facts that favor a genetic hypothesis. In the first place, Mongoloids show strong physical similarity. The uniformity of the syndrome argues for a unitary cause such as a gene-controlled metabolic defect, rather than for an exogenous cause which would be expected to produce more variable effects. Second, according to Oliver (1950) and Böök and Reed (1950) among others, there appears to be a moderately increased incidence among sibs. These findings are not supported by the work of Øster (1953), however, who studied 354 children born to mothers who had already produced Mongoloids. He found only four more cases, which is not exceptionally high for mothers of this age. Third, the high frequency of spontaneous abortions in mothers of Mongoloids suggests that the incidence in their families may be greater than is usually computed. The assumption here is that the aborted children would become Mongoloids.

Further evidence (Allen and Baroff, 1955) of heritability comes from twin data. MZ twins are always concordant with respect to Mongolism; DZ twins are rarely so. The latter point is particularly important, since DZ twins must be exposed to a similar maternal environment. Allen and Baroff concluded that the environmental agent, if in fact there were one, must operate very early in development before the first division of the fertilized ovum.

Another line of research has followed Penrose's (1954) finding that normal relatives of Mongoloids show an increased incidence of one trait of the syndrome, namely, distal triradius in the palms of the hands. He went on to hypothesize that Mongolism is caused by a biochemical deficiency in the early embryo which is compensated for by the mother, unless she is also deficient in the special substance needed. In both mother and child the deficiency is presumed to be genetic, but it is precipitated in the mother primarily by age factors. Thus far, the only biochemical error found in Mongoloids (excessive secretion of beta-aminoiso butyric acid) is not found in parents or sibs (Wright and Fink, 1957).

Many of these discordant findings fell into place with the discovery that Mongoloids have an extra chromosome, the result of *non-disjunction* (failure to separate) of a chromosome pair during gametogenesis (Jacobs et al., 1959). Chromosomal accidents of this kind are probably not uncommon, but the embryos are usually not viable. In this instance, chromosomal imbalance blights normal development but allows survival. The concordance of MZ twins and discordance of DZ twins is now understandable. In a sense Mongolism is genetic, but not inherited. The reasons for the high correlation between maternal age and incidence are not yet clear. Possibly changes in cellular viscosity associated with age may be responsible.

Genetic problems in Mongolism now center about the physiological effects of the supernumerary chromosome and the causes of nondisjunction. The history of this syndrome illustrates the value of supplementing statistical evidence with cytological observations. The usefulness of this collaboration in dealing with other types of mental deficiency has yet to be proved. In many of the endogenous deficiencies, which we shall now consider, more conventional genetic models have proved adequate.

Neurological Defects. Endogenous mental defects can be divided into two kinds, those associated with morphological or neurological changes and those arising from or accompanying various kinds of metabolic errors. The distinction is somewhat arbitrary, since the syndromes of the first group may, in fact, eventually be linked to biochemical abnormalities, though at present they are not. It should also be understood that often exogenous agents may play an important part in the etiology of many diseases in this category (Sarason, 1949). With these reservations in mind, we may proceed to a discussion of a few prototypes in each category.

The neurological and morphological disorders cover a wide variety of different syndromes. Among these a few may be selected as representative. Neurofibromatosis, or Recklinghausen's disease, is characterized by pigmentation and bone changes and neurofibromata. About 10% of patients also show intellectual deficits. Its incidence is about

3 or 4 per 10,000 births, and it appears to show an irregular type of dominant inheritance with probably about 90% penetrance (Borberg, 1951; Crowe, Schull, and Neel, 1956). In addition, Crowe, Schull, and Neel found presumptive evidence for somatic mutation, that is, the mutation of genes for the disease occurring some time after the start of development. This is indicated by the fact that some of their cases had no affected relatives and produced completely normal children. As Allen (1958) has indicated, exploration of this mechanism in neurofibromatosis might well yield exceedingly interesting and important data.

Belonging to the same group of diseases represented by neurofibromatosis are tuberous sclerosis, naevoid amentia (Sturge-Weber's disease), Hippel-Lindau's syndrome, and Albright's disease. All of these involve various types of dermoplastic defects associated with mental deficiency. Although the genetic basis of all of these have not yet been thoroughly worked out, at least the second two mentioned above appear to be transmitted by single dominant genes (Jervis, 1952; Kallman, 1953). Likewise, many of the so-called dystotic syndromes, that is, those involving abnormalities of the skeletal system, seem to be dependent on single dominants. Among these may be listed hyperteleorism (Craig's disease), associated with very wide placement of the eyes, acrocephalosyndactylia (Apert's disease), involving a "tower" skull (Ferriman, 1939), and arachnodactyly (Marfan's disease), characterized by spidery hands and feet. Others in the same group are carried by recessive genes. Primary microcephaly, which includes more than 1% of all defectives, is in this category. This syndrome involves small stature, a very narrow, long head with a receding forehead, and other gross physical deformities. Some forms are genetic, others exogenous in etiology. The various types of microcephaly have been discussed in detail by Böök, Schut, and Reed (1953). According to these authors, there is some evidence for heterozygous expression of the gene. Macrocephaly and megalocephaly are also recessive diseases. Similar rare defects of the head such as anencephaly, hemicephaly, acrania, holoacrania, and others have not been definitely assigned to specific genetic mechanisms.

Other groups of disorders that may be included in the present category are the muscular dystrophies involving degeneration of the muscular system, the cerebellar atrophies, the ataxias, such as Friedreich's ataxia, and the extra-pyramidal diseases. Many of the syndromes in these groups appear to be recessively determined (Jervis, 1952), though some, at least, Huntington's chorea, for example, are caused by dominant genes. Additional related syndromes have been discussed in more detail by Kallman (1953), Tyler (1954), and Schut (1954).

Biochemical Errors. The final category, which includes those defects dependent directly on certain biochemical errors, is perhaps the most interesting. Kallman (1953), following Jervis, has distinguished four classes according to the type of metabolic disorder, namely, those involving lipids, amino acids, carbohydrates, and pigments. We shall summarize Kallman's presentation here.

The prototype of the first group is amaurotic idiocy. There are several forms of the syndrome, some occurring in infancy (Tay-Sachs disease, Bielschowski's disease), another between 5 and 7 years (Spielmeyer-Vogt's disease), and others later in life (Kuf's disease). This class of defect involves slow physical development and profound mental impairment often with epileptic seizures or motor disability and a progressive course ending in death. At least some forms of amaurotic idiocy are known to be dependent on recessive inheritance, though the specific genes involved in the various forms may be different (Sjögren, 1931; Slome, 1933; Herndon, 1954). The primary effect of these genes is to produce a distortion and swelling of nerve cells which characteristically contain fatty granules (Kallman, 1953; Herndon, 1954). Other lipidoses include the xanthomatoses, Gaucher's disease, Niemann-Pick's disease, gargoylism, and dwarfism. All involve excessive lipid content of nerve cells, and all except possibly the xanthomatoses appear to be dependent on single, autosomal recessive genes (Jervis, 1952; Kallman, 1953; Herndon, 1954).

The prototype of the second class is phenylpyruvic oligophrenia. This disease involves an alteration in the metabolism of phenylalanine, an amino acid. It is responsible for about 0.5% to 1% of all institutionalized mental defectives. The evidence suggests that the amino acid is not completely oxidized by the organism, with the result that phenylpyruvic acid is excreted in the urine. First discovered by Fölling (1934), it was studied subsequently by many workers, including Penrose (1935, 1945) and Jervis (1939). The main body of evidence strongly suggests a simple autosomal recessive inheritance (Jervis, 1939, 1954).

The third group of mental defects relates to errors in carbohydrate metabolism. One of these, galactosuria, involves an excess of galactose in body fluids. Another, von Gierke's disease, is caused by a failure of the organism to break down glycogen with a resulting accumulation of this chemical in the central nervous system. Both diseases are accompanied by severe mental defect and appear to be dependent on hereditary factors which are probably recessive in nature (Childs and Sidbury, 1957).

Finally, faulty metabolism of pigments causes a syndrome known as Hallerworden-Spatz's disease. The main symptom is increasing muscle rigidity presumably resulting from accumulation of pigment in parts of the basal ganglia.

It will be clear even from the brief outline above that there are a vast number of metabolic errors regularly accompanied by mental defect. The problems involved in sorting them out genetically are enormous. Nevertheless there have been some advances directly translatable into useful modes of therapy. A good case in point is phenylketonuria, which has been corrected in a number of cases by putting patients on a diet deficient in phenylalanine (Bickel, Boscott, and Gerrard, 1955). With the rapid advances being made in biochemistry, we can expect that similar progress will be made in our understanding and therapy of other forms of mental defect.

EPILEPSY

Epilepsy is a condition characterized by convulsive seizures with loss of consciousness. Its incidence in the general population is probably somewhere around 1%. Conventionally, cases have been divided into two classes, idiopathic and symptomatic. Idiopathic epilepsy has been considered to be constitutional and functional; symptomatic epilepsy is an expression of trauma or toxicity. This division has not been universally accepted by workers in genetics. Alström (1950) prefers the terms "unknown origin" and "known origin." Lennox (1951) speaks of "metabolic" and "symptomatic" epilepsy. The symptomatic cases are not a genetic problem, except insofar as genotype might affect the probability of convulsive responses to brain injury. The question at issue is whether more thorough neuropathological study will bring more and more cases into the "known origin" category until the idiopathic class is finally reduced to zero.

The occurrence in rodents of differential genetic susceptibility to audiogenic seizures is proof that metabolic differences can play an important role in epileptiform attacks. Nachtsheim (1939, 1941) described "hereditary epilepsy" in the Vienna white rabbit. The seizures were set off by minimal stimulation and were not correlated with any obvious neurological defects. Animal seizures may not be exact models of human epilepsy, but the resemblance is so strong that the possibility of metabolic epilepsy in man must be seriously considered.

The relationship of epilepsy to other psychiatric disorders has been disputed. Rosanoff et al. (1934) and Conrad (1937) found a higher than average proportion of psychoses, psychopathic abnormality, and other mental disorders among the relatives of epileptics. Alström (1950) states that unselected series of epileptics do not show personality characteristics specific to the disease. Epileptics without brain injury usually have normal intelligence (Lennox and Jolly, 1954). We might have chosen to include epilepsy with "response patterns" because deviant motor behavior or lapses of awareness are its essential features. Conventionally, however, it is considered as a psychiatric disorder, and we have for convenience included it in this chapter.

The literature on heredity and epilepsy is too extensive to be listed in detail. Additional references may be found in the cited papers. Rosanoff et al. (1934b), Conrad (1935), Lennox (1946), and Slater (1953a) have employed the twin method. Rosanoff did not describe his case-finding procedure in detail, but he was aware of the need for a representative sample. Conrad started with a group of 17,030 epileptics on the record books of German hospitals and went back to their birth records to determine which were twins. A total of 30 MZ and 131 DZ pairs made up the final sample after deletions for incomplete data. Propositi were classified as being afflicted with symptomatic or idiopathic epilepsy (Table 9-16).

TABLE 9-16

**Concordance in Twins with Epilepsy:
Summary of Data of Rosanoff et al. (1934),
Conrad (1935), and Lennox (1946)**

Diagnosis	MZ		DZ		Author
	N	%C	N	%C	
Idiopathic	22	86.3	97	4.1	Conrad
No brain injury	16	83.3	16	6.2	Lennox
Symptomatic	8	12.5	34	0.0	Conrad
With brain injury	19	15.8	7	0.0	Lennox
Epilepsy	23	52.2	84	11.7	Rosanoff et al.

Lennox's sample, summarized in the same table, was obtained from office and clinic patients. The samples are biased, for Conrad's group was deficient in MZ pairs and Lennox's group deficient in DZ twins. Ordinarily about one-third of all twin births are monozygotic. However, the three studies are in essential agreement and argue for a high degree of heritability for epilepsy. The lack of perfect concordance for idiopathic epilepsy indicates that genes do not determine the disease inevitably. The lower concordance for symptomatic epilepsy is expected on a genetic hypothesis, though even here concordance is higher in MZ pairs. Slater was unable to find in his sample even a single case of concordance either for his MZ or DZ pairs. This may have been mainly because of the small sample he used. To use Lennox's analogy, the spark (environmental agent) must find combustible material (genetic substratum) to start a fire (epileptic seizure). Under this viewpoint, the difference between the two types of epilepsy might lie in the size of spark necessary to ignite the fire. The substratum might be so flammable that almost any minor accident would precipitate a seizure. Lennox et al. (1939, 1942) have thus been of the opinion that genotype does not determine actually epileptic convulsions but rather that it determines cerebral dysrhythmia. They found that in 41 MZ-twin pairs EEG records were identical in 35 cases, different in 1 case, and of doubtful similarity in the remaining 6 cases. Among 12 DZ pairs, only one case of intrapair similarity was found (Lennox et al., 1942).

The family studies have yielded less clear results. Stein (1933) in a study of the 6572 relatives of 1000 hospitalized epileptic propositi, found that 18.1% of the latter had families with a history of seizure cases. Of a control group of 1115 non-epileptic patients, only 4.6% of them had families with seizure history. Expectation of epilepsy in combined relatives of the propositi was 3.7%, three times as high as found by Stein among relatives of the control group (1.3%). This was somewhat higher than the expectancy figure of 2.6% obtained previously by Lennox and Cobb (1928) for relatives of epileptic index cases. Various other disorders also appeared in the kin of propositi. Conrad (1937) recorded epilepsy in 7.94% of the offspring of patients diagnosed as "idiopathic" cases, but found a risk of only 1.9% in the descendants of "symptomatic" propositi. Lennox (1951) ascertained the history of seizures in 20,000 near relatives of 4231 patients seen in offices or clinics. Relatives of patients with "metabolic epilepsy" whose seizures began in infancy had the highest morbidity rate, 6.4%. The risk for relatives of propositi whose seizures began at 30 years of age or later was only 1.3%. Metrakos et al. (Fraser, 1958a) found clear evidence for heredity in so-called centrencephalic epilepsy, involving seizure history, no obvious neuropathology, and a centrencephalic EEG pattern. Risk in sibs of propositi was estimated at 22% as compared to 4% in sibs of a control group. Only 5.5% of affected sibs were chronic epileptics, however.

In contrast with these investigators, Alström (1950) found the risk of epilepsy in relatives of epileptics to be insignificantly greater than the estimate for the general population of the United States. He utilized Strömgren's exact method for computing cumulative risks throughout the life span. The age of onset of seizures was high in his propositi; in view of Lennox's results, late onset would lower the expectation of epilepsy in relatives. Alström's sample included 5 MZ-twin pairs, none concordant. Although he discounted heredity in general as a factor in epilepsy, Alström described 11 families (out of a total of 897) where epilepsy appeared to be inherited as a mono-hybrid, as a recessive in 4 families and as a dominant in 7. Such divergence points up the error of considering epilepsy as a unitary trait. It is probable that it is a clinical category representing a heterogeneous collection of diseases varying in heritability.

The evidence from animal and human data is convincing with respect to the heritability of susceptibility to convulsions. There is no reason to suppose that the connection between genes and convulsions is the same in all species or even in all individuals within a species. Ginsburg's investigations (1954) of the physiological genetics of audiogenic seizures represent one attempt to open up this important area (page 328). Convulsions represent a bizarre disorganization of adaptive behavior; they are also an index of excitation level in the nervous system. The question may be raised as to whether seizure susceptibility is directly related to other parameters of behavior. If susceptibility is related to pathology or metabolic disturbance in the central nervous system, as the work of Lennox et al. seems to suggest, it is plausible to hypothesize that these variations would have general effects upon behavior. Unfortunately the cited evidence is conflicting, and more research directed specifically at this problem is needed to resolve the issue.

The genetics of idiopathic epilepsy has not yet been fully worked out, and, though several theories have been proposed, none of these is backed by crucial evidence. Lennox and his co-workers (Lennox et al., 1939) have suggested that epilepsy, as indicated by cerebral dysrhythmia, is dependent on a single dominant gene with incomplete penetrance. Alström (1950), however, though admitting the possibility of some dominant inheritance, qualified this suggestion by hypothesizing a system of modifying polygenes in addition. Before the matter can be decided, more information will be needed, especially with respect to the nosological aspects of the disease and the underlying biochemical or neurological changes involved.

10

Heredity and individual differences in behavior

The preceding five chapters have documented the evidence for the inheritance of behavior. Data from many species and many types of investigation support the view that hereditary influences upon behavior are not exceptional but are almost universal. The exact nature of the relationship between nature and nurture in the production of individual differences is, however, by no means settled. Behavioral characters are not evoked by particular genes as neatly as blood types or coat colors, although the notion of congruence between particular genes and particular modes of behavior still persists in some quarters.

The general issue of the significance of genetic contributions to individual differences may be approached in two ways, through population genetics and through physiological genetics. The first method seeks an answer to the question, *"How much* does genetics contribute?"*; the second is oriented to the inquiry, *"How* does genetics make its contribution?"* (See Anastasi, 1958*b*.) The first question has no logical meaning when applied to an individual, for his whole genotype and total life experience contribute to every aspect of his behavior, and their influences cannot be separated. With respect to populations, however, one may well ask how much of the observed variation in behavior is attributable to genetic differences and how much to environment. In the language of genetics this is equivalent to determining the heritability of a trait. The fact that heritability is an attribute of populations rather than of traits has been emphasized earlier (page 64). In a heterogeneous colony of laboratory rats, for example, one might expect to find significant heritability of activity. The heritability of the same trait in a closely inbred colony would probably be zero, though the rats might be quite variable. Yet in both colonies genes would affect activity level through the same physiological mechanisms, and the activity of the inbred animals would be determined by their genes through the same physiological processes operating in the heterogeneous strain.

The two approaches to the problem of individual differences complement each other. Knowledge of heritability is paramount when one attempts to change phenotypes by selection. Actually it is not essential to know how the genes work in order to have a successful selection program. The important thing is the size of their effect in relation to total variability. But one can also change phenotypes by manipulating the environment, and here it is important to know how genotypes interact with specific environmental factors. Possibly the most significant contribution of behavior genetics is its documentation of the fact that two individuals of superficially similar phenotypes may be quite different genotypically and respond in completely different fashion when treated alike. Knowledge of how genes produce effects on behavior is often sought for its practical importance. If one can counteract the effect of a genetic "lesion" by biochemical means, seriously defective individuals may be restored to health. The dual approach to the problem of individual differences has dictated a division of this chapter into two sections, one concerned with population genetics and the other with pathways between genes and traits.

POPULATION GENETICS AND BEHAVIOR

The Adaptive Value of Behavioral Variation. The adaptive nature of behavior is almost a truism. In order to survive, organisms must respond to stimuli in a way which results on the average in the satisfaction of tissue needs and the execution of reproductive functions. The accepted explanation for the correspondence between needs and behavior is the evolution of behavior mechanisms through natural selection.

Briefly, the natural-selection theory of behavioral evolution postulates three related processes. First, random genetic variation occurs within a population. Second, this results in variable behavior, some forms of which are better adapted than others to the environmental challenges which are encountered. Third, the better-adapted individuals are more successful in reproduction, and the genes which are necessary for superior adaptation increase. The process has no definite end point, and evolution is a contemporary process as well as a historical one. Obviously the evolution of behavior is explicable by this mechanism only to the extent that behavior is heritable. Superior adaptation not related to genes could be transmitted culturally but not biologically.

Two contrasting types of adaptive evolution have been recognized. In one, structures evolve which produce a relatively stereotyped response to critical stimuli impinging upon the organism. Through natural selection each stimulus-response pattern is stabilized as the one most likely to permit survival and reproduction. The second type of adaptation involves the evolution of structures which become organized in the course of their functioning to produce the most adaptive response to particular circumstances. The stimulus-response patterns themselves are not stabilized by natural selection but by learning. The two forms of adaptation are not mutually exclusive, and man still depends on innate protective reflexes, although learning plays so important a role in his behavior. The question has been raised as to whether in man and other mammals genetic sources of variation in behavior have become insignificant, since the development of specific behavior patterns can be related to events in the environment. Although no general quantitative answer can be given, it seems likely that heredity is a major contributor to the variation of behavioral traits, as it is to physiognomy and physique.

Allen (1957) has suggested that the central-nervous system of the higher mammals may show instability because of its rapid and recent structural evolution. Not enough time has elapsed for natural selection to have eliminated genes with deleterious effects upon brain function. The great leap forward which made man a cultural animal with a tradition and the ability to build upon the accomplishments of past generations was based upon an enlarged nervous system. Once the leap was made, cultural progress did not depend upon changing genotypes. This, however, is not the same as saying that all genotypes became equivalent with respect to psychological traits.

It would be interesting to systematically compare the importance of heredity in producing behavioral variation in different classes of animals, but data are too scanty to permit a true comparative survey. We shall first discuss the situation in laboratory populations and in wild animals. Following this we shall consider human populations.

Heritable Variation in Behavior in Laboratory and Wild Populations. The widespread occurrence of strain differences is evidence for the generality of genes which affect behavior. In most instances, the inbred strains of rats and mice employed in experiments have not been selected on the basis of behavior, and the genome of each strain may be considered as a sample gamete of the species made diploid. Clearly, the strains could not be so different if the original population had not been genetically variable.

A second example has been drawn from a non-laboratory domesticated species. Dog breeds have been selected both for behavior and for physical type, but the behavioral criteria have been loosely specified. Certainly the basis for selection has never been performance on controlled laboratory tests. Some results of an experiment in which five pure breeds of dog were raised under standard conditions and tested in a uniform manner are set forth in Table 10-1. The intraclass

TABLE 10-1

Contribution of Breed Differences to Total Variance of Behavior Tests Administered to Five Pure Breeds of Dogs

Name of Test	Measurement	Intraclass Correlation
Motivation	Speed of running	.382
Discrimination	Correct responses in first 64 trials	.000
Leash control	Demerits on first day	.537
Leash control	Demerits, days 6–10	.524
Spatial orientation	Errors, sixth trial	.053
(Elevated maze)	Errors, twelfth trial	.250
Obedience training	Duration of inhibition of movement	.149
Reactivity	Summated activity	.446
Reactivity	Tremor (electrically recorded)	.382
Reactivity	Change in heart rate, entrance of human	.245
Reactivity	Change in heart rate, loud sound	.070
Reactivity	Tail carriage	.402

correlations are a measure of the proportion of the variance attributable to breed differences. Although the importance of heredity differs from score to score, on some tests it was a particularly important factor. The same analysis also demonstrated significant effects of environmental factors common to members of a litter. With better environmental controls (rearing subjects individually rather than in litters) it is likely that the estimated heritability would have been slightly greater. The elimination of genetic variability within the pure breeds should also raise the intraclass correlations. The figures obtained are certainly not the maximal values attainable.

It would be extremely interesting to know the extent of naturally occurring heritable behavioral variation in wild populations of mammals. King (1958), working with subspecies of the deermouse *Peromyscus maniculatus,* has found differences in rate of development of behavior and in the frequency of specific response patterns. Similar studies on other species would yield valuable information on the amount of genetic variability available for selection in natural populations.

Heritable behavior variations are not limited to the higher vertebrate classes. Differences in behavior have been frequently found in laboratory populations of insects, and selection is effective in changing these phenotypes (Richards, 1951; Hirsch and Boudreau, 1958). The amount of heritable variation in behavior in nature is not known. Where such variation has been demonstrated, it is adaptive. Pittendrigh (1958), for example, showed that geographic races of *Drosophila pseudoobscura* and *D. persimilis* showed physiological and behavioral adaptations related to the supply of moisture in their habitats. Probably mutations affecting behavior are as frequent in nature as in the laboratory, but few possess selective advantages over a genotype coadapted in the course of thousands of generations.

Heritable Behavior Variation in Man. Methods for determining the degree of genetic contribution to behavior variation in man differ with the nature of the gene-character relationship. Characters inherited as simple recessives or dominants can be investigated by the techniques described in Chapter 4. An example of such a study in the Netherlands on the frequency of the gene for *microcephalia vera,* a form of feeble-mindedness inherited as a recessive, is presented in Table 10-2 (van den Bosch, 1957).

TABLE 10-2

Estimates of the Frequency of the Gene for Microcephalia vera in the Netherlands (van den Bosch, 1957)

Place	Gene Frequency	Total Population
Four large cities (Amsterdam, Rotterdam, Den Haag, Utrecht)	0.00187	2,333,346
Eight Isolates:		68,427
Huissen	0.0285	
Etten	0.0151	
Lemmen	0.0263	
Elst	0.0250	
Putten	0.0285	
Didam	0.0181	
Hardinxveld	0.0200	
Enkhizen	0.0164	

The most interesting feature of this table is the tenfold difference in gene frequency between the larger cities, in which panmixia is a reasonable assumption, and a number of isolates with moderate numbers of consanguineous marriages. The contribution of this gene to the population of mental defectives varies widely within the bounds of a single small country. The genetic isolates in the Netherlands are predominantly religious in nature. Although closely consanguineous marriages are not common (i.e., first cousins), it is apparent that restriction upon the choice of marriage partners leads to very unequal risks of acquiring a genetic disease. As such isolates break up, the recessive genes responsible for many defects are more widely distributed in the population. This distribution results in an equalization of the risk of abnormal children, but it also spreads the deleterious gene more widely.

It is clear from this one example that one cannot specify the risk of genetic disease population-wise in general terms. More extensive regional data collection is needed to determine the relative importance of genetic factors in the production of mental defect caused by specific genes.

Population-genetic models have been well tested with traits such as the ability to taste PTC (page 99) and have also been employed with such characters as handedness (Trankell, 1955; Merrell, 1957), dyslexia or word-blindness (Hallgren, 1950), enuresis (Hallgren, 1957), and schizophrenia (Slater, 1958). In the last four characteristics, the expression of the trait is modifiable by the environment, and various assumptions regarding penetrance must be made to achieve a fit to the standard models. The validity of such assumptions is difficult to prove, and their plausibility is somewhat dependent upon the nature of the trait investigated. The dominant mode of inheritance of PTC tasting has been established by population studies. Hallgren's hypothesis that dyslexia is inherited in a similar fashion has not been generally accepted, although the genetic evidence is of a nature similar to that of PTC (though not as extensive). The point is that PTC taste-blindness is readily conceivable as the resultant of a rather simple metabolic variant. The relating of word-blindness, a variation which does not influence intelligence in general, to a unit process on the metabolic level is difficult to integrate with modern neurological ideas.

Another use of population genetics is exemplified by Slater's (1958) computations from data on incidence of schizophrenia in a number of countries. He has undertaken to test Böök's hypothesis, that the disorder is caused by a partially dominant gene with complete manifestation of the disease only in homozygotes, by comparing results of several family studies. Agreement with the hypothesis was best with values of .015 for the frequency of a postulated gene (S) which has a calculated penetrance of .26 in the heterozygote. The consistency of the results from independent surveys suggests common etiological mechanisms in all populations. Psychiatric characters do not follow the classical models of population genetics perfectly, but the models do appear useful in computing morbidity risks.

The heritability of intelligence has been variously estimated, though some authors (e.g., Sarason & Gladwin, 1958) do not accept the results, on the basis that since environmental factors can affect intelligence, one may anticipate that all effects ascribed to heredity will eventually be traced to such factors as cultural deprivation or prenatal injury. To our knowledge, the highest heritability values proposed are those of Burt and Howard (1956) and Burt (1958), who ascribed about 69% of variance in intelligence to genetics, 17% to assortative mating (also genetic), and only about 14% to environmental factors and unreliability. These estimates may impress some as being over high, but it must be remembered that the equalization of educational opportunities will have the effect of increasing heritability, since environmental sources of variance will be simultaneously reduced.

Even though the heritability of intelligence under certain circumstances is high, too little is known of the interaction between heredity and environment to make accurate predictions concerning the effects of natural selection on this trait. A number of longitudinal surveys have been conducted in several countries, and in all surveys children from larger families obtained significantly lower test scores than those from small families. This might be expected to lead to a progressive decline in test intelligence, since in successive generations the population will be drawn predominantly from the larger families. But the predicted decline has not occurred (Anastasi, 1958a, pages 209 ff.). We live today in an era of rapid cultural and educational change, and the effects of these factors upon intelligence probably obscure any effects of genotypic changes.

Race and Class Differences. The racial diversity of man has long been recognized, but population genetics provided the first quantitative means of evaluating such differences. Races have been defined as relatively homogeneous groups of interbreeding individuals characterized by a particular set of gene frequencies. Do the well-established differences in gene frequencies imply psychological differences as well? Strains of animals show behavioral differences correlated with their diversity in genotypes, and it can be argued that the same must be true of human races. Such a view need not imply racial superiority, merely racial differences. The evidence to prove this point one way or the other does not exist, nor is it likely to be obtained in the near future. Nevertheless, there are reasons to discount the likelihood of such differences being very important. The most diverse human cultures have common features related to the perpetuation of the species. It is difficult to conceive of a society in which intelligence, cooperation, and physical vigor would not have positive selective value. Hence it is likely that natural selection tends to oppose the establishment of major heritable behavior differences between races. (Dobzhansky and Ashley-Montagu, 1947; Dobzhansky, 1950, 1957; Etkin, 1954).

A similar question may be asked regarding the genetic basis of intelligence differences between social classes. Although there is great overlap in the intelligence-test scores of individuals from different social classes, there are real differences in average performance on various psychological tests (Anastasi, 1958a, Chapter 15). In the opinion of some investigators, social-class differences in intelligence are simply a reflection of cultural stimulation. What we call intelligence may be the way well-trained middle- and upper-class children behave. Nevertheless, when it comes to accounting for individual variability within social classes, it is often difficult to identify the environmental factors responsible for a genius from the wrong side of the tracks or a mediocre student from a professional family. In view of the strong evidence for the heritability of intelligence (Chapter 7) and the occurrence of assortative mating with respect to intelligence, it is possible that some social-class differentiation exists with respect to genetic factors affecting intelligence, and this divergence may increase if social-class membership becomes more dependent upon competitive effort in a society with high social mobility (Tryon, 1958).

These opinions regarding race and class differences may appear to be contradictory. The point is that natural selection in man operates at the level of whole societies. Intelligence is necessary for survival of a society, but it is not necessary that all members of the society be superior, and in fact a complex society has niches for its dullards as well as its geniuses. The less able members of a society benefit from association with the talented leaders. Natural selection should effectively prevent the evolution of a race of morons, but it would not eliminate them from a society which had a need for unskilled workers.

The Eugenics Concept. The essential idea of eugenics is that artificial selection be substituted for natural selection in the evolution of man. The program has generally been divided into negative eugenics, concerned with the elimination of major defects, and positive eugenics, the encouragement of reproduction by the most able elements of the population. Negative eugenics is considered now to be chiefly a matter of counseling with voluntary action based upon genetic predictions (Reed, 1957). The counselor can be definite only with those characters which show single-factor patterns of inheritance, and these are relatively rare in behavior genetics.

Positive eugenics is less direct in its approach and might actually be described as an attempt to give direction to natural selection. Osborn (1951) has given an excellent account of the modern eugenics movement. The basic idea is to work toward a social organization which promotes the formation of stable families and provides satisfactory niches for those who are incapable of this responsibility. This type of eugenics is an approach to the "good society" which takes special account of man's inherent biological diversity. It involves controlled natural rather than artificial selection.

There is a popular belief that advances in science and medicine have tended to eliminate selection as a force in human populations except for underdeveloped areas. This misconception originates from a too literal interpretation of the phrases "struggle for existence" and "survival of the fittest." The unmarried, the childless, the parents of a single child, are the unfit in the evolutionary sense, since their genes are not perpetuated. Dobzhansky and Allen (1956) have even suggested that fitness in our society may be more adequately measured by the number of grandchildren than by the number of children, since parental influences play so important a role in the preparation of children for marriage and family life. The biological criterion of fitness has little resemblance to popular notions of vigor, eminence, or social desirability, but natural selection has no goal except the maximizing of fitness. Idiots and imbeciles, schizophrenics and neurotics, generally have birth rates below average. But the genetic significance of the birth-rate differential will depend upon the heritability of each trait. It need not be high, but it must be significantly above zero. For some types of mental defect and for the major psychoses there is good evidence of heritability sufficient to be important in selection. The heritability of milder intellectual deficiencies and personality disorders is less well established. However, from the evidence from studies with animals it is clear that almost any behavioral attribute is modifiable by selection. The safest conclusion is that in man, too, natural selection operates on polygenic systems and modifies reactive capacities related to fitness. The process must be slow and its direction apparent only over the course of many generations. In fact, whatever directedness the process has will be contingent upon the cultural milieu in which it operates. For example, societies which place a major emphasis upon fertility as a religious duty may well be less subjected to selection than those which make marriage and child-rearing a matter of personal choice.

The difficulties in accurately appraising the proportionate contribution of heredity to socially inadequate behavior are great and probably insuperable. Yet the denial of any importance to heredity rests upon the assumption that human behavior has been emancipated from any connection with its biological substratum. Belief in such a discontinuity must rest on faith rather than scientific evidence. Often it appears that disavowal of heredity as a factor in human-behavior problems arises from the fear that nothing can be done about genetic conditions. Actually there are two ways of control, by family limitation based on genetic counseling and through treatments undertaken to modify the phenotypic expression of "poor" genotypes. Procedures of the second type will become more common as physiological genetics advances. This means that the genes which are involved no longer decrease fitness and are not subjected to negative selection. Medical and social progress should be viewed as improving fitness, not as permitting the survival of the "unfit." Education in its broad sense may be considered as directing a genotype-environment transaction in which the nature of the genotype determines the optimum form of training.

Summary and Conclusions. The population aspects of behavior genetics have not been widely studied with quantitative techniques. Nevertheless, it appears that a considerable portion of the behavioral variability of both wild and laboratory races is attributable to heredity. Surveys of genetic variation in behavior in populations of small mammals would be very useful in developing general laws for the nature-nurture relationship.

In mammals and, more especially, in man the adaptive nature of behavior is largely insured through the process of learning. Genetic variation, however, provides a second mechanism for adjusting to different environmental conditions including perhaps different social roles. Both modes of behavioral adaptation are the product of organic evolution through natural selection. Since natural selection differs in several important ways from artificial selection as usually practiced in laboratory experiments, it would be highly instructive to study the evolution of behavior in the laboratory using natural selection instead of directed selection. Such experiments would test the hypothesis that major changes in the nature of selection will always influence behavior in a relatively permanent fashion by changing the composition of the gene pool.

Finally, the eugenics movement has been considered as a proposal to substitute directed for natural selection in human populations. As applied to deleterious characters inherited in simple Mendelian patterns, it is reasonable that man should use his scientific knowledge to prevent the conception of children likely to be severe social burdens. Beyond this, our knowledge of human genetics is insufficient to base further recommendations, particularly since we do not know the nature of the future society to which our descendants must be adapted.

PATHWAYS BETWEEN GENES AND BEHAVIOR

Although it is possible to demonstrate hereditary effects without understanding the mechanisms involved, there are good reasons for probing more deeply. The modification of heritable defects is more likely to be successful if we understand how the causative genes are acting. Furthermore, the discovery of a pathway of gene action gives more concreteness to the concept of heritable behavior. Proof that a particular psychological difference between strains fits a one-factor Mendelian model is more convincing when some physical link can be found between the presumptive genes and the observed behavioral variation. In short, behavior genetics becomes intellectually more satisfying as it bridges the gap between genes and psychological traits.

The general problem of the relationship between gene and character was treated briefly in Chapter 2. This problem is central to physiological genetics, and the difficulties are great even when concern is limited to physical traits. With respect to behavioral traits, there is relatively little which has been firmly established. Nevertheless, there is value in summarizing and generalizing to the extent now possible, in full realization that drastic changes may soon be required. Experimentation in the area is desirable, for genetics can become a useful tool for the behavioral scientist seeking to find a physiological explanation for individual differences (Fuller, 1951, 1957; Ginsburg, 1949, 1958).

The ordinary technique of physiological genetics research is to start with a specific well-developed phenotypic difference and to work backward toward genetic sources of variation. The reverse order is more suitable for presentation of general principles. Behavior is the response of an organism to stimulation of external or internal origin. Genes operate at the molecular level of organization, but they are peculiar kinds of molecules, highly individuated carriers of information, whose effects are describable in psychophysiological as well as chemical terms. Enzymes, hormones, and neurons may be regarded as successively complex intermediaries between genes and psychological characters. We shall consider each in turn.

The Path through Enzymes. According to the gene-enzyme hypothesis, the effects of genes upon behavior must always be related eventually to some metabolic effect of the gene within the cell. In this sense variations in hormones, nerve structure, and the like are the outcome of more basic enzymatic differences. It is convenient, however, to consider these more complex pathways separately, since the links between the primary gene functions and their structural consequences are known in only the most rudimentary fashion. In this section we will deal with experiments purporting to demonstrate a rather direct correlation between metabolic systems and behavior. The classic example of a gene-controlled metabolic lesion with important behavioral effects is phenylketonuria (see page 312). A block in the oxidation pathway of phenylalanine leads to the accumulation of phenylketone and related substances (Jervis, 1954). That the effects upon intelligence are produced by a toxic action of the abnormal metabolites is indicated by the fact that afflicted individuals with reduced phenylalanine intake are psychologically improved (Bickel et al., 1955). Without the raw material no toxic substance is produced.

Hyperphagia in the genetically obese mouse (page 183) can also be related to a metabolic block. Although there is some argument as to the exact nature of the biochemical lesion (Guggenheim and Mayer, 1952; Parson and Crispell, 1955), there is no doubt that some defect exists in the oxidation of short-chain fatty acids. Since obesity can be prevented by restricting food intake (Lane and Dickie, 1954) it is evident that hyperphagia is an essential link between the biochemical defect and the gross overweight.

Partial Metabolic Blocks. Phenylketonuria and hereditary obesity are examples of metabolic lesions which are compatible with life, but which produce phenotypic effects far beyond the ordinary range of the species. Both conditions are inherited as simple Mendelian recessives. The concept of less drastic metabolic lesions is also fundamental in Williams' genetotrophic theory of alcoholism (page 184). Williams speaks of partial genetic blocks which can apparently vary quantitatively and thus be responsible for biological and psychological variation within the normal range.

A somewhat similar hypothesis has been proposed by Ginsburg (1949, 1954, 1958) to account for strain differences in audiogenic seizure susceptibility in mice. Partial metabolic blocks within nerve cells result in a system which cannot react appropriately in the face of massive stimulation. Direct evidence in favor of this view has been obtained by Abood and Gerard (1955). These investigators found a deficiency of the enzyme ATPase and of oxidative phosphorylization in the brains of DBA mice during, and only during, the age period of susceptibility. Such a temporary imbalance of metabolism is quite different from the permanent defect of phenylketonuria.

Results with the chemical control of audiogenic seizures in mice have been interpreted as favoring the partial genetic-block hypothesis (Ginsburg, 1954). The procedure has been to inject mice with rather large doses of substances known to participate in energy-releasing reactions in cells or with related substances which compete with normal metabolites and thus block certain pathways. If different inbred strains have acquired susceptibility through separate mutations affecting different parts of the metabolic system, they might be expected to respond differentially to the same metabolite or anti-metabolite.

The DBA/1 strain was used primarily in this research since it is intermediate in seizure risk and can be used to test for both enhancement and reduction of susceptibility. Among the substances with enhancing effects were glutamine, α-methyl glutamic acid, and malic acid. Reduction of susceptibility was achieved with glutamic acid and lactic acid. Such compounds as dextrose, aspartic, and fumaric acids had no effect. Glutamic acid and related substances had differential effects between males and females within the DBA/1 strain. Other types of compounds reacted similarly on both sexes.

Diamox, which inhibits the enzyme carbonic anhydrase, reduced seizures in the two susceptible strains, DBA/1 and HS. But glutamic acid was effective only on DBA's. None of the enhancers produced susceptibility in the resistant strain C57BL.

The significance of these results to behavior genetics rests upon the extent to which they can be related to specific genetically regulated enzyme systems. Ginsburg (1954) states: "At present, we have no rationale with which to explain the mode of action of the substances on any common basis. . . . (It is a) fact that many of these substances are easily interconvertible, and the procedure of injecting a particular one into the intact animal does not insure that it remains in that form or that a significant amount accumulated in the central nervous system."

In view of the fact that most of the reported data are based upon a single dose level, it is possible that some of the differences are quantitative and not qualitative. Any disruption of metabolism sets up a series of changes. For example, susceptibility was enhanced *48* hours after injecting Diamox, although it was completely suppressed *one-half* hour after injection. The strain differences in enhancement could also be quantitative rather than qualitative. It may take a more powerful agent to produce any convulsions in C57BL's than to increase seizure risk of DBA's by 30%.

Brain Cholinesterase and Adaptive Learning. One of the most direct attempts to link body chemistry with heritable differences in behavior has already been described (page 221). Cholinesterase (ChE) is an enzyme which catalyses the breakdown of acetylcholine to choline and acetic acid. Acetylcholine is one of the chemical mediators in the peripheral and central nervous systems. High concentrations of an enzyme are commonly taken to indicate a high level of metabolism of the enzyme substrate. In this instance, the concentration of cholinesterase might be taken as a measure of readiness of synaptic transmission. Within limits, ease of transmission might be conducive to adaptive learning. The primary datum is the finding by Krech, Rosenzweig, and Bennett (1954, 1956, 1957) that rats showing superior performance in the Krech hypothesis apparatus have more cholinesterase in their brains than do poor performers.

In this apparatus, preference for a spatial "hypothesis" in maze running is considered to be more adaptive than a visual "hypothesis." Subjects using visual orientation were significantly lower in ChE between the ages of 150 to 400 days (Rosenzweig et al., 1958). At 100 and 500 days, however, visual-spatial preferences could be demonstrated in the absence of a biochemical difference. The facilitating effect of ChE is therefore insufficient as a complete explanation.

Superimposed upon the age variation were strain differences. Strain S_1, descendants of Tryon's maze-bright animals, were higher in ChE at 200 days and above than strain S_3. Within each group subjects having a spatial orientation had higher ChE activity, yet the ranges were such that spatially oriented rats of S_3 averaged less than visually oriented subjects of S_1. Certainly the absolute level of ChE is not the critical factor. Rats selected for high brain ChE were in fact more spatially oriented than those selected for low ChE (Roderick, 1958). Independence of biochemical and behavioral events is also shown by the fact that intracerebral injections of powerful ChE inhibitors failed to alter the hypothesis preferences of the same rat strains (Chow and John, 1958). A severe handicap to interpretation is the fact that the biochemical measurements must be made after the animal has been tested behaviorally, never in reverse order. Hence there is a possibility that the chemical findings are a function of behavior, rather than the reverse. At best, the relationship between ChE and learning is not simple.

Appraisal of the Enzyme System-Behavior Relationship. The reservations expressed with respect to interpretation of experiments on partial genetic blocks do not imply that the hypothesis is untenable. On the contrary, the attractiveness and reasonableness of the theory merit more attention than it has yet received. But this esthetic appeal should not exclude other approaches (see Kety, 1959). For example, differences in the rate of active transport across cell boundaries may have as much to do with behavioral variability as partial metabolic blocks. The difficulties in covering the gap between molecular and behavioral phenomena are formidable; the much narrower gap between the molecular level and histogenesis has few bridgeheads. We can explain some of the pigment variations in mammals in chemical terms, but the distribution of pigment over the body must be accounted for by growth gradients, differential migration of pigment cells, and similar phenomena of a biological nature.

The approach to the gene-behavior character relationship through enzyme studies has the advantage of being close to the gene end of the chain, but this advantage is counterbalanced by distance from behavioral events. One may employ genetic lesions, using Ginsburg's (1958) phrase, to "naturally dissect" the nervous system at the metabolic level, but this dissection is not the same as separating out natural units of behavior. More must be learned regarding the relationship between biochemical individuality and behavior before the findings of the biochemist can have psychological meaning. In the expanding area of psychochemistry, genetics will have a unique role, for genes are the only way in which permanent chemical characteristics can be built into an organism. Selective breeding for biochemical characters is well known in plants and can be achieved with animals for characters of psychological interest, such as cholinesterase concentration (Rosenzweig et al., 1958). The methods are laborious, but some shortcuts may be possible through the use of strains already available.

The Path through Hormones. The relationship between hormones and behavior was reviewed a few years ago by Beach (1948). The potential mechanisms through which hormones might control behavior were grouped under four headings.

(1) Hormones may affect behavior through effects upon the organism's normal development and maintenance activities. Such effects, exemplified by the multiple deficiencies of the cretin, are relatively non-specific.

(2) Hormones may control behavior through stimulation of structures employed in specific response patterns. For example, the postnatal growth of genital organs is dependent upon hormones, and adult sexual behavior cannot occur until these structures are fully developed.

(3) Behavior may be controlled through effects upon peripheral receptors, sensitizing them to particular forms of stimulation. This possibility has not been much explored, but there is some positive evidence for it.

(4) Behavior may be controlled through effects of hormones on the integrative functions of the central nervous system. This possibility has attracted considerable attention since Beach's review, and a number of studies have dealt with the effects of hormones directly injected into the brain (Fisher, 1956; Harris et al., 1958).

The fact that evidence can be found for each of these possibilities does not mean that all are involved in the production of heritable individual differences in behavior. A distinction must be made between psychophysiological actions of hormones in normal concentrations and psychopharmacological effects of large doses applied in artificial ways. The latter type of effect has little significance for the genetics of normal variation.

An additional complication in the analysis of the gene-hormone-behavior relationship is that genes might operate upon the source of the hormone, affecting the quantity and quality of the product or upon the target organs, affecting their response. Furthermore, the endocrine system is physiologically complex, with much interaction between components. None of the four types of mechanism described by Beach or the two means by which genes might act are mutually exclusive. The choice of pathways is more than adequate.

Evidence is abundant that individuals vary greatly in endocrine-gland structure and physiology (Williams, 1956, Chapter 6). A relationship between this variation and heredity is often inferred, but direct evidence is rare. However, strain differences in reaction to hormone injection have been demonstrated in animals for anterior-pituitary extract (Munro et al., 1943), cortisone (Wragg and Speirs, 1952), and in thyroid activity (Stockard et al., 1941; Chai et al., 1957).

Sex Hormones and Behavior. Since courtship behavior is intimately dependent upon hormones, it might be expected to provide good evidence on the points in question. Young's group (page 174) has maintained that individual and strain differences in the sexual activity of guinea pigs are functions of target-organ sensitivity rather than amount of sex hormones produced. The target locus has not been specified, but some portion of the central nervous system is a distinct possibility. Raising the metabolism of low sex-drive subjects by thyroxin did not elevate their courtship scores (Riss, 1955). Sexual behavior can be elicited provided the supply of sex hormones exceeds a threshold, whereas metabolic level, controlled in part by thyroxin, places an upper limit upon activity. Hormones, *per se*, do not seem to be the sources of individual differences among intact animals.

The relationship between sex hormones, experience, and behavior varies widely among species, and generalization from guinea pigs to carnivores or primates should be made cautiously. Many studies (summarized by Williams, 1956) have shown wide variations in sex hormones in humans, but there is no real evidence that such variations have any direct effect upon sexual behavior, provided they are not so extreme as to interfere with normal development. On the other hand, it would be wrong to conclude that, because even pseudo-hermaphrodites adopt the gender role of their rearing in spite of genetic or endocrine discordance (Money et al., 1955), endocrine variations have no psychological effect. Feminization of the male, or masculinization of the female features have obvious social repercussions (the somatopsychic effects of Anastasi, 1958a).

Androgens have effects upon aggressive behavior as well as courtship and mating (Beach, 1948, Chapter 5), and castration has been used for centuries as an aid in the management of male domestic animals. Are individual differences in aggressiveness caused by variation in androgen production? Injecting testosterone propionate into castrated female mice is much less effective in inducing fighting than the same treatment applied to castrated males (Tollman and King, 1956). Bevan et al (1957) found that strain differences in fighting were not abolished when castrated subjects received equal injections of male sex hormones. Variation in the responding system seems a likelier source of heritable individual differences in aggression than does androgen production.

Other Endocrine Systems. A decrease in the size of the adrenal glands has accompanied the domestication of the Norway rat (Rogers and Richter, 1948). Among domestic strains, Hall's emotional rats had larger adrenals and thyroids than his non-emotional stock (Yeakel and Rhoades, 1941). Wire-haired fox terriers, selected to be aggressive, were found by Elliot (personal communication) to have much larger adrenals than beagles or cocker spaniels. The reduction of eosinophils in the blood stream following cortisone was far greater in some inbred strains of mice than in others (Wragg and Speirs, 1952). Such observations suggest that the genes might affect behavior through the adrenal glands. However, neither adrenalectomy nor injections of excess cortisone altered the strain differences among mice with respect to activity, avoidance behavior, and emotional defecation (Fuller et al., 1956).

Variation in the thyroid glands of dog breeds was reported by Stockard et al. (1941). Some of the subjects of his experiments were conditioned in the classical Pavlovian manner. Thyroidectomy was deleterious to establishment of a conditioned response, but it is not clear from the published report that individual differences in conditionability (which were pronounced) were directly correlated with thyroid status. At the time of this research, radioactive-tracer methods for studying thyroid function were not available. Using such techniques, inbred mouse strains have been found to differ widely in rate of thyroid-hormone output (Chai et al., 1957; Amin et al., 1957). The high-output strains are those found in other studies to be more active.

Endocrine Variation in Man. A number of endocrine disorders in man, diabetes mellitus and Grave's disease (a form of hyperthyroidism) among them, are heritable (Bartels, 1953). In untreated diabetes mellitus, blood-sugar concentration fluctuates widely with accompanying changes of mood and appetite. The victim of Grave's disease is hyperactive, sometimes to the point of mania. Extreme variants in the endocrine system do have behavioral consequences related to the physiological disturbance, but the opposite relationship, that between extreme behavioral deviation and endocrine disorders, is not as clear.

To review adequately the literature of endocrinological psychiatry would lead too far afield, but a few comments will suffice as illustration. Schizophrenics are frequently extreme deviants in endocrine function tests, but the relationships are not perfect, observers are not in agreement as to the nature of the deviations, and the effects of institutionalization are confounded with possible genetic effects (Kety, 1959). Bleuler and his co-workers (1948) have carried out extensive investigations on psychotic patients with endocrine disorders such as acromegaloidy, fatty dysplasia, virilization (in women), and infantilism. Familial investigations have generally shown a hereditary basis for both the psychosis and the endocrinopathy, but except for acromegaloidy, the correlations of the psychosis with the endocrine dysfunctions were no greater than those predicted from random association of independent variables. In acromegaloidy, a behavior syndrome attributable to diencephalic disturbance was prominent. Although not causally related, an endocrine dysfunction may affect the course of psychotic disease. For example, Bleuler reports that schizophrenia in a physically infantile person differs from the disease in one whose genital development is normal. Sexual fantasies and aberrations are less frequent in infantile persons.

In summary, the pathway from genes to behavior through the endocrine system is real but narrow. Although much exploration is yet to be done, it is likely that variations in target-organ response will have greater significance for behavior genetics than variations in hormone output. In fact, strain differences in response to hormones seem to be very common.

The Path through the Nervous System. Despite the importance of variation in the nervous system as a path whereby genes might come to influence behavior, few studies have dealt directly with the problem. We have previously given cursory attention to the large variety of heritable neurological defects which produce profound changes in behavior due to interference with anatomical pathways. Genes which lead to major neurological defects have been found in many species and show considerable uniformity in their manifestations. One group of these, the lipidoses (Herndon, 1954), is characterized by abnormal lipid deposition in the brain, but these have not yet been related to specific enzymatic processes. An interesting feature of some lipidoses and heritable ataxias (Schut, 1954), and of Huntington's chorea is their long latency. Onset of the disease follows long periods of apparently normal functioning. How the presence of the causative gene becomes manifest only at a late stage of development is not clear. Perhaps a developmental error occurs early, but function is adequate until a defective part wears out. Many neurological diseases are progressive, and it is often difficult to specify exactly when they began. In these instances of gross defect in the nervous system, the behavioral correlates depend upon the region of the nervous system affected. At present the primary metabolic lesions have not been identified.

The simplest quantitative attribute of the nervous system is its size. Mere mass of the brain is considered to be a good measure of the psychological capacity of related species (Rensch, 1956). But brain weight by itself has not proved a reliable indicator of psychological differences within a species (see Lashley, 1947, for discussion). It is natural, therefore, to look for less crude morphological differences which might be correlated with behavior. A number of interrelated questions must be asked. (1) Is there substantial individual variation in the fine structure of the central nervous systems of the higher vertebrates? (2) Is such variation heritable? (3) What significance does it have for behavior?

Fine Structure Variation. Textbooks on neuroanatomy usually describe morphology in terms of a single normal pattern, yet uniformity is certainly not the rule. Lashley and Clark (1946) have sharply criticized the architectonic method of dividing the cerebral cortex into small units based on common cell structure and arrangement. We quote from their account of quantitative comparisons between several specimens of macaques and spider monkeys. "Individual variations in cell size, density, and arrangement (in homologous areas of different brains) exceed many interareal differences and make quantitative criteria, upon which the parcellations have been carried out, unreliable." In their own studies variation in cell density and cell size of the order of 25 to 100% was common. Lashley (1947) cites Alexander's statement, "The myeloarchitectural pattern of the normal thalamus shows a surprising number of individual variations . . . human thalami are almost as different in appearance as human faces." The existence of so much individual variation gives a strong affirmative answer to our first question.

Unfortunately, no evidence bearing on the heritability of this type of quantitative variation is known to us. In a sense, the spatial arrangement of nerve cells is like the patterning of dermal ridges, which are highly individualistic. Three dimensions are involved instead of two, and the number of elements involved is much greater. Since the ridge count of fingerprints is inherited (Holt, 1952, 1957), it is reasonable to surmise that the arrangement of nerve cells is also. Direct evidence is lacking, but the difficulties which would be encountered in obtaining it are not insurmountable.

The same lack of data is found when we consider the psychological consequences of structural variation in nerve-cell arrangement. Psychologists have often ablated a portion of an animal's brain and observed the effects upon behavior, but we have no means of knowing whether the quantitative variation observed by Lashley and Clark (1946) is psychologically significant. In our current state of knowledge regarding cerebral physiology, we must guess regarding the effect of altering the spatial relationships of neurons by a factor of 50%. Genetics may provide a means for controlling cell density through selection and bring the problem into the experimental sphere. Ablation of a bit of cortex makes a hole in the nerve net—often with little effect upon behavior. Variations in the size of the mesh may have more important effects than do small lesions.

Evaluating the behavioral significance of fine neural-structure variation when there is so little evidence must be speculative. It seems reasonable that the functions of a nerve network would be altered when the number of connections is increased, and it is conceivable that the structure of the network is a heritable character. A full-scale research program in the area would repay the effort, for even negative results would be important. It is perhaps pertinent that Powers (1951) could not always find a neurological correlate for flightlessness in certain mutants of Drosophila.

Sensorimotor Variation. Heritable peripheral variation is well known to affect behavior. A simple example is the differential thermal preference of mice shown to be dependent upon skin thickness (Herter and Sgovina, 1938). There is, however, no convincing evidence that differences in temperament and intelligence are related to any obscure inherited sensorimotor deficits or advantages. Tryon (1931, 1939) was unable to show any correlation between sensory factors and the maze-bright–maze-dull differentiation in his rats. In human beings, even extreme sensory deficits are compatible with high intelligence if adequate educational procedures are employed (Anastasi, 1958a, Chapter 5). Without such special treatment, however, intelligence is greatly impaired in these circumstances.

Peripheral variations have special significance in social species, for they serve as cues for discriminatory responses or determine success in competition. The heavy dog wins his fights and becomes dominant. The myopic boy reads because glasses interefere with sports. The girl with regular features is the "belle of the ball." These events affect the development of personality, yet genes affecting weight, the length of the eyeball, or the shape of the nose are not usually considered as "behavior genes." Such correlations between heritable anatomical characters and psychological traits emphasize the difficulty in proving that any gene is behaviorally neutral. Dominance and love of reading and dancing are not commonly spoken of as heritable behavior because the nature of the genotype-phenotype relation is so obviously a function of culture. Standards of feminine beauty change and even differ between social classes. The shape of a nose seems less critical than society's response to its contours. But to limit genetic effects upon behavior to invariant relationships between a particular gene and a particular trait would be to restrict them unduly. A continuum exists between quite direct relationships and those which are so complex that they may be overlooked. More research is needed on the later manifestations of sensorimotor variation in young organisms and their modification in different environments.

Genes and Psychological Components. The search for anatomical and physiological channels through which genes contribute to variation in behavior has been successful to a limited extent. A few enzymes have been implicated; hormones play a significant role; neurological defects have behavioral consequences. But many behavioral differences clearly shown to be heritable have not been reduced to problems in biochemistry or electrophysiology. Perhaps investigators have not looked in the right places. We have already suggested the fine structure of the nervous system as a likely hunting ground. Or it may be that behavior measures are the only reliable indicators of certain kinds of inherited organic characters. Physiological and anatomical techniques have limitations, since the measuring devices themselves impair the intactness of the subjects.

These limitations have stimulated some psychologists to use behavior tests themselves to define psychological components which could have genetic significance. The idea is that traits might be found by methods such as factor analysis which are biologically more real than test scores chosen empirically. (Eysenck and Prell, 1951; Cattell, 1953; Blewett, 1954; Thurstone, Thurstone, and Strandskov, 1953; Thompson, 1956; Royce, 1957). Results of observations on the heritability of factor scores have been previously presented. At this time we shall be concerned with the general implications of the method in behavior genetics.

Factor analysis begins with a matrix of intercorrelations between a number of measures and by a series of statistical manipulations determines a smaller number of factors which can "explain" the variances of the original scores. There is no mathematically unique solution of such a matrix. Many psychologists have employed Thurstone's (1947) concepts of "simple structure" and "positive manifold." The first means that each test shall have loadings on as few factors as possible; the latter requires rotation of axes to eliminate significant negative factor loadings on all tests. Thus the description of the traits is the most parsimonious possible, and high ratings on factors never imply low scores on any tests. This requirement is probably defensible in the area of intelligence testing in which Thurstone was particularly interested, but its validity in the realm of temperament is less obvious. Both these criteria are intrinsic to the original matrix; that is, they are applied to the relationships between the dependent variables as expressed in the test intercorrelations. Having no definite relationship to causal factors (independent variables), they do not necessarily lead to factors which make biological sense. By itself, factor analysis leads to more parsimonious description, not to hypothesis testing.

A possible method of accomplishing a rapprochement between factors and external criteria has been proposed by Eysenck (1950).

Basically, his method involves rotating axes to maximal agreement of the first factor with some criterion test included in the matrix. For example, tetrachoric correlations might be employed to measure the success with which each of a set of tests discriminated between two genetically defined subgroups. Rotation of axes would continue to extract the factor which most nearly matched the criterion. The method is a serious attempt to relate factors to psychological and biological facts obtained independently of the test scores. However, the method has not been adequately tested and its potential contribution to behavior genetics remains to be determined.

Another attempt to relate factor theory to genetics emphasizes the multiple-factor control of independent processes which can collectively be called intelligence (Royce, 1957). Royce's model (Figure 10-1)

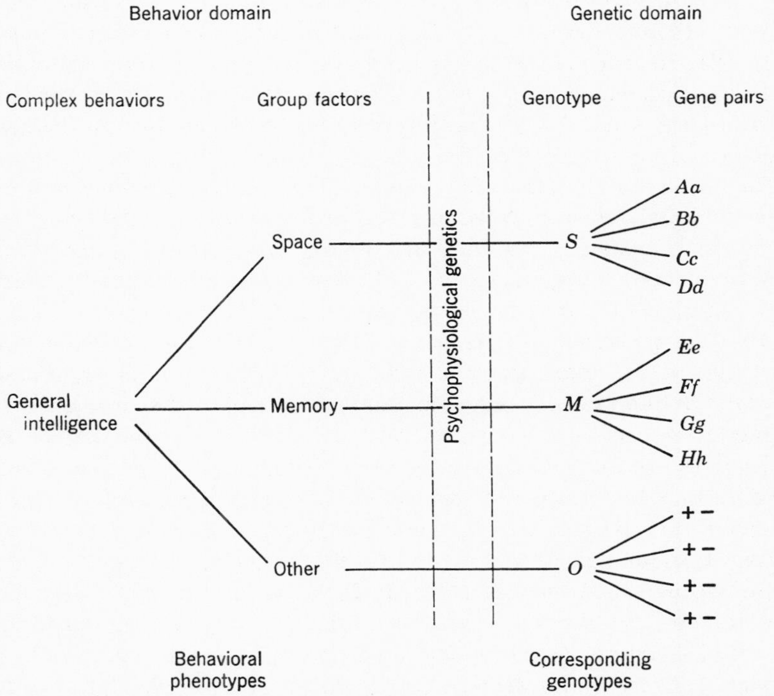

FIGURE 10-1. Royce's (1957) concept of the relationship between the multiple-factor theory of psychology and the multiple-factor theory of genetics. Capital letters signify a plus effect upon the trait or phenotype. Thus a high space-factor score would be given by *ABCD*, a low score by *abcd*. This model we have called "congruent," since there is a part-for-part correspondence between gene blocks and psychological factors.

assigns blocks of genes to various group factors. The relationship between the genotypes, *S*, *M*, etc., and their respective mental traits
Space, Memory, etc., is not stated in the theory. Presumably the action
is direct, since other genes are postulated to have indirect effects
through the nervous or endocrine systems. The most notable feature
of the Royce model is the idea of congruence between genetic and
psychological elements, a concept which is implicit in much hypothesizing in behavior genetics. In the Royce model, it leads to a distinction
between direct and indirect (nervous and endocrine) actions of genes
upon intelligence, but the nature of direct action is not defined.

In the hands of more biochemically oriented investigators, all genetic
effects are considered to be chemical. When combined with the concept of congruence, however, this leads to a sort of biochemical
phrenology in which enzyme systems replace bumps on the cranium,
each enzyme controlling a psychological function. But when single
genes are found which affect behavior, they affect not one but a variety
of intellectual and temperamental traits. Phenylketonurics are low in
all the Primary Mental Abilities. About two-thirds show abnormal
neurological symptoms in addition to mental defects; bizarre behavior
such as echolalia and echopraxia may be more common than in some
other defectives. Psychotic episodes and epilepsy are relatively common
(Jervis, 1954). A simple biochemical lesion does not affect a limited
segment of behavior but modifies development in many ways. Since
psychological factors are not congruent with gene systems, factor
analysis will not automatically yield a genetic analysis.

The Genetic Meaning of Factors. A discussion of the genetic meaning
of factors must start with a consideration of the genetic significance
of phenotypic correlations, the raw material for the analysis. The
subject has been discussed previously (page 77), but we shall review
it with special reference to factor-analytic concepts.

Correlations between traits may arise from genic, chromosomal,
gametic, or environmental communalities. A diagram of genic communality is shown on the left-hand side of Figure 10-2. The correlation between traits ϕ and θ is a function of the contribution of
physiological character l to each. This character is, in turn, controlled by gene *D*. Both ϕ and θ have genetic variances (from genes
A, *B*, *C*, *E*, *F*) which are either specific or shared with other traits.
The short arrows extending from physiological-level traits are considered to run to other behavioral traits omitted from the figure.

On the right-hand side of Figure 10-2 is a diagram of chromosomal
communality. The covariation between traits θ and Σ is dependent
upon the linkage of genes *F* and *G*. It will not be important in large

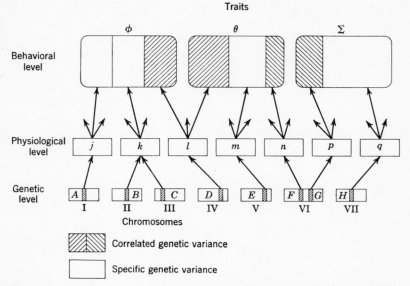

FIGURE 10-2. Gene and Chromosomal Communality. The pleiotropic effects of gene D, operating through a physiological process l, results in covariation of traits ϕ and θ. This model is "non-congruent," for there is no precise correspondence between genes and traits defined on the behavioral level. The short arrows extending upward from the physiological level traits are intended to represent effects upon other behavioral traits here omitted for the sake of clarity. Environmental sources of trait variance are likewise omitted from this diagram.

Chromosomal communality is depicted by the covariance between θ and Σ, which is dependent upon linkage between genes F and G in chromosome VI.

random-breeding populations, but may be significant in small groups of related individuals.

Gametic communality is illustrated in Figure 10-3. The associations of traits ϕ and θ and their opposites, ϕ' and θ', are maintained only as long as a non-random mating system is followed. Since assortative mating is characteristic of humans (with respect to social class, intelligence, etc.) it is conceivable that factors could be generated by the gametic correlations produced (Price, 1936; Bartlett, 1937; Thompson, 1956). The critical issue is, of course, whether assortative mating is partly based upon genic and gametic communalities or solely upon environmental ones.

The diagrams of genetic communalities were drawn, for simplicity of exposition, without reference to environmental variance. In Figure 10-4, traits ϕ and θ are shown with both environmental and genetic contributions to variance. A portion of each type of variance

Traits

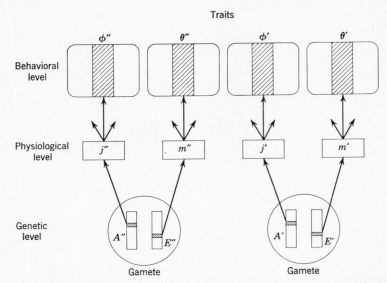

FIGURE 10-3. Gametic Communality. The covariance between ϕ'' and θ'' is maintained by the association of chromosomes I and II bearing genes A'' and E''. Covariance of ϕ' and θ' (lower-ranking than ϕ'' and θ'') is similarly maintained either by inbreeding or by assortative mating between individuals of similar rank in ϕ and θ.

is common to the two traits; other portions are independent. Some such arrangement is probably representative of the actual situation. If traits ϕ and θ are subsumed under a common factor, Z, because of their covariance, this is a function of event II as well as gene C. If this figure is representative of the true relationships between variables affecting behavior, one would not expect a simple factor analysis to lead to purely biologically or purely environmentally determined factors. Possibly this limitation can be removed by developing new techniques which include genetic characteristics in the original correlation matrix.

Specific Movements as Behavior Traits. In one sense the use of specific movements as units for behavior genetics stands almost at the opposite pole from the factor-analytic approach. The objective is not parsimony in the description of behavior differences, but the analysis of gross general differences into a number of precisely described acts. In another sense, the two approaches have something in common. Both methods seek to define basic units of behavior which can then be related to genetic and environmental determinants. The careful description of interspecific differences in behavior has been the concern

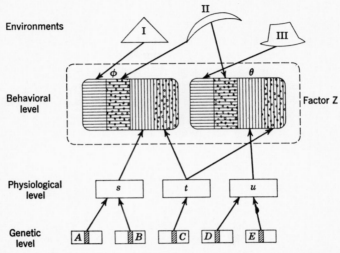

FIGURE 10-4. Specific and Common Variances of Genetic and Environmental Origin. Traits ϕ and θ may be subsumed under factor Z because of their intercorrelation. Factor Z exists because of common effects of gene C and event II. The factor provides a more parsimonious description of the traits, but it does not imply a single agent responsible for the covariation. Horizontal lines = environmental variances; vertical lines = genetic variances; dotted areas = covariances of ϕ and θ.

of a number of biologists. It has been stated that behavior patterns are as useful in the taxonomy of some groups as are anatomical characters (Lorenz, 1950). Although most of the investigations in this area have been concerned with tracing the evolutionary history of behavior, a few studies using specific movements as genetic characters have been cited previously (Clark et al., 1954; von Hörmann-Heck, 1957; Baltzer, 1952; Caspari, 1951; Haskins and Haskins, 1958). Significantly, all these experiments employed fish or insects. There are suggestions, however, that the specific movements made by dogs in an emotionally disturbing situation are partly determined by heredity (Fuller, 1955).

Non-congruence of Genes and Behavior. In contrast with the model made explicit by Royce (1957) and adopted implicitly by many others, we have argued for a lack of correspondence between genes and behavior traits. Single genes characteristically affect many forms of behavior; single psychological traits have variance ascribable to many genes. Between the genetic and behavioral levels of description is a network of physiological processes. We propose that behavior is insensitive to a substantial portion of the metabolic shunting which occurs in this network, for a neuron may not be concerned with the source of its energy provided it gets enough. In such a situation any one of a number of alternative genetically controlled pathways may be equivalent from the viewpoint of behavior integration. In other cases the behavioral consequences of a genetic substitution may depend upon a particular balance of physiological factors. In these instances a particular form of behavior would be responsive to changes in genotype, but the inheritance patterns would be complicated since the phenotypic consequences would be functions of the interplay of independent interacting characters. Finally one might expect to find behavioral traits which are correlated strongly with single physiological characters. Such traits would respond well to selection, and would probably show additive inheritance in interstrain crosses. We have chosen to call this a non-congruent model, since it does not postulate a one-to-one correspondence between genes (or groups of genes) and particular behavior traits. In fact, a gene substitution might have opposite effects upon behavior depending upon either the presence of other genes or life-history differences.

If the non-congruent model is generally applicable, the task of the investigator in behavior genetics is made more difficult. The classical biometrical methods are applicable only in situations where genetic effects can be made approximately additive through some scale transformation. If the contribution of a gene to a behavioral trait varies with circumstances in a highly irregular fashion, suitable scale transformations may not be possible. The relationships between genotype and phenotype must still be lawful, but each specific combination of genotype and life history may have its own rules of developing response patterns. The problem of complex interactions of this type is not unique to behavior genetics, and animal breeders have been forced to become interested in the non-additive effects of genes upon quantitative physical characters (Lerner, 1958, Chapter 6). Nevertheless, the complexity inherent in the regulation of behavior by many factors gives the non-congruent model special significance for our branch of genetics.

Confirmation of the non-congruence model requires manipulation of genotypes instead of phenotypes. The methods are exactly opposite to selection in which phenotypes are manipulated in order to change genotypes. Such procedures are possible only with species in which a large reservoir of controllable genetic variation is available. Drosophila is the animal of choice from the genetic point of view, but its behavior repertoire is limited. The mouse, with its numerous mutations and inbred strains, is the most suitable mammal. Manipulating genes, chromosomes, and gametes rather than selecting for phenotype will be the next important phase of behavior genetics. The conceptual framework of these experiments will be the use of genes as treatments affecting behavior, rather than the determination of the heritability of traits. Studies of heritability will be carried out in the framework of population genetics rather than as attempts to identify particular genes with particular forms of behavior.

The above paragraph suggests a new approach to the genetic part of behavior genetics. Opportunities for innovation also exist on the behavioral side. Hull (1951), who is well known for the development of an elaborate series of formal laws relating behavior to antecedent conditions and stimulus characteristics, hypothesized that "both individual and species differences appear in natural molar behavior as variable values of the 'constants' involved. . . . We believe that this area goes much deeper than ordinary molar principles, cutting across them sharply. Quite possibly it even includes such things as basic physiological determiners." Eysenck (1956) and Thompson and Kahn (1955) have attempted to relate individual differences in behavior to Hullian constructs, but the field for genetic experimentation to test the value of such concepts is still open.

Another approach to finding suitable dimensions of behavior for genetic analysis is through neurophysiology. Various kinds of problem-solving behavior (spatial versus temporal alternation, for example) may be differentially affected by brain lesions (Pribram, 1958). These experimental results are leading to new views concerning the old question of localization versus non-specificity in cortical functions. Possibly processes separable by surgical techniques are also separable by means of genetic selection. Likewise, behavior which is differentially affected by drugs may prove especially sensitive to heritable changes in body chemistry. Behavior genetics will profit from a closer relationship to other branches of experimental psychology, and it can reciprocate by providing additional tools for the analysis of behavior.

Summary. Genetic effects upon behavior are sometimes mediated through metabolic lesions which interfere with a specific enzymatic reaction. Partial genetic blocks have also been implicated as causes of behavioral variability, but the evidence for this is less clear.

Endocrine disorders are generally correlated with behavioral changes, but this does not mean that quantity of hormone—provided it is within the normal range—has critical effects upon behavior. Heritable variations in target-organ sensitivity are probably more important than variations in hormone output as sources of individual psychological differences.

Except for gross defects which impair normal functioning, little is known of the behavioral significance of structural variation in the nervous system. The relationships of neuron density and patterning to individual psychological differences may be worth exploring.

The search for more suitable units of behavioral description for use in genetic studies has converged on factor analysis. The method has promise, but must be interpreted with full understanding of the possible genetic meanings of correlation coefficients.

A working model for the gene-behavioral character relationship emphasizes the non-congruence of the two levels of description. Non-congruence implies multiple-factor control of psychological traits and the existence of complex gene interactions in the development of phenotypes. In spite of this complexity the evidence for lawful genetic effects upon behavior has been amply demonstrated. Further analysis of the gene-character relationship may be possible from experiments in which genotypes are manipulated and phenotypic effects measured.

References

Abood, L. G., and Gerard, R. W. Phosphorylation defect in the brains of mice susceptible to audiogenic seizure. In: *Biochemistry of the Developing Nervous System*, H. Waelsch, ed. New York: Academic Press, 467–472, 1955.

Agar, W. E., Drummond, F. H., and Tiegs, O. W. Third report on a test of McDougall's lamarckian experiment on the training of rats. *J. exp. Biol.* **25**, 103–122 (1948).

Agar, W. E., Drummond, F. H., Tiegs, O. W., and Gunson, M. M. Fourth (final) report on a test of McDougall's lamarckian experiment on the training of rats. *J. exp. Biol.* **31**, 308–321 (1954).

Allee, W. C., Emerson, A. E., Park, O., Park, T., and Schmidt, K. P. *Principles of Animal Ecology*. Philadelphia: Saunders, 1949.

Allen, G. Genetic aspects of mental disorder. In: *The Nature and Transmission of the Genetic and Cultural Characteristics of Human Populations*. New York: Milbank Foundation, 112–121, 1957.

Allen, G. Patterns of discovery in the genetics of mental deficiency, *Amer. J. ment. Defic.* **62**, 840–849 (1958).

Allen, G., and Baroff, G. S. Mongoloid twins and their siblings. *Acta. Genet.* **5**, 294–326 (1955).

Allison, A. C. Aspects of polymorphism in man. *Cold Spring Harbor Symp. Quant. Biol.* **20**, 239–255 (1955).

Allport, G. W. *Personality, a Psychological Interpretation*. New York: Holt, 1937.

Alström, C. H. A study of epilepsy in its clinical, social and genetic aspects. *Acta. Psychiat. Neurol. Suppl.* **63**, 1–284 (1950).

Amin, A., Chai, C. K., and Reineke, E. P. Differences in thyroid activity of several strains of mice and F_1 hybrids. *Amer. J. Physiol.* **191**, 34–36 (1957).

Anastasi, A. The nature of psychological traits. *Psychol. Rev.* **55**, 127–138 (1948).

Anastasi, A. *Psychological Testing*. New York: Macmillan, 1954.

Anastasi, A. *Differential Psychology*, 3rd ed. New York: Macmillan, 1958a.

Anastasi, A. Heredity, environment and the question "how?" *Psychol. Rev.* **65**, 197–208 (1958b).

Anastasi, A., and Foley, J. P. Jr. A proposed reorientation in the heredity-environment controversy. *Psychol. Rev.* **55**, 239–249 (1948).

Anastasi, A., and Foley, J. P. Jr. *Differential Psychology*. New York: Macmillan, 1949.

Anastasi, A., Fuller, J. L., Scott, J. P., and Schmitt, J. R. A factor analysis of the performance of dogs on certain learning tests. *Zoologica* **40**, 33–46 (1955).

Anderson, E. E. The interrelationship of drives in the male albino rat. I. Intercorrelations of measures of drives. *J. comp. Psychol.* **24**, 73–118 (1937).

Anderson, E. E. The interrelationship of drives in the male albino rat. II. Intercorrelations between 47 measures of drives and of learning. *Comp. Psychol. Monogr.* **14**, No. 6, 1–119 (1938a).

Anderson, E. E. The interrelationship of drives in the male albino rat. III. Interrelations among measures of emotional, sexual and exploratory behavior. *J. genet. Psychol.* **53**, 335–352 (1938b).

Anderson, L. D., and Scheidmann, N. V. A study of triplets. *Genet. Psychol. Monogr.* **14**, 93–176 (1933).

Anderson, O. D. The spontaneous neuro-muscular activity of various pure breeds of dog and of inter-breed hybrids of the first and second generation. *Amer. J. Physiol.* **126**, 422–423 (1939).

Anliker, J., and Mayer, J. An operant conditioning technique for studying feeding-fasting patterns in normal and obese mice. *J. appl. Physiol.* **8**, 667–670 (1956).

Antonitis, J. J., Crary, D. D., Sawin, P. B., and Cohen, C. Sound-induced seizures in rabbits. *J. Hered.* **45**, 279–284 (1954).

Ashby, W. An approach to the solution of mental dysfunction through brain enzyme studies. *Amer. J. Psychiat.* **106**, 491–496 (1950).

Ashley-Montagu, M. F. Comments on comparative studies in human biology. *Science* **100**, 383–384 (1944).

Ashman, R. The inheritance of simple musical memory. *J. Hered.* **43**, 51–52 (1952).

Ashman, R. A. An attempt to discover behavioral effects of single-gene differences in mice. Student report, R. B. Jackson Lab. Bar Harbor, Maine, 1957.

Bagg, H. J. Individual differences and family resemblances in animal behavior. *Amer. Nat.* **50**, 222–236 (1916).

Bagg, H. J. Individual differences and family resemblances in animal behavior. *Arch. Psychol.* **6**, 1–58 (1920).

Bakwin, R. M. Similarities and differences in identical twins. *J. genet. Psychol.* **38**, 373–397 (1931).

Baltzer, F., Einige Beobachtungen über Sicheltänze bei Bienenvölkern verchiedener Herkunst. *Arch. Julius Klaus Stiftung* **27**, 197–206 (1952).

Banker, H. J. Genealogical correlation of student ability. *J. Hered.* **19**, 503–508 (1928).

Barahal, H. S. Is dementia praecox hereditary? *Psychiat. Quart.* **19**, 478–502 (1945).

Barnicot, N. A. Taste deficiency for phenylthiourea in African Negroes and Chinese. *Ann. Eugenics* **15**, 248–254 (1950).

Barnicot, N. A., Harris, H., and Kalmus, H. Taste thresholds of further eighteen compounds and their correlation with P. T. C. thresholds. *Ann. Eugenics* **16**, 119–128 (1951).

Barr, M. L., and Hobbs, G. E. Chromosomal sex in transvestites. *Lancet* **266**, 1109–1110 (1954).

Barrows, S. L. The inheritance of the ability to taste brucine. *M. A. Thesis*, Stanford University, 1945.

Bartels, E. D. Endocrine disorders. In: *Clinical Genetics*, A. Sorsby, ed. London: Butterworth, 529–543, (1953).

Bartlett, M. J. Note on the development of correlation among genetic components of ability. *Ann. Eugenics* **7**, 299–302 (1937).

Bassett, G. C. Habit formation in a strain of albino rats with less than normal brain weight. *Behav. Monogr.* **2**, 1–46 (1914).

Bastock, M. A gene mutation which changes a behaviour pattern. *Evolution* **10**, 421–439 (1956).

Bastock, M., and Manning, A. The courtship of *Drosophila melanogaster*. *Behaviour* **8**, 85–111 (1955).

Bateman, A. J. Analysis of data on sexual isolation. *Evolution* **3**, 174–177 (1949).

Beach, F. A. A review of physiological and psychological studies of sexual behavior in mammals. *Physiol. Rev.* **27**, 240–307 (1947).

Beach, F. A. *Hormones and Behavior*. New York: Paul B. Hoeber, 1948.

Beadle, G. W. Biochemical Genetics. *Chem. Rev.* **37**, 15–96 (1945).

Beadle, G. W. Genes and biological enigmas. In: *Science in Progress*, 6th ser. New Haven: Yale Univ. Press, Ch. 9, 184–249, 1949.

Beadle, G. W. What is a gene? *Amer. Inst. biol. Sci. Bull.* **5**, 15 (1955).

Bemmelen, J. F. van. Heredity of mental faculties. *Proc. Roy. Acad. Sci., Amsterdam* **30**, 769–795 (1927).

Benda, C. E. *Mongolism and Cretinism*. New York: Grune and Stratton, 1946.

Bender, L., and Gruggett, A. E. A study of certain epidemiological factors in a group of children with childhood schizophrenia. *Amer. J. Orthopsychiat.* **26**, 131–143 (1956).

Benedict, S. R. Uric acid in its relations to metabolism. *J. lab. & clin. Med.* **2**, 1–15 (1916).

Bevan, W., Levy, G. W., Whitehouse, J. M., and Bevan, J. M. Spontaneous aggressiveness in two strains of mice castrated and treated with one of three androgens. *Physiol. Zool.* **30**, 341–349 (1957).

Bickel, H., Boscott, R. J., and Gerrard, J. Observations on the biochemical error in phenylketonuria and its dietary control. In: *Biochemistry of the Developing Nervous System*, H. Waelsch, ed. New York: Academic Press, 417–430, 1955.

Bindra, D., and Thompson, W. R. An evaluation of defecation and urination as measures of fearfulness. *J. comp. physiol. Psychol.* **46**, 43–45 (1953).

Blair, W. F. Interbreeding of natural populations of vertebrates. *Amer. Nat.* **85**, 9–30, 1951.

Blair, W. F., and Howard, W. E. Experimental evidence of sexual isolation between three forms of mice of the cenospecies, *Peromyscus maniculatus*. *Contr. Lab. vert. Biol. Univ. Mich.* **26**, 1–19 (1944).

Blakeslee, A. F. Unlike reaction of different individuals to fragrance in verbena flowers. *Science* **48**, 298–299 (1918).

Blakeslee, A. F., and Fox, A. L. Our different taste worlds. *J. Hered.* **23**, 96–110 (1932).

Blakeslee, A. F., and Salmon, M. R. Odour and taste blindness. *Eugen. News* **16**, 105–109 (1931).

Blakeslee, A. F., and Salmon, T. N. Genetics of sensory thresholds: individual taste reactions for different substances. *Proc. Nat. Acad. Sci.* **21**, 84–90 (1935).

Blatz, W. E. Collected studies on the Dionne quintuplets. *Univ. Toronto Stud. Child Dev. Series*, 1937.

Bleuler, M. Der Rorschachsche Formdeutversuch bei Geschwistern. *Zeitschr. ges. Neurol. Psychiat.* **118**, 366–398 (1929).

Bleuler, M. Vererbungsprobleme bei Schizophrenen. *Ztschr. ges. Neurol Psychiat.* **127**, 321–388 (1930).

Bleuler, M. The delimitation of influences of environment and heredity on mental disposition. *Char. & Pers.* **1**, 286–300 (1933).

Bleuler, M. Untersuchungen aus den Grenzgebiet zwischen Psychopathologie und Endokrinologie. *Arch. f. Psychiat.* **180**, 271–528 (1948).

Blewett, D. B. An experimental study of the inheritance of intelligence. *J. ment. Sci.* **100**, 922–933 (1954).

Böök, J. A. A genetic and neuropsychiatric investigation of a North Swedish population. *Acta Genet.* **4**, 1–100, 345–414 (1953a).

Böök, J. A. Schizophrenia as a gene mutation. *Acta genet.* **4**, 133–139 (1953b).

Böök, J. A., and Reed, S. C. Empiric risk figures in mongolism. *J. Amer. Med. Assoc.* **143**, 730–732 (1950).

Böök, J. A., Schut, J. W., and Reed, S. C. A clinical and genetic study of microcephaly. *Amer. J. ment. Defic.* **57**, 637–660 (1953).

Borberg, A. Clinical and genetic investigations into tuberous sclerosis and Recklinghausen's neurofibromatosis. *Acta. Psychiat. Neurol. Supp.* **71** (1951).

Borges, P. R., and Kvedar, B. J. A mutation producing resistance to several transplantable neoplasms in the C57 black strain of mice. *Cancer Res.* **12**, 19–24 (1952).

Borgström, C. A. Eine Serie von kriminellen Zwillingen. *Arch. Rassenbiol.* **33**, 334–343 (1939).

Bosch, J. van den Microcephaly in the Netherlands. *Acta. genet.* **7**, 398–402 (1957).

Boyd, W. C. Taste reactions to antithyroid substances. *Science* **112**, 153 (1950).

Boyd, W. C. Taste blindness to phenylthiocarbamide and related compounds. *Psychol. Bull.* **48**, 71–74 (1951).

Boyd, W. C., and Boyd, L. G. Sexual and racial variations in ability to taste phenylthiocarbamide with some data on inheritance. *Ann. Eugen.* **8**, 45–51 (1937).

Bracken, H. v. Vererbungheit und Ordnung in Binnenleben von Zwillingspaaren. *Ztschr. pädag. Psychol.* **37**, 65–81 (1936).

Bracken, H. v. Wahrnehmungstaüschungen und Scheinbare Nachbildgröze bei Zwillingen. *Arch. ges. Psychol.* **103**, 203–230 (1939).

Bracken, H. v. Erbbiologische untersuchungen uber die Handschrifteigenart. *Dtsch. Zeitsch. ges. gerichte. Med.* **33**, 64–72 (1940a).

Bracken, H. v. Untersuchungen an Zwillingen uber die quantitativen und qualitativen Merkmale des Schreibdrucks. *Zeitschr. Ang. Psychol.* **58**, 367–384 (1940b).

Bramwell, B. S. The Order of Merit: the holders and their kindred. *Eugen. Rev.* **36**, 84–91 (1944).

Brand, H. *The Study of Personality.* New York: Wiley, 1954.

Broadhurst, P. L. Determinants of emotionality in the rat. I. Situational factors. *Brit. J. Psychol.* **48**, 1–12 (1957).

Broadhurst, P. L. Determinants of emotionality in the rat. II. Antecedent factors. *Brit. J. Psychol.* **49**, 12–20 (1958a).

Broadhurst, P. L. Determinants of emotionality in the rat. III. Strain differences. *J. comp. physiol. Psychol.* **51**, 55–59 (1958b).

Broadhurst, P. L. Studies in psychogenetics. In: *Experiments in Personality,* H. J. Eysenck, ed. London: Routledge & Kegan Paul, 1960.

Brockhausen, K. Ueber erbbiologische Untersuchungen involutiver Psychosen, inbesondere über erstmalig in der Involution auftretende Melancholien. *Zeitschr. ges. Neurol. Psychiat.* **157**, 17–34 (1937).

Brockhausen, K. Erbbiologische utersuchungen uber depressive Psychosen des Rückbildungsalters. *Allg. Zeitschr. Psychiat.* **112**, 179–183 (1939).

Brody, D. Twin resemblances in mechanical ability, with reference to the effects of practice on performance. *Child Dev.* **8**, 207–216 (1937).

Brody, E. G. Genetic basis of spontaneous activity in the albino rat. *Comp. psychol. Monog.* **17**, No. 5., 1–24 (1942).

Brody, E. G. A note on the genetic basis of spontaneous activity in the albino rat. *J. comp. physiol. Psychol.* **43**, 281–288 (1950).

Brown, F. A. Jr., and Hall, B. U. The directive influence of light upon *Drosophila melanogaster* and some of its eye mutants. *J. exp. Zool.* **74**, 205–221 (1936).

Brown, F. W. Heredity in psychoneuroses. *Proc. Roy. Soc. Med.* **35**, 785–790 (1942).

Brugger, C. The genetic uniformity of mental deficiency without marked physical signs. *Proc. 7th internat. Congr. Genet. Cambridge,* p. 82 (1939).

Brugger, C. Die genetische Einheitlichkeit der klinisch unkomplizierten Schwach-sinnformen. *Schweiz. Archiv. Neurol. Psychiat.* **45**, 140–145 (1940).

Brunner, W. Über den Vererbungs der verschiedenen Typen der angeborenen Rotgrünblindheit. *Graefe's Arch. Ophthalmol.* **124**, 1–52 (1930).

Burks, B. S. The relative influence of nature and nurture upon mental development; a comparative study of foster parent-foster child resemblance and true parent-true child resemblance. *27th Yearbook Nat. Soc. Stud. Educ.* (Part I) 219–316 (1928).

Burks, B. S. Review of twins. A study of heredity and environment. *J. abnorm. soc. Psychol.* **33**, 128–133 (1938).

Burks, B. S. A study of identical twins reared apart under differing types of family relationship. In: *Studies in Personality.* Q. McNemar and M. A. Merrill, eds. New York: McGraw-Hill, Ch. 3, 1942.

Burlingame, M., and Stone, C. P. Family resemblances in maze-learning ability of white rats. *27th Yearbook Nat. Soc. Stud. Educ.* (Part I) 89–99 (1928).

Burns, M. *The Genetics of the Dog.* Edinburgh: Commonwealth Agric. Bur., 1952.

Burrows, W. H., and Byerly, T. C. The effect of certain groups of environmental factors upon the expression of broodiness. *Poultry Sci.* **17**, 324–330 (1938).

Burt, C. The inheritance of mental ability. *Amer. Psychol.* **13**, 1–15 (1958).

Burt, C., and Howard, M. The multifactorial theory of inheritance and its application to intelligence. *Brit. J. stat. Psychol.* **9**, 95–131 (1956).

Byrns, R., and Healy, J. The intelligence of twins. *J. genet. Psychol.* **49**, 474–478 (1936).

Carmena, M. Schreibdruck bei Zwillingen, *Zeitschr. ges. Neurol. Psychiat.* **103**, 744–752 (1935).

Carr, R. M., and Williams, C. D. Exploratory behavior of three strains of rats. *J. comp. physiol. Psychol.* **50**, 621–623 (1957).

Carter, H. D. Family resemblances in verbal and numerical abilities. *Genet. Psychol. Monogr.* **12**, 1–104 (1932).

Carter, H. D. Twin similarities in personality traits. *J. genet. Psychol.* **43**, 312–321 (1933).

Carter, H. D. Twin similarities in emotional traits. *Char. & Pers.* **4**, 61–78 (1935).

Carter, H. D. Resemblance of twins in speed of association. *Psychol. Bull.* **36**, 641 (abst.) 1939.

Carter, H. D. Ten years of research on twins: contributions to the nature-nurture problem. *39th Yearbook Nat. Soc. Stud. Educ.* (Part I) Bloomington, Ill.: Public School Pub. Co., 235–255, (1940).

Caspari, E. On the biological basis of adaptedness. *Amer. Scientist* **39**, 441–451 (1951).

Caspari, E. Genetic basis of behavior. In: *Behavior and Evolution,* Roe and Simpson, eds. New Haven: Yale Univ. Press, 103–127 (1958).

Castle, W. E. *Mammalian Genetics.* Cambridge: Harvard Univ. Press, 1940.

Castle, W. E. Influence of certain color mutations on body size in mice, rats and rabbits. *Genetics* **26,** 177–191 (1941).

Cattell, R. B. *The Description and Measurement of Personality.* New York: World Book Co., 1946.

Cattell, R. B. Research designs in psychological genetics with special reference to the multiple variance method. *Amer. J. hum. Genetics* **5,** 76–93 (1953).

Cattell, R. B. The chief invariant psychological and psycho-physical functional unities found by P-technique. *J. clin. Psychol.* **11,** 319–343 (1955).

Cattell, R. B. *Theory and Method in Psychological Genetics.* (Privately circulated manuscript) 1956.

Cattell, R. B., Blewett, D. B., and Beloff, J. R. The inheritance of personality. *Amer. J. human Genetics* **7,** 122–146 (1955).

Cattell, R. B., and Malteno, E. V. Contributions concerning mental inheritance. V. Temperament. *J. genet. Psychol.* **57,** 31–47 (1940).

Cattell, R. B., Stice, G. F., and Kristy, N. F. A first approximation to nature-nurture ratios for eleven primary personality factors in objective tests. *J. abn. soc. Psychol.* **54,** 143–159 (1957).

Cattell, R. B. and Willson, J. L. Contributions concerning mental inheritance. I. Of intelligence. *Brit. J. educ. Psychol.* **8,** 129–149 (1938).

Chai, C. K., Amin, A., and Reineke, E. P. Thyroidal iodine metabolism in inbred and F_1 hybrid mice. *Amer. J. Physiol.* **188,** 499–502 (1957).

Chamberlain, H. D. The inheritance of left handedness. *J. Hered.* **19,** 557–559 (1928).

Charles, E. Collateral and ancestral correlation for sex-linked transmission irrespective of sex. *Genetics* **27,** 97–104 (1933).

Chase, H. W. On the inheritance of acquired modifications of behavior. *Amer. J. Psychol.* **28,** 175–190 (1917).

Childs, B., and Sidbury, J. B. A survey of genetics as it applies to problems in medicine. *Pediatrics* **20,** 177–218 (1957).

Child, I. L. The relation of somatotype to self-ratings on Sheldon's temperamental traits. *J. Pers.* **18,** 440–453 (1950).

Chow, K. L., and John, E. R. Effects of intracerebral injection of anticholinesterase drugs on behavior in rats. *Science* **128,** 781–782 (1958).

Clark, E., Aronson, L. R., and Gordon, M. Mating behavior patterns in two sympatric species of Xiphophorin fishes: their inheritance and significance in sexual isolation. *Bull. Amer. Mus. Nat. Hist. N. Y.* **103,** 135–226 (1954).

Clark, F. H. Geotropic behavior on a sloping plane of arboreal and non-arboreal races of mice of the genus *Peromyscus. J. Mammal.* **17,** 44–47 (1936).

Cloudman, A. M., and Bunker, L. E. Jr. The varitint-waddler mouse. *J. Hered.* **36,** 259–263 (1945).

Cobb, M. V. A preliminary study of the inheritance of arithmetical abilities. *J. educ. Psychol.* **8,** 1–20 (1917).

Coburn, C. A. Heredity of wildness and savageness in mice. *Behav. Monogr.* **4,** (5), 1–71 (1922).

Cohen, J., and Ogden, D. P. Taste blindness to phenyl-thio-carbamide as a function of saliva. *Science* **110,** 532–533 (1949a).

Cohen, J., and Ogden, D. P. Taste blindness to phenyl-thio-carbamide and related compounds. *Psychol. Bull.* **46**, 490–498 (1949*b*).

Cole, J. Paw preference in cats related to hand preference in animals and man. *J. comp. physiol. Psychol.* **48**, 137–140 (1955).

Cole, W. H. Note on the relation between the photic stimulus and the rate of locomotion in *Drosophila*. *Science* **55**, 678–679 (1922).

Conrad, H. S. On kin resemblances in physique vs. intelligence. *J. educ. Psychol.* **22**, 376–382 (1931).

Conrad, H. S., and Jones, H. E. A second study of family resemblances in intelligence: environmental and genetic implications of parent-child and sibling correlations in the total sample. *Yearbook Nat. Soc. Stud. Educ.* **39**, (Part II) 97–141 (1940).

Conrad, K. Erbanlage und Epilepsie. Untersuchung an einer serie von 253 Zwillingspaaren. *Zeitschr. ges. Neurol. Psychiat.* **153**, 271–326 (1935).

Conrad, K. Ergebnisse einer Nachkommenschaftuntersuchung an Epileptikern. *Zeitschr. ges. Neurol. Psychiat.* **159**, 521–528 (1937).

Crawford, M. P. The social psychology of the vertebrates. *Psychol. Bull.* **36**, 407–446 (1939).

Crew, F. A. E. Inheritance of educability. A first report on an attempt to examine Prof. McDougall's conclusions relating to his experiment for the testing of the hypothesis of Lamarck. *Proc 6th internat. Cong. Gen.* **1**, 121–134 (1932).

Crew, F. A. E. A repetition of McDougall's Lamarckian experiment. *J. Genet.* **33**, 61–102 (1936).

Cromwell, H., and Rife, D. C. Dermatoglyphics in relation to functional handedness. *Hum. Biol.* **14**, 516–526 (1942).

Crook, M. N., and Thomas, M. Family relationships in ascendance-submission. *Pub. Univ. Calif. Educ. Philos. & Psychol.* **1**, 189–192 (1934).

Crook, M. N. Intra-family relationship in personality test performance. *Psychol. Rec.* **1**, 479–502 (1937).

Crowe, F. W., Schull, W. J., and Neel, J. V. *Multiple Neurofibromatosis.* Springfield, Ill.: Thomas, 1956.

Crozier, W. J., and Pincus, G. Analysis of the geotropic orientation of young rats. *J. gen. Physiol.* **13**, I, II. 57–119 (1929). **15**, III. 201–242 (1931). **15**, IV. 243–256 (1931). **15**, V. 421–436 (1932). **15**, VI. 437–462 (1932). **20**, X. 111–144 (1936).

Cunha, A. B. da, Dobzhansky, T., and Sokoloff, A. On food preferences of sympatric species of Drosophila. *Evolution* **5**, 97–101 (1951).

Curtis, R. L. Quantitative measurement of hereditary circling behavior in the BUD and BUE mouse strains. *Physiol. Zool.* **29**, 299–308 (1956).

Dahlberg, G. *Mathematical Methods for Population Genetics.* New York: Interscience Press, 1947.

Dahlberg, G. Biometric evaluation of findings. In: *Clinical Genetics*, A. Sorsby, ed. London: Butterworth, 83–100, 1953.

Damon, A. Physique in hereditary mental defect; anthropometric study of 97 "Old American" female morons. *Hum. Biol.* **13**, 459–472 (1941).

Danforth, C. H. Relation of genic and endocrine factors in sex. In: *Sex and Internal Secretions.* E. Allen, ed. Baltimore: Williams & Wilkins, Ch. 6, 1939.

Darke, R. A. Heredity as an etiological factor in homosexuality. *J. nerv. ment. Dis.* **107**, 251–268 (1948).

Davenport, C. B., and Scudder, T. M. *Naval Officers; their heredity and development.* Washington: Carnegie Inst., 1918.

Davis, B. D. Genetic and environmental control of enzyme formation. *Proc. Assoc. Res. nerv. ment. Dis.* **33**, 23–38 (1954).

Dawson, W. M. Inheritance of wildness and tameness in mice. *Genetics* **17**, 296–326 (1932).

Dember, W. N., and Kristofferson, A. B. The relation between free alcohol consumption and susceptibility to audiogenic seizures. *Quart. J. Stud. Alc.* **16**, 86–95 (1955).

Dempster, E. R., and Lerner, I. M. Heritability of threshold characters. *Genetics* **35**, 212–236 (1950).

Denenberg, V. H. Learning differences in two separated lines of mice. *Science* **130**, 451–452 (1959).

Dice, L. R. Inheritance of waltzing and of epilepsy in mice of the genus *Peromyscus*. *J. Mammal.* **16**, 25–35 (1935).

Dice, L. R. The importance of cooperative studies of the biology of man. *Science* **99**, 457–461 (1944).

Dickerson, G. E., and Gowen, J. W. Hereditary obesity and efficient food utilization in mice. *Science* **105**, 496–498 (1947).

Dobzhansky, T. The Genetic Nature of Differences among Men. In: *Evolutionary Thought in America*, S. Persons, ed. New Haven: Yale Univ. Press, 86–155, 1950.

Dobzhansky, T. The biological concept of heredity as applied to man. In: *The Nature and Transmission of the Genetic and Cultural Characteristics of Human Populations*. New York: Milbank Memorial Fund, 11–19, 1957.

Dobzhansky, T., and Allen, G. Does natural selection continue to operate in modern mankind? *Amer. Anthropol.* **58**, 591–604 (1956).

Dobzhansky, T., and Koller, P. An experimental study of sexual isolation in *Drosophila*. *Biol. Zentralbl.* **58**, 589–607 (1938).

Dobzhansky, T., and Ashley-Montagu, M. F. Natural selection and the mental capacities of mankind. *Science* **105**, 587–590 (1947).

Dobzhansky, T., and Streisinger, C. Experiments on sexual isolation in Drosophila. II. Geographic strains of *D. prosaltans*. *Proc. Nat. Acad. Sci.* **30**, 340–345 (1944).

Dunn, L. G. *Genetics in the 20th Century*. New York: Macmillan, 1951.

Dürrwachter, G. Untersuchungen uber Phototaxis und Geotaxis einiger *Drosophila* —Mutanten nach Aufzucht in verschiedenen Lichtbedingungen. *Zeitschr. Tierpsychol.* **14**, 1–28 (1957).

Earle, E. L. The inheritance of ability to learn to spell, *Columbia Univ. Contrib. Phil., Psychol. & Educ.* **2**, 41–44 (1903).

Eckle, C., and Ostermeyer, G. Erbcharacterologische Zwillungsuntersuchungen. *Beitr. Z. angew. Psychol.* **82**, 255 (1939).

Elderton, E. M. A summary of the present position with regard to the inheritance of intelligence. *Biometrika* **14**, 378–408 (1923).

Elsässer, G. Endogen geisteskranken Elternpaare und ihre Nachkommen. *Zeitschr. ges. Neurol. Psychiat.* **165**, 108–112 (1939).

Elsässer, G. *Die Nachkommen geisteskranken Elternpaare*. New York: Stechert-Haffner, 1952.

Ermisch, H. Psychophysische und psychologische Untersuchungen an verschiedenen Hühnerrassen. *Zeitschr. Psychol.* **137**, 209–244 (1936).

Essen-Möller, E. Psychiatrische untersuchungen an einer Serie von Zwillingen. *Acta Psychiat. Neurol. Suppl.* **23** (1941).

Essen-Möller, E. *Psychiatrische Geisteskranken Elternpaare*. Stuttgart: Thieme, 1952.

Etkin, W. Social behavior and the evolution of man's mental faculties. *Amer. Naturalist* **88,** 129–142 (1954).

Eysenck, H. J. *Dimensions of Personality.* London: Routledge & Kegan Paul, 1947.

Eysenck, H. J. Criterion analysis—an application of the hypothetico-deductive method to factor analysis. *Psychol. Rev.* **57,** 38–53 (1950).

Eysenck, H. J. Neuroticism in twins. *Eugen. Rev.* **43,** 79–82 (1951).

Eysenck, H. J. The inheritance of extraversion-introversion. *Acta Psychologica* **12,** 95–110 (1956).

Eysenck, H. J. The continuity of abnormal and normal behavior. *Psychol. Bull.* **55,** 429–432 (1958).

Eysenck, H. J., and Prell, D. B. The inheritance of neuroticism: an experimental study. *J. ment. Sci.* **97,** 441–465 (1951).

Falek, A. Handedness, a family study. *Amer. J. hum. Genet.* **11,** 52–62 (1959).

Farris, E. J., and Yeakel, E. H. The susceptibility of albino and gray Norway rats to audiogenic seizures. *J. comp. Psychol.* **35,** 73–80 (1943).

Farris, E. J., and Yeakel, E. H. Emotional behavior of gray Norway and Wistar albino rats. *J. comp. Psychol.* **38,** 109–117 (1945).

Fennell, R. A. The relation between heredity, sexual activity, and training to dominance-subordination in game cocks. *Amer. Nat.* **79,** 142–151 (1945).

Ferriman, D. The genetics of true oxycephaly and acrocephalosyndactyly. *Proc. 7th intern. Genet. Cong. Cambridge* 120, (1939).

Finch, F. H. A study of the relation of age interval to degree of resemblance of siblings in intelligence. *J. genet. Psychol.* **43,** 389–404 (1933).

Finlayson, A. The Dach family. A study in the hereditary lack of emotional control. *Eugen. Record Office. Bull.* **15,** (1916).

Fish, H. S., and Richter, C. P. Comparative number of fungiform and foliate papillae on tongues of domestic and wild Norway rats. *Proc. Soc. Exp. Biol.* **63,** 352–353 (1946).

Fisher, A. E. Maternal and sexual behavior induced by intracranial chemical stimulation. *Science* **124,** 228–229 (1956).

Fisher, R. A. The correlation between relatives on the supposition of Mendelian inheritance. *Trans. Roy. Soc. Edinb.* **52,** 399–433 (1918).

Flanagan, J. C. *Factor Analysis in the Study of Personality.* Stanford, Calif.: Stanford Univ. Press, 1935.

Fölling, A. Uber Auscheidung von Phenylbrenztraubensaüre in den Harn als Stoffwechselanomalie in Verbindung mit Imbezillität. *Zeitschr. f. physiol. Chem.* **227,** 169–176 (1934).

Forster, M. C. A study of father-son resemblance in vocational interests and personality traits. *Ph.D. Thesis, Univ. Minn.,* 1931.

Fox, A. L. The relationship between chemical constitution and taste. *Proc. Nat. Acad. Science* **18,** 115–120 (1932).

Franceschetti, A. Première observation d'une fratrie issue de deux daltoniens de type different. *Bull. schweiz. Akad. de med. Wissensch.* **5,** 227–232 (1949).

Franceschetti, A., and Klein, D. Two families with parents of different types of red-green blindness. *Acta genet.* **7,** 255–259 (1957).

Frary, L. G. Enuresis; A genetic study. *Amer. J. Dis. Child.* **49,** 557–578 (1935).

Fraser, F. C. Recent advances in genetics in relation to pediatrics. *J. Pediatrics,* **52,** 734–757 (1958a).

Fraser, F. C. Genetic counseling in some common pediatric diseases. In: *The Pediatric Clinics of North America.* Philadelphia: W. B. Saunders, 1958b.

Fredericson, E. The wall-seeking tendency in three inbred mouse strains (*Mus musculus*). *J. genet. Psychol.* **82**, 143–146 (1953).

Fredericson, E., and Birnbaum, E. A. Competitive fighting between mice with different hereditary backgrounds. *J. genet. Psychol.* **85**, 271–280 (1954).

Freedman, D. G. Constitutional and environmental interactions in rearing of four breeds of dogs. *Science* **127**, 585–586 (1958).

Freeman, F. N. *Mental Tests.* New York: Houghton Mifflin, 1926.

Freeman, F. N., Holzinger, K. J., and Mitchell, B. C. The influence of environment on the intelligence, school achievement, and conduct of foster-children. *Yearbook Nat. Soc. Stud. Educ.* **27**, (Part I) Ch. 9 (1928).

Fremming, K. H. *Morbid risk of mental diseases and other mental abnormalities in an average Danish population.* Copenhagen: Munksgaard, 1947.

Friedman, M., and Byers, S. O. Observations concerning the causes of the excess excretion of uric acid in the Dalmatian Dog. *J. biol. Chem.* **175**, 727–735 (1948).

Frings, H., and Frings, M. Otitis media and audiogenic seizures in mice. *Science* **113**, 689–690 (1951).

Frings, H., and Frings, M. The production of stocks of albino mice with predictable susceptibilities to audiogenic seizures. *Behaviour* **5**, 305–319 (1953).

Frings, H., Frings, M., and Hamilton, M. Experiments with albino mice from stocks selected for predictable susceptibilities to audiogenic seizures. *Behaviour* **9**, 44–52 (1956).

Frisch, K. v. *Bees, their Vision, Chemical Senses, and Language.* Ithaca: Cornell Univ. Press. 1950

Frisch, K. v. Orientierungsvermögen und Sprache der Bienen. *Naturwissenschaften* **38**, 105–112 (1951).

Frischeisen-Köhler, I. The personal tempo and its inheritance. *Char. & Pers.* **1**, 301–313 (1933a).

Frischeisen-Köhler, I. *Das personliche Tempo. Eine erbbiologische Untersuchung.* Leipzig: G. Thieme, 1933b.

Fuller, J. L. Gene mechanisms and behavior. *Amer. Naturalist* **85**, 145–157 (1951).

Fuller, J. L. Cross-sectional and longitudinal studies of adjustive behavior in dogs. *Ann. N. Y. Acad. Sci.* **56**, 214–224, (1953).

Fuller, J. L. Hereditary differences in trainability of pure-bred dogs. *J. genet. Psychol.* **87**, 229–238 (1955).

Fuller, J. L. The path between genes and behavioral characters. *Eugen. Quart.* **3**, 209–212 (1956).

Fuller, J. L. The genetic base: pathways between genes and behavioral characters. In: *The Nature and Transmission of the Genetic and Cultural Characteristics of Human Populations.* New York: Milbank Foundation, 101–111, 1957.

Fuller, J. L., Chambers, R. M., and Fuller, R. P. Effects of cortisone and of adrenalectomy on activity and emotional behavior of mice. *Psychosomatic Med.* **18**, 234–242 (1956).

Fuller, J. L., Easler, C., and Smith, M. E. Inheritance of audiogenic seizure susceptibility in the mouse. *Genetics* **35**, 622–632 (1950).

Fuller, J. L., and Jacoby, G. A., Jr. Central and sensory control of food intake in genetically obese mice. *Amer. J. Physiol.* **183**, 279–283 (1955).

Fuller, J. L., and Scott, J. P. Heredity and learning ability in infrahuman mammals. *Eugen. Quart.* **1**, 28–43 (1954).

Fuller, J. L., and Smith, M. E. The kinetics of sound-induced convulsions in some inbred mouse strains. *Amer. J. Physiol.* **172**, 661–670 (1953).

Fuller, J. L., and Williams, E. Gene-controlled time constants in convulsive behavior. *Proc. Nat. Acad. Sci.* **37**, 349–356 (1951).

Galton, F. *English Men of Science. Their Nature and Nurture.* London: Macmillan, 1874.

Galton, F. *Hereditary Genius.* New York: Appleton, 1883a.

Galton, F. *Inquiry into Human Faculty.* London: Macmillan, 1883b.

Gardner, I. C., and Newman, H. H. Mental and physical tests of identical twins reared apart. *J. Hered.* **31**, 119–126 (1940).

Gardner, I. C., and Newman, H. H. Studies of quadruplets. VI. The only living one-egg quadruplets. *J. Hered.* **34**, 259–263 (1943).

Garrod, A. E. *Inborn Errors of Metabolism.* London: Oxford Univ. Press, 1909.

Gates, N., and Brash, H. An investigation of the physical and mental characteristics of a pair of like twins reared apart from infancy. *Ann. Eugen.* **11**, 89–101 (1941).

Gates, R. R. *Human Genetics,* Vols. 1 & 2, New York: Macmillan, 1946.

Gates, W. H. Linkage tests of the new shaker mutation with other factors in the house mouse, *Mus musculus. Amer. Naturalist* **68**, 173–174 (1934).

Gerard, R. W. Biological roots of psychiatry. *Science* **122**, 225–230 (1955).

Gesell, A. The method of co-twin control. *Science* **95**, 446–448 (1942).

Ginsburg, B. E. Genetics and Social Behavior—a theoretical synthesis. *R. B. Jackson Mem. Lab. 20th Comm. Lect.,* Bar Harbor, Maine, 101–124 (1949).

Ginsburg, B. E. Genetics and the physiology of the nervous system. *Proc. Assoc. Res. nerv. ment. Disease,* **33**, 39–56, Baltimore: Williams & Wilkins, 1954.

Ginsburg, B. E. Genetics as a tool in the study of behavior. *Perspect. Biol. Med.* **1**, 397–424 (1958).

Ginsburg, B. E., and Allee, W. C. Some effects of conditioning on social dominance and subordination in inbred strains of mice. *Physiol. Zool.* **15**, 485–506 (1942).

Gjerde, C. M. Parent-child resemblance in vocational interests and personality traits. *Ph.D. Thesis, Univ. of Minn.,* 1949.

Glaser, O. Hereditary deficiencies in sense of smell. *Science* **48**, 647–648 (1918).

Glass, H. B., and Li, C. C. The dynamics of racial intermixture—an analysis based on the American negro. *Amer. J. hum. Genet.* **5**, 1–20, (1953).

Glass, H. B. Genetic aspects of adaptability. *Proc. Assoc. Res. nerv. ment. Dis.* **33**, 367–377 (1954).

Goldschmidt, R. *The Mechanism and Physiology of Sex Determination.* (translated from German by W. J. Dakin) London: Methuen & Co., 1923.

Goldschmidt, R. *Physiological Genetics.* New York: McGraw-Hill, 1938.

Goodale, H. D., Sanborn, R., and White, D. Broodiness in the domestic fowl. Data concerning its inheritance in the Rhode Island Red breed. *Mass. Agr. Exp. Sta. Bull.* **199**, 93–116 (1920).

Goodenough, F. L. *Mental Testing.* New York: Rinehart, 1949.

Gordon, K. The influence of heredity on mental ability. Report of the children's department. *State Board of Control, Calif.,* 1919.

Gottlieb, J. S., Ashby, M. C., and Knott, J. R. Studies in primary behavior disorders and psychopathic personality. II. The inheritance of electrocortical activity. *Amer. J. Psychiat.* **103**, 823–827 (1947).

Gottlober, A. B. The inheritance of brain potentials. *J. exper. Psychol.* **22**, 193–200 (1938).

Gottschaldt, K. Erbpsychologie der elementar Funktionen der Begabung. In: *Handbuch der Erbbiologie des Menschen.* Berlin: Springer 5(1) 445–537, 1939.

Goy, R. W., and Young, W. C. Strain differences in the behavioral responses of female guinea pigs to alpha-estradiol benzoate and progesterone. *Behaviour* **10,** 340–354 (1957a).

Goy, R. W., and Young, W. C. Somatic basis of sexual behavior in guinea pigs. *Psychosomatic Med.* **19,** 144–151 (1957b).

Graham, C. H., and Hsia, Y. Color defect and color theory. *Science* **127,** 675–682 (1958).

Grant, M. *Passing of the Great Race.* New York: Scribner, 1921.

Graves, E. A. Inter-relationships in performance in the albino rat. *J. comp. Psychol.* **22,** 179–186 (1936).

Gray, J. L., and Moshinsky, P. Studies in genetic psychology. The intellectual resemblance of collateral relatives. *Proc. Roy. Soc. Edinb.* **53,** 188–207 (1933).

Griffiths, W. J. Transmission of convulsions in the white rat. *J. comp. Psychol.* **34,** 263–277 (1942).

Griffiths, W. J. Absence of audiogenic seizures in wild Norway and Alexandrine rats. *Science* **99,** 62–63 (1944).

Griffiths, W. J. Audiogenic fits produced by magnesium deficiency in tame domestic Norway rats and in wild Norway and Alexandrine rats. *Amer. J. Physiol.* **149,** 135–141 (1947).

Griffits, C. H. The influence of family on school marks. *School & Soc.* **24,** 713–716 (1926).

Grüneberg, H. *Animal Genetics and Medicine.* New York: Paul B. Hoeber, 1947.

Grüneberg, H. *The Genetics of the Mouse,* 2nd ed. The Hague: Nijhoff, 1952.

Grunt, J. A., and Young, W. C. Differential reactivity of individuals and the response of the male guinea pig to testosterone propionate. *Endocrinology* **51,** 237–249 (1952).

Grunt, J. A., and Young, W. C. Consistency of sexual behavior patterns in individual male guinea pigs following castration and androgen therapy. *J. comp. physiol. Psychol.* **46,** 138–144 (1953).

Guggenheim, K., and Mayer, J. Studies of pyruvate and acetate metabolism in the hereditary obesity-diabetes syndrome in mice. *J. Biol. Chem.* **198,** 259–265 (1952).

Guhl, A. M., and Eaton, R. C. Inheritance of aggressiveness in the fowl. *Poultry Sci.* **27,** 665 (1948).

Gun, W. T. J. *Studies in Hereditary Ability.* London: Allen & Unwin, 1928.

Gun, W. T. J. The heredity of the Tudors. *Eugen. Rev.* **22,** 111–116 (1930a).

Gun, W. T. J. The heredity of the Stewarts. *Eugen. Rev.* **22,** 195–201 (1930b).

Haldane, J. B. S. A method for investigating recessive characters in man. *J. Genet.* **25,** 251–255 (1932).

Haldane, J. B. S. Suggestions as to the quantitative measurement of rates of evolution. *Evolution* **3,** 51–56 (1949).

Haldane, J. B. S. *The Biochemistry of Genetics.* New York: Macmillan, 1954.

Hall, C. S. Emotional behavior in the rat. I. Defection and urination as measures of individual differences in emotionality. *J. comp. Psychol.* **18,** 385–403 (1934).

Hall, C. S. Emotional behavior in the rat. III. The relationship between emotionality and ambulatory activity. *J. comp. Psychol.* **22,** 345–352 (1936).

Hall, C. S. The inheritance of emotionality. *Sigma Xi Quart.* **26,** 17–27 (1938).

Hall, C. S. Temperament: a survey of animal studies. *Psychol. Bull.* **38,** 909–943 (1941).

Hall, C. S. Genetic differences in fatal audiogenic seizures between two inbred strains of house mice. *J. Hered.* **38,** 2–6 (1947).

Hall, C. S. The genetics of behavior. In: *Handbook of Experimental Psychology,* S. S. Stevens, ed. New York: Wiley, 304–329, 1951.

Hall, C. S., and Klein, S. J. Individual differences in aggressiveness in rats. *J. comp. Psychol.* **33,** 371–383 (1942).

Hall, C. S., and Lindsay, M. The relation of the thyroid gland to the spontaneous activity of the rat. *Endocrinology* **22,** 66–79 (1938).

Hall, C. S., and Lindzey G. *Theories of Personality.* New York: Wiley, 1957.

Hallgren, B. Specific dyslexia (congenital word blindness) *Acta Psychiat. Neurol. Scand. Supp.* **65,** 1–287 (1950).

Hallgren, B. Enuresis, a clinical and genetic study. *Acta Psychiat. Neurol. Scand. Supp.* **114,** 1–159 (1957).

Harlow, H. F. Mice, monkeys, men, and motives. *Psychol. Rev.* **60,** 23–32 (1953).

Harris, G. W., Michael, R. P., and Scott, P. P. Neurological site of action of stilbesterol in eliciting sexual behaviour. In: *Neurological Basis of Behaviour,* Ciba Foundation Symposium. Boston: Little Brown, 236–251, 1958.

Harris, H., and Kalmus, H. Chemical specificity in genetical differences of taste sensitivity. *Ann. Eugen.* **15,** 32–45 (1949).

Harris, H., Kalmus, H., and Trotter, W. R. Taste sensitivity to phenylthiourea in goitre and diabetes. *Lancet* **2,** 1038–1039 (1949).

Harris, V. T. An experimental study of habitat selection by prairie and forest races of the deermouse, *Peromyscus maniculatus. Contr. Lab. Vert. Biol., Univ. Mich.* **56,** 1–53 (1952).

Hart, H. Correlations between intelligence quotients of siblings. *School & Society* **20,** 382 (1924).

Haskins, C. P., and Haskins, E. F. Note on the inheritance of behavior patterns for food selection and cocoon spinning in F_1 Hybrids of *Callosamia promethea* × *C. angulifera. Behaviour* **13,** 89–95 (1958).

Hays, F. A. Characteristics of non-broody and intense broody lines of Rhode Island Reds. *Mass. Agr. Exp. Sta. Bull.* No. 311 (1933).

Hays, F. A. Inheritance of broodiness in Rhode Island Reds. *Mass. Agr. Exp. Sta. Bull.* No. 377 (1940).

Hebb, D. O., and Thompson, W. R. The social significance of animal studies. In: *Handbook of Social Psychology,* G. Lindzey, ed. Cambridge: Addison-Wesley, 1954.

Hebb, D. O., and Williams, K. A method of rating animal intelligence. *J. gen. Psychol.* **34,** 59–65 (1946).

Hermann, E. Messungen an Handschrift-problem von Zwillingspaaren unter 14 Jahren. *Zeitschr. Psychol.* **147,** 238–255 (1939).

Hermann, L., and Hogben, L. The intellectual resemblance of twins. *Proc. Roy. Soc. Edinb.* **53,** 105–129 (1933).

Herndon, C. N. Genetics of the lipidoses. *Proc. Assoc. nerv. ment. Dis.* **33,** 239–258 (1954).

Heron, W. T. The inheritance of maze learning ability in rats. *J. comp. Psychol.* **19,** 77–89 (1935).

Heron, W. T. The inheritance of brightness and dullness in maze learning ability in the rat. *J. genet. Psychol.* **59,** 41–49 (1941).

Heron, W. T., and Skinner, B. F. The rate of extinction in maze-bright and maze-dull rats. *Psychol. Rec.* **4,** 11–18 (1940).

Heron, W. T., and Yugend, S. Basal metabolism and maze learning in rats. *J. genet. Psychol.* **48,** 471–474 (1936).

Herskovits, M. J. Comparative studies in human biology. *Science* **100**, 50–51 (1944).

Herter, K. Das thermotaktische Optimum bei Nagetieren, ein mendelndes Art-und Rassenmerkmal. *Zeitschr. vergl. Physiol.* **23**, 605–650 (1936).

Herter, K. Die Beziehungen zwischen Vorzugstemperatur und die Hautbeschaffenheit ber Mäusen. *Zoöl. Anz. Suppl.* **11**, 48–55 (1938).

Herter, K., and Sgonina, K. Vorzugstemperatur und Hautbeschaffenheit bei Mäusen. *Zeitschr. vergl. Physiol.* **26**, 366–415 (1938).

Heston, W. E. Development of inbred strains in the mouse and their use in cancer research. *R. B. Jackson Mem. Lab. 20th Commen. Lect.* Bar Harbor, Maine, 1949.

Hildreth, G. H. The resemblance of siblings in intelligence and achievement. *Teachers College, Columbia Univ., Cont. to Educ.* **186**, 1–65 (1925).

Hildreth, G. H. The development and training of hand dominance: I. Characteristics of handedness. *J. genet. Psychol.* **75**, 197–220 (1949). II. Developmental tendencies in handedness. **75**, 221–254 (1949). III. Origin of handedness and lateral dominance. **75**, 255–275 (1949). IV. Developmental problems associated with handedness. **76**, 39–100 (1950).

Hill, D., and Watterson, D. Electroencephalographic studies of psychopathic personalities. *J. Neur. Psychiat.* **5**, 47–65 (1942).

Hinde, R. A. The behaviour of certain Cardueline F_1 inter-species hybrids. *Behaviour* **9**, 202–213 (1956).

Hirsch, J., and Boudreau, J. C. The heritability of phototaxis in a population of *Drosophila melanogaster*. *J. comp. physiol. Psychol.* **51**, 647–651 (1958).

Hirsch, J., and Tryon, R. C. Mass screening and reliable individual measurement in the experimental behavior genetics of lower organisms. *Psychol. Bull.* **53**, 402–410 (1956).

Hirsch, N. D. M. *Twins, Heredity and Environment.* Cambridge: Harvard Univ. Press, 1930.

Hoch, P. H., and Zubin, J., eds. *Depression.* New York: Grune & Stratton, 1954.

Hoch, P. H., and Zubin, J., eds. *Psychopathology of Childhood.* New York: Grune & Stratton, 1955.

Hoffeditz, E. L. Family resemblances in personality traits. *J. soc. Psychol.* **5**, 214–227 (1934).

Hoffman, H. *Familienpsychosen in schizophrenen Erbkreis.* Berlin: Karger, 1926.

Hofstetter, H. W. Accommodative convergence in identical twins. *Amer. J. Optom.* **25**, 480–491, 1948.

Hofstetter, H. W., and Rife, D. C. Miscellaneous optometric data on twins. *Amer. J. Optom.* **30**, 139–150 (1953).

Hogben, L. The correlation of relatives on the supposition of sex-linked transmission. *J. Genet.* **26**, 418–432 (1932a).

Hogben, L. The factorial analysis of small families with parents of undetermined genotype. *J. Genet.* **26**, 75–79 (1932b).

Hogben, L. The limits of applicability of correlation techniques in human genetics. *J. Genet.* **27**, 379–406 (1933a).

Hogben, L. A matrix notation for Mendelian populations. *Proc. Roy. Soc. Edinb.* **53**, 7–25 (1933b).

Hogben, L. *An Introduction to Mathematical Genetics.* New York: Norton, 1946.

Holt, S. B. Genetics of dermal ridges: inheritance of total finger ridge-count. *Ann. Eugen.* **17**, 140–161 (1952).

Holt, S. B. Quantitative genetics of dermal ridge-patterns on fingers. *Proc. First Int. Cong. Hum. Genet., Acta genet.* **6**, 473–476 (1957).

Holzinger, K. J. The relative effect of nature and nurture influences on twin differences. *J. educ. Psychol.* **20**, 241–248 (1929).

Hopkins, C. Y. Taste differences in compounds having the NCS linkage. *Canad. J. Res. B.* **20**, 268–273 (1942).

Hörmann-Heck, S. v. Untersuchungen über den Erbgang einiger Verhaltensweisen bei Grillen bastarden. *Zeitschr. Tierpsychol.* **14**, 137–183 (1957).

Horowitz, N. H., and Leupold, U. Some recent studies bearing on the one gene–one enzyme hypothesis. *Cold Spring Harbor Symposia Quant. Biol.* **16**, 65–74 (1951).

Howells, T. H. The hereditary differential in learning—a reply to F. A. Pattie. *Psychol. Rev.* **53**, 302–305 (1946).

Huestis, R. R., and Otto, T. P. The grades of related students. *J. Hered.* **18**, 225–226 (1927).

Hughes, K. R., and Zubek, J. P. Effect of glutamic acid on the learning ability of bright and dull rats. I. Administration during infancy. *Canad. J. Psychol.* **10**, 132–138 (1956).

Hughes, K. R., and Zubek, J. P. Effect of glutamic acid on the learning ability of bright and dull rats. II. Duration of the effects. *Canad. J. Psychol.* **11**, 182–184 (1957).

Hull, C. L. *Principles of Behavior.* New York: Appleton-Century-Crofts, 1943.

Hull, C. L. *Essentials of Behavior.* New Haven: Yale Univ. Press, 1951.

Humphrey, E., and Warner, L. *Working Dogs.* Baltimore: Johns Hopkins Press, 1934.

Hunt, H. F., and Otis, L. S. Conditioned and unconditioned emotional defecation in the rat. *J. comp. physiol. Psychol.* **46**, 378–382 (1953).

Hurst, C. C. A genetic formula for the inheritance of intelligence in man. *Proc. Roy. Soc. Lond.* **112** (Series B) 80–97 (1932).

Hurst, C. C. The genetics of intellect. *Eugen. Rev.* **26**, 33–45 (1934).

Hurst, L. A. Genetics of schizophrenia: Reply to Pastore. *Psychol. Bull.* **48**, 402–412 (1951).

Hurst, L. A. The genetics of schizophrenia: Further rejoinder to Pastore. *Psychol. Bull.* **49**, 544–546 (1952).

Huxley, J. S. *Evolution, the Modern Synthesis.* London: Allen & Unwin, 1942.

Hylkema, B. S. Kinlische Anwendung der Bestimmung der Verschmelzungsfrequenz. *Arch. f. Ophth.* **146**, 110–127; 241–252 (1943).

Jacobs, P., Baikie, A. G., Court-Brown, W. M., and Strong, J. A. The somatic chromosomes in Mongolism. *Lancet*, No. 7071, 710 (1959).

Jacobsen, A. W., and Macklin, M. T. Hereditary sexual precocity; report of a family with 27 affected members. *Pediatrics* **9**, 682–695 (1952).

James, W. T. Dominant and submissive behavior in puppies as indicated by food intake. *J. genet. Psychol.* **75**, 33–43 (1949).

James, W. T. Social organization among dogs of different temperaments, terriers and beagles, raised together. *J. comp. physiol. Psychol.* **44**, 71–77 (1951).

Jervis, G. A. The genetics of phenylpyuvic oligophrenia. *J. ment. Sci.* **85**, 719–762 (1939).

Jervis, G. A. Medical aspects of mental deficiency. *Amer. J. ment. Defic.* **57**, 175–188 (1952).

Jervis, G. A. Phenylpyruvic oligophrenia (phenylketonuria) In: Genetics and the

Inheritance of Integrated Neurological and Psychiatric Patterns. *Proc. Assoc. nerv. ment. Dis.* **33**, 259–282 (1954).

Jolly, R. Die Heredität der Psychosen. *Arch. Psychiat. Nervenkr.* **52**, 492–715 (1913).

Jones, H. E. A first study of parent-child resemblances in intelligence. *Yearbook Nat. Soc. Stud. Educ.* **27** (Part I), 61–72 (1928).

Jones, H. E. Homogamy in intellectual abilities. *Amer. J. Sociol.* **35**, 369–382 (1929).

Jones, H. E. Environmental influences on mental development. In: *Manual of Child Psychology*, 2nd ed. L. Carmichael, ed. New York: Wiley, Ch. 11, 1954.

Jost, H., and Sontag, L. W. The genetic factor in autonomic nervous system function. *Psychosomatic Med.* **6**, 308–310 (1944).

Juel-Nielsen, N., and Mogensen, A. Uniovular twins brought up apart. *Acta genet.* **7**, 430–433 (1957).

Kallman, F. J. *The Genetics of Schizophrenia.* New York: J. J. Augustin, 1938.

Kallman, F. J. The genetic theory of schizophrenia. *Amer. J. Psychiat.* **103**, 309–322 (1946).

Kallman, F. J. Modern concepts of genetics in relation to mental health and abnormal personality development. *Psychiat. Quart.* **21**, 535–553 (1947).

Kallman, F. J. Heredity and constitution in relation to the treatment of mental disorders. In: *Failures in Psychiatric Treatment,* P. H. Hoch, ed. New York: Grune & Stratton, 1948*a*.

Kallman, F. J. Genetics in relation to mental disorders. *J. ment. Sci.* **94**, 250–257, (1948*b*).

Kallman, F. J. Twin and sibship study of overt male homosexuality. *Amer. J. hum. Genet.* **4**, 136–146 (1952*a*).

Kallman, F. J. Comparative twin studies on the genetic aspects of male homosexuality. *J. nerv. ment. Dis.* **115**, 283–298 (1952*b*).

Kallman, F. J. The genetic aspects of mental disorders in the aging. Comparative twin data on the involutional and senile periods of life. *J. Hered.* **43**, 89–96, (1952*c*).

Kallman, F. J. *Heredity in Health and Mental Disorder.* New York: Norton, 1953.

Kallman, F. J. The genetics of psychotic behavior patterns. *Proc. Assoc. Res. nerv. ment. Dis.* **33**, 357–366 (1954*a*).

Kallman, F. J. Genetic Principles in Manic-depressive Psychosis. In: *Depression,* Hoch and Zubin, eds. New York: Grune & Stratton, 1954*b*.

Kallman, F. J., and Barrera, S. E. The heredo-constitutional mechanisms of predisposition and resistance to schizophrenia. *Amer. J. Psychiat.* **98**, 544–550 (1942).

Kallman, F. J., Deporte, J., Deporte, E., and Feingold, L. Suicide in twins and only children. *Amer. J. hum. Genet.* **1**, 113–126 (1949).

Kallman, F. J., Feingold, L., and Bondy, E. Comparative adaptation, social and psychometric data on the life histories of senescent twin pairs. *Amer. J. hum. Genet.* **3**, 65–73 (1951).

Kallman, F. J., and Roth, B. Genetic aspects of preadolescent schizophrenia. *Amer. J. Psychiat.* **112**, 599–606 (1956).

Kallman, F. J., and Sander, G. Twin studies on aging and longevity. *J. Hered.* **39**, 89–96 (1948).

Kallman, F. J., and Sander, G. Studies on senescence. *Amer. J. Psychiat,* **106**, 29–36 (1949).

Kalmus, H. Tune deafness and its inheritance. *Proc. Int. Cong. Genetics, Stockholm,* 605, 1949.

Kanner, L. To what extent is early infantile autism determined by constitutional inadequacies? *Proc. Assoc. Res. nerv. ment. Dis.* **33,** 378–385 (1954).

Kant, O. Incidence of psychosis and other mental abnormalities in families of recovered and deteriorated schizophrenic patients. *Psychiat. Quart.* **16,** 176–186 (1942).

Katz, J. J., and Halstead, W. C. Protein organization and mental functions. *Comp. Psychol. Monogr.* **20,** 1–38 (1950).

Kaufman, L. On the mode of inheritance of broodiness. *Proc. Eighth Wor. Poultry Cong. Copenhagen.* 301–304 (1948).

Keeler, C. E. The association of the black (non-agouti) gene with behavior in the rat. *J. Hered.* **33,** 371–384 (1942).

Keeler, C. E. Coat color, physique, and temperament; materials for the synthesis of hereditary behavior trends in the lower mammals and man. *J. Hered.* **38,** 271–277 (1947).

Keeler, C. E. Materials for the synthesis of hereditary behavior trends in mammals. *J. comp. physiol. Psychol.* **41,** 75–81 (1948).

Keeler, C. E., and King, H. D. Multiple effects of coat color genes in the Norway rat with special reference to temperament and domestication. *J. comp. Psychol.* **34,** 241–250 (1942).

Kempthorne, O. *An Introduction to Genetic Statistics.* New York: Wiley, 1957.

Kennard, M. A. Inheritance of electroencephalogram patterns in children with behavior disorders. *Psychosomatic Med.* **11,** 151–157 (1949).

Kerr, M. Temperamental differences in twins. *Brit. J. Psychol.* **27,** 51–59 (1936).

Kety, S. S. Biochemical theories of schizophrenia. *Science* **129,** 1528–1532, 1590–1596 (1959).

King, J. A. Closed social groups among domestic dogs. *Proc. Amer. Phil. Soc.* **98,** 327–336 (1954).

King, J. A. Maternal behavior and behavioral development in two subspecies of *Peromyscus maniculatus. J. Mammal.* **39,** 177–190 (1958).

Kinsey, A. C., Pomeroy, W., and Martin, C. E. *Sexual Behavior in the Human Male.* Philadelphia: Saunders, 1948.

Kirkpatrick, C. A comparison of generations in regard to attitudes toward feminism. *J. genet. Psychol.* **49,** 343–361 (1936).

Kirkpatrick, C., and Stone, S. Attitude measurement and the comparison of generations. *J. appl. Psychol.* **5,** 564–582 (1935).

Kline, N., and Tenney, A. M. Prognosis in topectomies and lobectomies relative to body type. *A.M.A. Arch. Neurol. Psychiat.* **63,** 323–325 (1951).

Knight, A. R. *Intelligence and Intelligence Tests.* London: Methuen, 1933.

Knott, J. R., Platt, E. B., Coulson, A. M., and Gottlieb, J. S. A familial evaluation of the electroencephalogram of patients with primary behavior disorder and psychopathic personality. *EEG clin. Neurophysiology* **5,** 363–370 (1953).

Knox, C. W., and Olsen, M. W. A test of cross-bred chickens, Single Comb White Leghorns and Rhode Island Reds. *Poultry Sci.* **17,** 193–199 (1938).

Koch, A. B., and Stroud, J. B. Correlations between some personality test scores of siblings and intercorrelations between the scores. *J. educ. Psychol.* **25,** 542–546 (1934).

Koch, H. L. Some measurements of a pair of Siamese twins. *J. comp. Psychol.* **7,** 313–333 (1927).

Koller, J. Beitrag zur Erblichkeitsstatistik der Geisteskranken in Canton Zürich. *Arch. Psychiat.* **27,** 268–294 (1895).

Koller, S. Über den Erbgang der Schizophrenie. *Zeitschr. Neurol. Psychiat.* **164**, 199–228 (1939).

Kramer, E., and Lauterbach, C. E. Resemblances in the handwriting of twins and siblings. *J. educ. Res.* **18**, 149–152 (1928).

Kranz, H. *Lebensschicksale kriminellen Zwillinge.* Berlin: Springer, 1936.

Krech, D. Behavior genetics and biochemistry. Paper presented in symposium on *Genetics and Behavior.* APA Convention, New York. 1957.

Krech, D., Rosenzweig, M. R., Bennett, E. L., and Krueckel, B. A. Enzyme concentrations in the brain and adjustive behavior patterns. *Science* **120**, 994–996 (1954).

Krech, D., Rosenzweig, M. R., and Bennett, E. L. Dimensions of discrimination and level of cholinesterase activity in the cerebral cortex of the rat. *J. comp. physiol. Psychol.* **49**, 261–268 (1956).

Krechevsky, I. Hypotheses vs. "chance" in the presolution period in sensory discrimination learning. *Univ. Calif. Publ. Psychol.* **6**, 27–44 (1932).

Krechevsky, I. The hereditary nature of "hypotheses." *J. comp. Psychol.* **16**, 99–116 (1933).

Kretschmer, E. *Physique and Character.* London: Kegan Paul, 1936.

Kretschmer, E. *Korperbau und Character,* 20th ed. Berlin: Springer. 1951.

Kruse, M. Food satiation curves for maze-bright and maze-dull rats. *J. comp. Psychol.* **31**, 13–21 (1941).

Kulp, D. H., and Davidson, H. H. Sibling resemblance in social attitudes. *J. educ. Sociol.* **7**, 133–140 (1933).

Kuo, Z. Y. A psychology without heredity. *Psychol. Rev.* **31**, 427–448 (1924).

Kuo, Z. Y. The net result of the anti-heredity movement in psychology. *Psychol. Rev.* **36**, 181–199 (1929).

Kuppusawny, B. Laws of heredity in relation to general mental ability. *J. gen. Psychol.* **36**, 29–43 (1947).

Lacey, J. I., Bateman, D. E., and Van Lehn, R. Autonomic response specificity. *Psychosomatic Med.* **15**, 8–21 (1953).

Landauer, W. Rumplessness of chicken embryos produced by injection of insulin and other chemicals. *J. exp. Zool.* **98**, 65–77 (1945).

Lane, P., and Dickie, M. M. Fertile, obese male mice. *J. Hered.* **45**, 56–58 (1954).

Lang, T. Studies on the genetic determination of homosexuality. *J. nerv. ment. Dis.* **92**, 55–64 (1940).

Larsson, T., and Sjögren, T. A methodological, psychiatric and statistical study of a large Swedish rural population. *Acta Psychiat. Neurol., Suppl.* **89**, (1954).

Lashley, K. S. Structural variation in the nervous system in relation to behavior. *Psychol. Rev.* **54**, 325–334 (1947).

Lashley, K. S. In search of the engram. In: *Physiological Mechanisms in Animal Behavior.* New York: Academic Press, 1950.

Lashley, K. S., and Clark, G. The cytoarchitecture of the cerebral cortex of Ateles; a critical examination of architectonic studies. *J. comp. Neurol.* **85**, 223–306 (1946).

Lauterbach, C. E. Studies in twin resemblance. *Genetics* **10**, 525–568 (1925).

Lawrence, E. M. An investigation into the relation between intelligence and inheritance. *Brit. J. Psychol. Monogr. Suppl.* **16**, (1931).

Leiner, M. Kurze Mitteilung uber den Brutpflegeinstinkt von Stichlingsbastarden. *Zeitschr. Tierpsychol.* **4**, 167–169 (1940).

Lennox, W. G., and Cobb, S. *Epilepsy.* Baltimore: Williams & Wilkins, 1928.

Lennox, W. G. Sixty-six twin pairs affected by seizures. *Proc. Assoc. Res. nerv. ment. Disease* **26**, 11–34 (1946).

Lennox, W. G. The heredity of epilepsy as told by relatives and twins. *J. Amer. Med. Assoc.* **146**, 529–536 (1951).

Lennox, W. G., Gibbs, E. L., and Gibbs, F. A. The inheritance of epilepsy as revealed by the electroencephalogram. *J. Amer. Med. Assoc.* **113**, 1002–1003 (1939).

Lennox, W. G., Gibbs, E. L., and Gibbs, F. A. Twins, brain waves and epilepsy. *Arch. Neurol. Psychiat.* 47, 702–704 (1942).

Lennox, W. G., Gibbs, E. L., and Gibbs, F. A. The brain-wave pattern, an hereditary trait. Evidence from 74 "normal pairs of twins." *J. Hered.* **36**, 233–243 (1945).

Lennox, W. G., and Jolly, D. H. Seizures, brain waves and intelligence tests of epileptic twins. *Proc. Assoc. Res. nerv. ment. Dis.* **33**, 325–345 (1954).

Leonhard, K. *Die Defeckt-schizophrenen Krankheitsbilder.* Leipzig: Thieme, 1936.

Leopold, A. S. The nature of heritable wildness in turkeys, *Condor.* **46**, 133–197 (1944).

Lerner, I. M. *Population Genetics and Animal Improvement.* Cambridge, Eng.: University Press, 1950.

Lerner, I. M. *Genetic Homeostasis.* New York: Wiley, 1954.

Lerner, I. M. *The Genetic Basis of Selection.* New York: Wiley, 1958.

Levene, H. A new measure of sexual isolation. *Evolution* **3**, 315–321 (1949).

Levine, L. Studies on sexual selection in mice. I. Reproductive competition between albino and black-agouti males. *Amer. Naturalist* **92**, 21–26 (1958).

Lewis, A. J. The offspring of parents both mentally ill. *Acta. genet.* **7**, 349–365 (1957).

Lewis, W. L., and Warwick, E. J. Effectiveness of selection for body weight in mice. *J. Hered.* **44**, 233–238 (1953).

Li, C. C. *Population Genetics.* Chicago: Univ. Chicago Press, 1955.

Lindenov, H. The Ear. In: *Clinical Genetics,* A. Sorsby, ed. St. Louis: Mosby, 368–381, 1953.

Lindzey, G. Emotionality and audiogenic seizure susceptibility in five inbred strains of mice. *J. comp. physiol. Psychol.* **44**, 389–393 (1951).

Lord, E. M., and Gates, W. H. Shaker, a new mutation in the house mouse, *Mus musculus. Amer. Naturalist* **63**, 435–442 (1929).

Lorenz, K. Der Kumpan in der Umwelt des Vogels. *J. Ornithol.* **83**, 137–213, 289–413 (1935).

Lorenz, K. The comparative method in studying innate behavior patterns. In: *Physiological Mechanisms in Animal Behavior.* New York: Academic Press, 221–268, 1950.

Ludwig, K. Recht-Links Problem in Tierreich und beim Menschen. *Monogr. Gesamtgebiet Physiol. Pflanz. Tiere.* 27, Berlin, 1932.

Lush, J. L. *Animal Breeding Plans.* Ames: Iowa State College Press, 1945.

Lüth, K. F. Über Vererbung und Konstitutionelle Beziehungen der vorwiegenden Form—und Farbbeachtung. *Zeitschr. mensch. Vererb. Konstitutionslehre* **19**, 61–81 (1935).

Luxenburger, H. Vorläufigen Bericht über psychiatrische Serienuntersuchungen an Zwillingen. *Zeitschr. ges. Neurol. Psychiat.* **116**, 297–326 (1928).

Luxenburger, H. Psychiatrische-neurologische Zwillingspathologie. *Zentralbl. ges. Neurol. Psychiat.* **14**, 56–57, 145–180 (1930).

Luxenburger, H. Untersuchungen an schizophrenen Zwillingen und ihren Geschwistern zur Prufung der Realität von Manifestationsschwankungen. *Zeitschr. Neurol. Psychiat.* **154**, 351–394 (1935).

Luxenburger, H. Bemerkungen zum Vortrag von F. Lenz: Medeln die Geisteskrankheiten. *Zeitschr. ind. Abstamm. u. Vererbunglehre* **73**, 505–558 (1937).

Luxenburger, H. Die Schizophrenie und ihr Erbkreis. In: *Hdbk. d. Erbbiologie,* G. Just, ed. **5**. Berlin: Springer, 1939.

Lynn, J. G., and Lynn, D. R. Smile and hand dominance in relation to basic modes of adaptation. *J. abnorm. soc. Psychol.* **38**, 250–276 (1943).

Madsen, I. N. Some results with the Stanford revision of the Binet-Simon tests. *School & Soc.* **19**, 559–562 (1924).

Mahut, H. Breed differences in the dog's emotional behaviour. *Canad. J. Psychol.* **12**, 35–44 (1958).

Maier, N. R. F. Studies of abnormal behavior in the rat. XIV. Strain differences in the inheritance of susceptibility to convulsions. *J. comp. Psychol.* **35**, 327–335 (1943).

Maier, N. R. F., and Glaser, N. M. Studies of abnormal behavior in the rat. V. The inheritance of the "neurotic pattern." *J. comp. Psychol.* **30**, 413–418 (1940).

Mainland, R. C. Absence of olfactory sensation. *J. Hered.* **36**, 143–144 (1945).

Malan, M. Zur Erblichkeit der Orientierungsfähigkeit im Raum. *Zeitschr. Morph. Anthrop.* **39**, 1–23 (1940).

Mandl, A. M. The value of littermate controls in endocrinological research. *Collected Papers* **3**, 49–57. London: Laboratory Animals Bureau, 1955.

Mann, C. W. Intelligence tests and testing. In: *Encyclopedia of Psychology,* P. L. Harriman, ed. New York: Philosophical Library, 1946.

Mardones, R. J. On the relationship between deficiency of B vitamins and alcohol intake in rats. *Quart. J. Stud. Alc.* **12**, 563–575 (1952).

Mardones, R. J., Segovia, N. M., and Hederra, A. D. Heredity of experimental alcohol preference in rats. II. Coefficient of heredity. *Quart. J. Stud. Alc.* **14**, 1–2 (1953).

Marinescu, G., Kreindler, A., and Copelman, L. Essai d'une interpretation physiologique du test psychologique de Rorschach. Son application à l'étude de la dynamique cérébral des jumeaux. *An. Psichol.* **1**, 14–26 (1934).

Martin, R. F., and Hall, C. S. Emotional behavior in the rat. V. The incidence of behavior derangements resulting from air-blast stimulation in emotional and non-emotional strains of rats. *J. comp. Psychol.* **32**, 191–204 (1941).

Mather, K. *Biometrical Genetics.* New York: Dover Publications, 1949.

Mather, K. Comment on Dr. B. Woolf's paper. In: *Quantitative Inheritance,* E. C. R. Reeve, and C. H. Waddington, eds. London: H. M. Stationery Office, 1952.

Mayer, J. Decreased activity and energy balance in the hereditary obesity-diabetes syndrome of mice. *Science* **117**, 504–505 (1953).

Mayer, J., Dickie, M. M., Bates, M. W., and Vitale, J. J. Free selection of nutrients by hereditarily obese mice. *Science* **113**, 745–746 (1951).

Mayr, E. Experiments on sexual isolation in *Drosophila.* VII. The nature of the isolating mechanisms between *D. pseudobscura* and *D. persimilis. Proc. Nat. Acad. Sci.* **32**, 128–137 (1946).

MacArthur, J. W. Selection for small and large body size in the house mouse. *Genetics* **34**, 194–209 (1949).

McClelland, D. C. *Personality.* New York: Dryden Press, 1951.

McDougall, W. An experiment for the testing of the hypothesis of Lamarck. *Brit. J. Psychol.* **17**, 267–304 (1927).

McDougall, W. Fourth report on a Lamarckian experiment. *Brit. J. Psychol.* **28**, 328–345, 365–395 (1938).

McEwen, R. S. The reactions to light and to gravity in *Drosophila* and its mutants. *J. exp. Zool.* **25**, 49–106 (1918).

McEwen, R. S. Relative phototropism of vestigial and wild type *D. melanogaster. Biol. Bull.* **49**, 354–364 (1925).

McLaren, A., and Michie, D. Variability of response in experimental animals. A comparison of the reactions of inbred, F_1 hybrid, and random bred mice to a narcotic drug. *J. Genet.* **54**, 440–455 (1956).

McNemar, Q. Twin resemblances in motor skills and the effect of practice thereon. *J. genet. Psychol.* **42**, 70–97 (1933).

Meggendorfer, F. Ueber die hereditare Disposition zur Dementia senilis. *Zeitschr. Neurol. Psychiat.* **101**, 387–405 (1926).

Meggendorfer, F. Alterspsychosen. In: *Handbuch der Erbbiologie des Menschen*, G. Just, ed. Vol. 5(2) Berlin: J. Springer, 1939.

Merrell, D. J. Selective mating in *Drosophila melanogaster. Genetics* **34**, 370–389 (1949).

Merrell, D. J. Inheritance of manic-depressive psychosis. *A. M. A. Arch. Neurol. Psychiat.* **66**, 272–279 (1951).

Merrell, D. J. Selective mating as a cause of gene frequency changes in laboratory populations of *D. melanogaster. Evolution* **7**, 287–296 (1953).

Merrell, D. J. Dominance of eye and hand. *Hum. Biol.* **29**, 314–328 (1957).

Merriman, C. The intellectual resemblance of twins. *Psychol. Monogr.* **33**, (5), (1924).

Miguel, C. Schreibdruck bei Zwillingen. *Zeitschr. Neurol. Psychiat.* **152**, 19–24 (1935).

Miller, N. E. Experiments on motivation. *Science* **126**, 1271–1278 (1957).

Miller, N. E., Bailey, C. J., and Stevenson, J. A. A. F. Decreased "hunger" but increased food intake resulting from hypothalamic lesions. *Science* **112**, 256–259 (1950).

Mitsuda, H. v. Klinisch-Erbbiologische Untersuchung der Endogen Psychosen. *Acta. Genet.* **7**, 371–377 (1957).

Mjöen, F. Die Bedeutung der Tonhöheunterscheidsempfindlichkeit für die Musikalität und ihr Verhalten bei der Vererbung. *Hereditas* **7**, 161–188 (1925).

Mohr, J. Taste sensitivity to phenylthiourea in Denmark. *Ann. Eugen.* **16**, 282–286 (1951).

Money, J., Hampson, J. G., and Hampson, J. L. An examination of some basic sexual concepts: the evidence of human hermaphroditism. *Bull. Johns Hopkins Hosp.* **97**, 301–319 (1955).

Montgomery, K. C. Exploratory behavior and its relation to spontaneous alternation in a series of maze exposures. *J. comp. physiol. Psychol.* **45**, 287–294 (1952).

Moore, K. L., and Barr, M. L. Nuclear morphology according to sex in human tissues. *Acta Anat.* **21**, 197–208 (1954).

Mordkoff, A. M., and Fuller, J. L. Heritability in activity within inbred and cross-bred mice: A study in behavior genetics. *J. Hered.* **50**, 6–8 (1959).

Moss, F. A. *Comparative Psychology.* New York: Prentice-Hall, 1946.

Munn, N. L. *Handbook of Psychological Research on the Rat.* New York: Houghton Mifflin, 1950.

Munro, S. S., Kosin, I. L., and Macartney, E. L. Quantitative genic hormone inter-actions in the fowl. I. Relative sensitivity of five breeds to an anterior pituitary extract possessing both thyrotropic and gonadotropic properties. *Amer. Naturalist* **77**, 256–273 (1943).

Murphy, G. *Personality: A biosocial approach to origins and structure.* New York: Harpers, 1947.

Nachtsheim, H. Krampfbereitschaft und Genotypus. I. Die Epilepsie der Weissen Wiener Kaninchen. *Zeitschr. mensch. Vererbgs. u. Konstit. lehre* **22**, 791–810 (1939). II. Weitere Untersuchungen zur Epilepsie der Weissen Wiener-Kaninchen **25**, 229–244 (1941). III. Das Verhalten epileptischer und nichtepileptischer Kaninchen im Cardiazokrampf **26**, 22–74 (1942).

Neel, J. V. The detection of the genetic carriers of hereditary disease. *Amer. J. hum. Genet.* **1**, 19–36, 1949.

Neel, J. V., and Schull, W. J. *Human Heredity.* Chicago: Univ. Chicago Press, 1954.

Neu, D. M. A critical review of the literature on "absolute pitch." *Psychol. Bull.* **44**, 249–266 (1947).

Newcomb, T., and Svehla, G. Intra-family relationships in attitude. *Sociometry* **1**, 180–205 (1937).

Newman, H. H. Identical twins: The differences between those reared apart. *Eugen. Rev.* **22**, 29–34 (1930).

Newman, H. H., Freeman, F. N., and Holzinger, K. J. *Twins: A study of heredity and environment.* Chicago: Univ. of Chicago Press, 1937.

Nichols, J. Effects of captivity on adrenal glands of wild Norway rats. *Amer. J. Physiol.* **162**, 5–7 (1950).

Nicolay, E. Messungen an Handschrift-problem von Zwillingspaaren uber 14 Jahren. *Arch. ges. Psychol.* **105**, 275–295 (1939).

Noyes, A. P., and Kolb, L. *Modern Clinical Psychiatry,* 5th ed. Philadelphia: Saunders, 1958.

Oliver, C. P. Mongolism: multiple occurrence in sibships. *Eugen. News* **35**, 35–39 (1950).

Oransky, W. zur Frage über Vererbung der Enuresis nocturna. *Deutsche Zeitschr. Nervenh.* **104**, 308 (1928). Cited by Hallgren, 1957.

Osborn, F. *Preface to Eugenics.* New York: Harper & Bros., 1951.

Øster, J. *Mongolism.* Copenhagen: E. Munksgaard, 1953.

Östlyngen, E. Possibilities and limitations of twin research as a means of solving problems of heredity and environment. *Acta. Psychol.* **6**, 59–90 (1949).

Outhit. M. C. A study of the resemblance of parents and children in general intelligence. *Arch. Psychol.* **149**, 1-60 (1933).

Owen, R. D. Immunogenetic consequences of vascular anastamoses between bovine twins. *Science* **102**, 400–401 (1945).

Parson, W., and Crispell, K. R. Studies of acetate metabolism in the hereditary obesity-diabetes syndrome of mice utilizing C^{14} acetate. *Metabolism* **4**, 227–230 (1955).

Pastore, N. *The Nature-Nurture Controversy.* New York: Kings Crown Press, 1949a.

Pastore, N. The genetics of schizophrenia. *Psychol. Bull.* **46**, 285–302 (1949b).

Pastore, N. Genetics of schizophrenia: a rejoinder. *Psychol. Bull.* **49**, 542–544 (1952).

Patton, R. A. Purulent otitis media in albino rats susceptible to sound-induced seizures. *J. Psychol.* **24,** 313–317 (1947).

Patzig, B. Untersuchungen zur Frage des Erbganges und der Manifestierung schizophrener Erkrankungen. *Zeitschr. Neurol.* **161,** 521–532 (1938).

Pawlowski, A. A., and Scott, J. P. Hereditary differences in the development of dominance in litters of puppies. *J. comp. physiol. Psychol.* **49,** 353–358 (1956).

Pearson, J. S., and Kley, I. B. Discontinuity and correlation. A reply to Eysenck. *Psychol. Bull.* **55,** 433–435 (1958).

Pearson, K. On the laws of inheritance in man. II. On the inheritance of the mental and moral characters in man, and its comparison with the inheritance of the physical characters. *Biometrika* **3,** 131–190 (1904).

Pearson, K. Nature and nurture. In: *Vol. 6, Eugen. Lab. Lect. Series.* London: Dulan, 1910.

Pearson, K. Inheritance of psychical characters. *Biometrika* **12,** 367–372 (1918).

Penrose, L. S. Relative aetiological importance of birth order and maternal age in mongolism. *Proc. Roy. Soc., Lond.* **115,** 431–450 (1934).

Penrose, L. S. Inheritance of phenylpyruvic amentia. *Lancet* **2,** 192–194 (1935).

Penrose, L. S. A search for linkage between the A, B, O agglutinogens and phenylketonuria. *Amer. J. ment. Def.* **50,** 4–7 (1945).

Penrose, L. S. Genetical influences on the intelligence level of the population. *Brit. J. Psychol.* **40,** 128–136 (1950).

Penrose, L. S. The genetical background of common diseases. *Acta. Genet.* **4,** 257–265 (1953).

Penrose, L. S. Observations in the aetiology of mongolism. *Lancet* **2,** 505–509 (1954).

Peterson, T. D. The relationship between certain attitudes of parents and children. *Purdue Univ. Stud. Higher Educ.* **31,** 127–144 (1936).

Petrovsky, S. Erblichkeit und Enuresis nocturna. *Sov. Psichoneur.* **10,** 10 (1934). Cited by Hallgren, 1957.

Phillips, J. C. Note on wildness in ducklings. *J. anim. Behav.* **2,** 363–364 (1912).

Pickford, R. W. The genetics of intelligence. *J. Psychol.* **28,** 129–145 (1949).

Pintner, R. The mental indices of siblings. *Psychol. Rev.* **25,** 252–255 (1918).

Pintner, R., and Forlano, G. Sibling resemblance in two personality tests. *School & Soc.* **42,** 70–72 (1935).

Pittendrigh, C. S. Adaptation, natural selection, and behavior. In: *Behavior and Evolution,* G. G. Simpson and A. Roe, eds. New Haven: Yale Univ. Press, 390–416, 1958.

Planansky, K. Heredity in schizophrenia. *J. nerv. ment. Dis.* **122,** 121–142 (1955).

Pollock, H. M., and Malzberg, B. Hereditary and environmental factors in the causation of manic-depressive psychoses and dementia praecox. *Amer. J. Psychiat.* **96,** 1227–1247 (1940).

Pollock, H. M., Malzberg, B., and Fuller, R. G. Hereditary and environmental factors in the causation of dementia praecox and manic-depressive psychoses. *Psychiat. Quart.* **8,** 77, ibid. **8,** 337 (1934).

Pollock, H. M., Malzberg, B., and Fuller, R. G. *Hereditary and Environmental Factors in the Causation of Manic-depressive Psychoses and Dementia Praecox.* Utica, N. Y.: State Hospital Press, 1939.

Pope, A., Caveness, W., and Livingstone, K. E. Architectonic distribution of acetylcholinesterase in the frontal isocortex of psychotic and nonpsychotic patients. *A. M. A. Arch. Neurol. Psychiat.* **68,** 425–443 (1952).

Popham, R. E. A critique of the genetotropic theory of the etiology of alcoholism. *Quart. J. Stud. Alc.* **14,** 228–237 (1953).

Portenier, L. Twinning as a factor influencing personality. *J. educ. Psychol.* **30,** 542–547 (1939).

Potter, J. H. Dominance relations between different breeds of domestic hens. *Physiol. Zool.* **22,** 261–280 (1949).

Poulsen, H. Morphological and ethological notes on a hybrid between a domestic duck and a domestic goose. *Behaviour* **3,** 99–104 (1950).

Powers, M. E. The central nervous system of winged but flightless *D. melanogaster. J. exp. Zool.* **115,** 315–340 (1951).

Pribram, K. H. Neocortical function in behavior. In: *Biological and Biochemical Bases of Behavior,* Harlow & Woolsey, eds. Madison: Univ. Wisconsin Press, 151–172, 1958.

Price, B. Homogamy and the intercorrelation of capacity traits. *Ann. Eugen.,* **7,** 22–27 (1936).

Price, B. Primary biases in twin studies: a review of prenatal and natal difference producing factors in monozygotic pairs. *Amer. J. hum. Genet.* **2,** 293–352 (1950).

Punnett, R. C., and Bailey, P. G. Genetic studies in poultry. II. Inheritance of egg colour and broodiness. *J. Genet.* **10,** 277–292 (1920).

Rabin, A. I. Genetic factors in the selection and rejection of Szondi pictures: a study of twins. *Amer. J. Orthopsychiat.* **22,** 551–556 (1952).

Ramaley, F. Inheritance of left-handedness. *Amer. Naturalist* **47,** 730–738 (1913).

Raney, E. Reversed lateral dominance in identical twins. *J. exp. Psychol.* **23,** 304–312 (1938).

Raney, E. Brain potentials and lateral dominance in identical twins. *J. exp. Psychol.* **24,** 21–39 (1939).

Reed, J. G. A study of the alcohol consumption and amino-acid excretion of rats of different inbred strains. *Univ. Texas Publ.,* No. 5109, 144–149 (1951).

Reed, S. C. Counseling in medical genetics, *Acta. genet.* **7,** 473–480 (1957).

Reed, S. C., Williams, C. M., and Chadwick, L. E. Frequency of wing beat as a character for separating races, species and geographical varieties in *Drosophila. Genetics* **27,** 349–361 (1942).

Reeve, E. C. R., and Waddington, C. H. *Quantitative Inheritance.* London: H. M. Stationery Office, 1952.

Reinöhl, F. *Die Vererbung der geistigen Begabung.* Munich-Berlin: Lehmanns, 1939.

Rensch, B. Increase of learning capability with increase of brain size. *Amer. Naturalist* **90,** 81–95 (1956).

Rhine, J. B., and McDougall, W. Third report on a Lamarckian experiment. *Brit. J. Psychol.* **24,** 213–235 (1933).

Richards, O. W. The reaction to light and its inheritance in grain-weevils, *Calandra granaria. Proc. Zool. Soc., London* **121,** 311–314 (1951).

Richardson, H. M. Studies of mental resemblance between husbands and wives and between friends. *Psychol. Bull.* **36,** 104–120 (1939).

Richardson, J. S. The correlation of intelligence quotients of siblings of the same chronological age levels. *J. juv. Res.* **20,** 186–198 (1936).

Richter, C. P. Domestication of the Norway rat and its implications for the problems of stress. *Proc. Assoc. Res. nerv. ment. Dis.* **29,** 19–47 (1950).

Richter, C. P. Domestication of the Norway rat and its implications for the study of genetics in man. *Amer. J. hum. Genet.* **4,** 273–285 (1952).

Richter, C. P. The effects of domestication and selection on the behavior of the Norway rat. *J. Nat. Canc. Inst.* **15**, 727–738 (1954).

Richter, C. P., and Rice, K. K. Comparison of the effects produced by fasting on gross bodily weight of wild and domesticated Norway rats. *Amer. J. Physiol.* **179**, 305–308 (1954).

Richter, C. P., Rogers, P. V., and Hall, C. E. Failure of salt replacement therapy in adrenalectomized recently captured wild Norway rats. *Endocrinology* **46**, 233–242 (1950).

Richter, C. P., and Uhlenhuth, E. H. Comparison of the effects of gonadectomy on spontaneous activity of wild and domesticated Norway rats. *Endocrinology* **54**, 311–322 (1954).

Rife, D. C. Handedness with special reference to twins. *Genetics* **25**, 178–186 (1940).

Rife, D. C. An application of gene frequency analysis to the interpretation of data from twins. *Hum. Biol.* **22**, 136–145 (1950).

Riss, W. Sex drive, oxygen consumption and heart rate in genetically different strains of male guinea pigs. *Amer. J. Physiol.* **180**, 530–534 (1955).

Riss, W., Valenstein, E. S., Sinks, J., and Young, W. C. Development of sexual behavior in male guinea pigs from genetically different stocks under controlled conditions of androgen treatment and caging. *Endocrinology* **57**, 139–146 (1955).

Roberts, E., and Card, L. E. Inheritance of broodiness in the domestic fowl. *Proc. Fifth World. Poult. Cong. Rome,* **2**, 353–358 (1934).

Roberts, J. A. F. Studies on a child population V. The resemblance in intelligence between sibs. *Ann. Eugen.* **10**, 293–312 (1940).

Roberts, J. A. F. The genetics of oligophrenia. *Cong. Int. Psychiat., Paris: Rapports* **6**, 55–117 (1950).

Roberts, J. A. F., Norman, R. M., and Griffiths, R. Studies on a child population: I. Definition of the sample, method of ascertainment, and analysis of the results of a group intelligence test. *Ann. Eugen.* **6**, 319–338 (1935).

Roberts, J. A. F., Norman, R. M., and Griffiths, R. Studies on a child population. III. Intelligence and family size. *Ann. Eugen. Camb.* **8**, 178–215 (1937a). IV. The form of the lower end of the frequency distribution of the Stanford-Binet intelligence quotients and the fall of low intelligence quotients with advancing age. **8**, 319–334 (1937b).

Roderick, T. H. The genetics of variation in cholinesterase activity in the cerebral cortex of the rat. *Doctoral dissertation, U. of Calif., Berkeley.* 1958.

Roff, M. Intra-family resemblances in personality characteristics. *J. Psychol.* **30**, 199–227 (1950).

Rogers, P. V., and Richter, C. P. Anatomical comparison between the adrenal glands of wild Norway, wild Alexandrine, and domestic Norway rats. *Endocrinology* **42**, 46–55 (1948).

Rosanoff, A. J., Handy, L. M., and Plesset, I. R. Etiology of manic-depressive syndromes with special reference to their occurrence in twins. *Amer. J. Psychiat.* **91**, 725–762 (1935).

Rosanoff, A. J., Handy, L. M., and Rosanoff, I. A. Criminality and delinquency in twins. *J. crim. Law and Criminol.* **24**, 923–934 (1934a).

Rosanoff, A. J., Handy, L. M., and Rosanoff, I. A. Etiology of epilepsy with special reference to its occurrence in twins. *A.M.A. Arch. Neurol. Psychiat.* **31**, 1165–1193 (1934b).

Rosanoff, A. J., Handy, L. M., Plesset, I. R., and Brush, S. The etiology of so-called schizophrenic psychoses. *Amer. J. Psychiat.* **91**, 247–286 (1934c).

Rosenberg, R. Heredity in the functional psychoses. *Amer. J. Psychiat.* **101**, 157–165 (1944).

Rosenzweig, M. R., Krech, D., and Bennett, E. L. Brain enzymes and adaptive behavior. In: *Ciba Found. Sympos. Neurological Basis of Behavior.* Boston: Little, Brown & Co., 337–355, 1958.

Ross, S., Ginsburg, B. E., and Denenberg, V. H. The use of the split-litter technique in psychological research. *Psychol. Bull.* **54**, 145–151 (1957).

Rothenbuhler, W. C. Genetics of a behavior difference in honey bees. *Proc. 10th Int. Cong. Genet., Montreal,* **2**, 242 (1958).

Royce, J. R. Factorial analysis of animal behavior. *Psychol. Bull.* **47**, 235–259 (1950).

Royce, J. R. A factorial study of emotionality in the dog. *Psychol. Monogr.* **69** (22) (1955).

Royce, J. R. Factor theory and genetics. *Educ. Psychol. Measurement* **17**, 361–376 (1957).

Rüdin, E. *Zur Vererbung und Neuenstehung der Dementia Praecox.* Berlin: Springer, 1916.

Rüdin, E. Ueber Vererbung geistigen Störungen. *Zeitschr. Neurol. Psychiat.* **81**, 459 ff. (1923).

Rüdin, E. Ein Beitrag zur Frage der Zwangskrankheit, in besonderer ihrer hereditären Beziehungen. *Arch. Psychiat.* **191**, 14–54 (1953).

Rundquist, E. A. The inheritance of spontaneous activity in rats. *J. comp. Psychol.* **16**, 415–438 (1933).

Rundquist, E. A., and Bellis, C. J. Respiratory metabolism of active and inactive rats. *Amer. J. Physiol.* **106**, 670–675 (1933).

Runner, M. N. Inheritance of susceptibility to congenital deformation-embryonic instability. *J. Nat. Cancer. Inst.* **15**, 637–649 (1954).

Runner, M. N., and Gates, A. Sterile, obese mothers. *J. Hered.* **45**, 51–56 (1954).

Russell, E. S. Review of the pleiotropic effects of W-series genes on growth and differentiation. In: *Aspects of Synthesis and Order in Growth*, D. Rudnick, ed. Princeton, N. J.: Princeton Univ. Press, 113–126, 1955.

Russell, W. L. Inbred and hybrid animals and their value in research. In: *Biology of the Laboratory Mouse*, G. D. Snell, ed. (reprinted, New York: Dover) 325–348, 1941.

Sadovnikova-Koltzova, M. P. Genetic analysis of temperament of rats. *J. exp. Zool.* **45**, 301–318 (1926).

Sarason, S. B. *Psychological Problems in Mental Deficiency.* New York: Harpers, 1949.

Sarason, S. B., and Gladwin, T. Psychological and cultural problems in mental subnormality. *Genet. Psychol. Monogr.* **57**, 3–289 (1958).

Saudek, R. A British pair of identical twins reared apart. *Char. & Pers.* **3**, 17–39 (1934).

Sawin, P. B., and Curran, R. H. Genetic and physiological background of reproduction in the rabbit. I. The problem and its biological significance. *J. exp. Zool.* **120**, 165–201 (1952).

Sawin, P. B., and Crary, D. D. Genetic and physiological background of reproduction in the rabbit. II. Some racial differences in the pattern of maternal behavior. *Behaviour* **6**, 128–145 (1953).

Schoenheimer, R. *The Dynamic State of the Body Constituents.* Cambridge: Harvard. Univ. Press, 1942.

Schopbach, R. R., Keeler, C. E., and Greenberg, H. A. Some variations in basal metabolic levels of rats. *Growth* **7,** 83–95 (1943).

Schulz, B. Empirische untersuchungen uber die Bedeutung beidseitigen Belastung mit endogenen Psychosen. *Zeitschr. Neurol. Psychiat.* **165,** 97–108 (1939).

Schulz, B. Kinder schizophrenen Elternpaare. *Zeitschr. Neurol. Psychiat.* **168,** 332–381 (1940a).

Schulz, B. Erkrankungshalter schizophrenen Eltern und Kinder. *Zeitschr. Neurol. Psychiat.* **168,** 709–721 (1940b).

Schuster, E., and Elderton, E. M. The inheritance of ability. *Eugen. Lab. Mem.* **1,** 1–42 (1907).

Schut, J. W. The hereditary ataxias. *Proc. Assoc. Res. nerv. ment. Dis.* **33,** 293–324 (1954).

Schwesinger, G. C. *Heredity and Environment.* New York: Macmillan, 1933.

Scott, J. P. Genetic differences in the social behavior of inbred strains of mice. *J. Hered.* **33,** 11–15 (1942).

Scott, J. P. Effects of single genes on the behavior of Drosophila. *Amer. Naturalist* **77,** 184–190 (1943).

Scott, J. P. Genetics as a tool in experimental psychological research. *Amer. Psychol.* **4,** 526–530 (1949).

Scott, J. P. *Animal Behavior.* Chicago: Univ. of Chicago Press, 1958.

Scott, J. P., and Charles, M. S. Genetic differences in the behavior of dogs: a case of magnification by thresholds and by habit formation. *J. genet. Psychol.* **84,** 175–188 (1954).

Scott, J. P., and Fuller, J. L. *Manual of Dog Testing Techniques.* Bar Harbor, Maine: R. B. Jackson Mem. Lab. (mimeographed), 1950.

Scott, J. P., and Fuller, J. L. Research on genetics and social behavior. *J. Hered.* **42,** 191–197 (1951).

Searle, L. V. The organization of hereditary maze-brightness and maze-dullness. *Genet. Psychol. Monogr.* **39,** 279–325 (1949).

Segall, G. Taste-blind identical twins with diabetes and other striking pathological characteristics. *J. Hered.* **39,** 228–232 (1948).

Sen Gupta, N. N. *Heredity in Mental Traits.* London: Macmillan, 1941.

Setterfield, W., Schott, R. G., and Snyder, L. H. Studies in human inheritance. XV. The bimodality of the threshold curve for the taste of phenylthiocarbamide. *Ohio J. Sci.* **36,** 231–235 (1936).

Sheldon, W. H., and Stevens, S. S. *The Varieties of Temperament.* New York: Harper, 1942.

Shields, J. Personality differences and neurotic traits in normal twin school children. A study in psychiatric genetics. *Eugen. Rev.* **45,** 213–246 (1954).

Shields, J. Twins brought up apart. *Eugen. Rev.* **50,** 115–123 (1958).

Siemens, H. W. *Die Zwillingspathologie.* Berlin: Springer, 1924.

Silveira, A. Human genetics as an approach to the classification of mental disease. *Arq. Neuropsichiat.* **10,** 41–46 (1952).

Silverman, W., Shapiro, F., and Heron, W. T. Brain weight and maze learning in rats. *J. comp. Psychol.* **30,** 279–282 (1940).

Sims, V. M. The influence of blood relationship and common environment on measured intelligence. *J. educ. Psychol.* **22,** 56–65 (1931).

Sinnott, E. D., Dunn, L. C., and Dobzhansky, T. *Principles of Genetics.* New York: McGraw-Hill, 1958.

Sirlin, J. L. Vacillans, a neurological mutant in the house mouse linked with brown. *J. Genet.* **54,** 42–48 (1956).

Sjögren, T. Die juvenile amaurotische Idiotie. Klinische und erblichkeitsmedizinische Untersuchungen. *Hereditas* **14,** 197–426 (1931).

Sjögren, T. *Genetic-statistical and Psychiatric Investigations of a West Swedish Population.* Copenhagen: E. Munksgaard, 1948.

Skinner, B. F. A method of maintaining an arbitrary degree of hunger. *J. comp. Psychol.* **30,** 139–145 (1940).

Slater, E. The inheritance of manic-depressive insanity and its relation to mental defect. *J. ment. Sci.* **82,** 626–633 (1936).

Slater, E. Zur Erbpathologie des manisch-depressiven Irreseins: Die Eltern und Kinder von Manisch-Depressiven. *Zeitschr. Neurol. Psychiat.* **163,** 1–47 (1938).

Slater, E. Genetics in psychiatry. *J. ment. Sci.* **90,** 17–35 (1944).

Slater, E. Genetic investigations in twins. *J. ment. Sci.* **99,** 44–52 (1953*a*).

Slater, E. Psychiatry, In: *Clinical Genetics,* A. Sorsby, ed. London: Butterworth 332–349, 1953*b*.

Slater, E. Psychotic and neurotic illnesses in twins. *Medical Research Council, Special Report No. 278.* London: H. M. Stationery Office, 1953*c*.

Slater, E. The monogenic theory of schizophrenia. *Acta Genet.* **8,** 50–56 (1958).

Slome, E. The genetic basis of amaurotic family idiocy. *J. Genet.* **27,** 363–376 (1933).

Smith, G. Psychological tests with twins. *Hereditas* **33,** 420–421 (1947).

Smith, G. Psychological studies in twin differences. *Studia psychologica et paedagogica-Ser. altera Investigations* **3,** Lund: Gleerup, 1949.

Smith, G. Twin differences with reference to the Muller-Lyer illusion. *Lunds Universitet Arsskrift N. F. Aud.* 1. **50,** 1–27 (1953).

Smith, W. I., and Ross, S. The social behavior of vertebrates; a review of the literature (1939–1950) *Psychol. Bull.* **49,** 598–627 (1952).

Snyder, L. H. Inherited taste deficiency. *Science* **74,** 151–152 (1931).

Snyder, L. H. The inheritance of taste deficiency in man. *Ohio J. Sci.* **32,** 436–440 (1932).

Snyder, L. H., and David, P. R. Penetrance and expression. In: *Clinical Genetics,* A. Sorsby, ed. London: Butterworth & Co., 9–26, 1953.

Snyder, L., and Davidson, D. F. Studies in human inheritance, XVIII. The inheritance of taste deficiency to diphenylguanidine. *Eugen. News* **22,** 1–2 (1937).

Sontag, L. W. The genetics of differences in psychosomatic patterns in childhood. *Amer. J. Orthopsychiat.* **20,** 479–489 (1950).

Sorensen, M. I., and Carter, H. D. Twin resemblances in community of free association responses. *J. Psychol.* **9,** 237–246 (1940).

Sorokin, P. A. *Society, Culture and Personality.* New York: Harpers, 1947.

Sorsby, A. *Genetics in Ophthalmology.* London: Butterworth, 1951.

Sorsby, A. The eye, In: *Clinical Genetics,* A. Sorsby, ed. London: Butterworth, 350–367, 1953.

Southwick, W. E. Sterilization policy, economic expendiency and fundamental inheritance, with special reference to the inheritance of the intelligence quotient. *J. ment. Sci.* **85,** 707–718 (1939).

Spearman, C. *The Abilities of Man.* London: Macmillan, 1927.

Spieth, H. T. Mating behavior and sexual isolation in the *Drosophila virilis* species group. *Behaviour* **3,** 105–145 (1951).

Spieth, H. T. Mating behavior within the genus *Drosophila* (Diptera) *Bull. Amer. Mus. Nat. Hist.* **99,** 395–474 (1952).

Srb, A. M., and Owen, R. D. *General Genetics.* San Francisco: W. H. Freeman, 1953.

Stalker, H. D. Sexual isolation studies in the species complex *Drosophila virilis. Genetics* **27,** 238–257 (1942).

Stamm, J. S. Genetics of hoarding: Hoarding differences between homozygous strains of rats. *Jour. comp. physiol. Psychol.* **47,** 157–161 (1954).

Stamm, J. S. Hoarding and aggressive behavior in rats. *J. comp. physiol. Psychol.* **48,** 324–326 (1955).

Stamm, J. S. Genetics of hoarding: II. Hoarding behavior of hybrid and back-crossed strains of rats. *J. comp. physiol. Psychol.* **49,** 349–352 (1956).

Stanton, H. M. The inheritance of specific musical capacities. *Iowa Stud. Psychol.* **8,** 157–204 (1922).

Starch, D. The inheritance of abilities in school studies. *School & Soc.* **2,** 608–610 (1915).

Starch, D. The similarity of brother and sister in mental traits. *Psychol. Rev.* **24,** 235–238 (1917).

Stein, C. Hereditary factors in epilepsy: A comparative study of 1000 institutionalized epileptics and 1115 non-epileptic controls. *Amer. J. Psychiat.* **12,** 989–1037 (1933).

Stephens, F. E., and Thompson, R. B. The care of Millan and George, identical twins reared apart. *J. Hered.* **34,** 109–114 (1943).

Stern, C. *Principles of Human Genetics.* San Francisco: W. H. Freeman, 1949.

Stockard, C. R., Anderson, O. D., and James, W. T. *Genetic and Endocrinic Basis for Differences in Form and Behavior.* Philadelphia: Wistar Inst. Press, 1941.

Stocks, P., and Karn, M. N. A biometric investigation of twins and their brothers and sisters. *Ann. Eugen.* **5,** 1–55 (1933).

Stone, C. P. Wilderness and savageness in rats. In: *Studies in the Dynamics of Behavior.* K. S. Lashley, ed. Chicago: Univ. of Chicago Press, 1932.

Stone, C. P. *Comparative Psychology,* 3rd ed. New York: Prentice-Hall, 1951.

Strandskov, H. H. Human genetics and anthropology. *Science* **100,** 570–571 (1944a).

Strandskov, H. H. Further comments on comparative studies in human biology. *Science* **100,** 146–147 (1944b).

Strandskov, H. H. A twin study pertaining to the genetics of intelligence. *Caryologia Suppl., Att. 9th Internat. Cong. Genet.* 811–813 (1954).

Strandskov, H. H., and Edelen, E. W. Monozygotic and dizygotic twin birth frequencies in the total, the "white" and the "colored" U. S. populations. *Genetics* **31,** 438–446 (1946).

Strecker, E. A. *Fundamentals of Psychiatry.* Philadelphia: Lippincott, 1947.

Streisinger, G. Experiments on sexual isolation in Drosophila. IX. Behavior of males with etherized females. *Evolution* **2,** 187–188 (1948).

Strömgren, E. *Beitrage zur psychiatrischen Erblehre.* Copenhagen: Munksgaard, 1938.

Strömgren, E. Statistical and genetical population studies within psychiatry. *Congrés intern. de Psychiat.,* Vol. 6. Paris: Hermann, 1950.

Strong, E. K., Jr. *Vocational Interests of Men and Women.* Stanford: Stanford Univ. Press, 1943.

Sturtevant, A. H. Experiments on sex recognition and the problem of sexual selection in Drosophila. *J. anim. Behav.* **5,** 351–366 (1915).

Sturtevant, A. H. A gene in *Drosophila melanogaster* that transforms females into males. *Genetics* **30,** 297–299 (1945).

Sünner, P. Die psychoneurologische Belastung bei dem manisch-depressiven Irresein auf grund der Diem-Kollerschen Belastungsberechnung. *Zeitschr. Neurol. Psychiat.* **77**, 453–470 (1922).

Sward, K., and Friedman, M. B. Jewish temperament. *J. appl. Psychol.* **19**, 70–84 (1935).

Szondi, L. Instinct and education: experimental researches on the instinct tendencies of twins. *Psychol. Stud. Univ. Budapest* **3**, 79–111 (1939).

Tallman, G. G. A comparative study of identical and non-identical twins with respect to intelligence resemblances. *27th Yearbook Nat. Soc. Stud. Educ.* (Part 1) Bloomington, Ill.: Public School Pub. Co., 83–86 (1928).

Tarcsay, I. Testing of will-temperament in twins. *Psychol. Stud. Univ. Budapest* **3**, 79–111 (1939).

Tebb, G., and Thoday, J. M. Reversal of mating preferences by crossing strains of *Drosophila melanogaster.* Nature **177**, 707 (1956).

Terry, C. S. *The Origin of the Family of Bach Musicians.* Oxford: Oxford Press, 1929.

Terry, M. C. Diabetes mellitus in identical negro twins and the association of taste-blindness and diabetes. *J. Hered.* **39**, 279–280 (1948).

Terry, M. C., and Segall, G. The association of diabetes and taste blindness. *J. Hered.* **38**, 135–137 (1947).

Thompson, W. R. Exploratory behavior as a function of hunger in "bright" and "dull" rats. *J. comp. physiol. Psychol.* **46**, 323–326 (1953a).

Thompson, W. R. The inheritance of behavior; behavioral differences in fifteen mouse strains. *Canad. J. Psychol.* **7**, 145–155 (1953b).

Thompson, W. R. The inheritance and development of intelligence. *Proc. Assoc. Res. nerv. ment. Dis.* **33**, 209–231 (1954).

Thompson, W. R. The inheritance of behavior. Activity differences in five inbred mouse strains. *J. Hered.* **47**, 147–148 (1956).

Thompson, W. R. Influence of prenatal maternal anxiety on emotionality in young rats. *Science* **125**, 698–699 (1957a).

Thompson, W. R. Traits, factors and genes. *Eugen. Quart.* **4**, 8–16 (1957b).

Thompson, W. R. Social Behavior. In: *Behavior and Evolution,* G. G. Simpson and A. Roe, eds. New Haven: Yale Univ. Press, 1958.

Thompson, W. R., and Bindra, D. Motivational and emotional characteristics of "bright" and "dull" rats. *Canad. J. Psychol.* **6**, 116–122 (1952).

Thompson, W. R., and Fuller, J. L. The inheritance of activity in the mouse. *Amer. Psychol.* **12**, 433 (1957).

Thompson, W. R., and Kahn, A. Retroaction effects in the exploratory activity of "bright" and "dull" rats. *Canad. J. Psychol.* **9**, 173–182 (1955).

Thorndike, E. L. *The Measurement of Twins.* New York: Science Press, 1905.

Thorndike, E. L. The resemblance of siblings in intelligence. *27th Yearbook Nat. Soc. Stud. Educ.* (Part 1) Bloomington, Ill.: Public School Pub. Co., 41–54, 1928.

Thorndike, E. L. The causation of fraternal resemblance. *J. genet. Psychol.* **64**, 249–264 (1944a).

Thorndike, E. L. The resemblance of siblings in intelligence test scores. *J. genet. Psychol.* **64**, 265–267 (1944b).

Thorne, F. C. Approach and withdrawal behavior in dogs. *J. genet. Psychol.* **56**, 265–272 (1940).

Thurstone, L. L. *Multiple Factor Analysis.* Chicago: Univ. of Chicago Press, 1947.

Thurstone, T. G., Thurstone, L. L., and Strandskov, H. H. *A Psychological Study of Twins.* Chapel Hill: Univ. North Carolina, Psychometric Laboratory. No. 4, 1953.

Tinbergen, N. *The Study of Instinct.* Oxford: Oxford Univ. Press, 1951.

Tinbergen, N., and Perdeck, A. C. On the stimulus situation releasing the begging response in the newly hatched herring gull chick (*Larus a. argentatus*, Pontopp). *Behaviour* **3**, 1–38 (1950).

Tjio, J. H., and Levan, A. The chromosome number of man. *Hereditas* **42**, 1–6 (1956).

Tollman, J., and King, J. A. The effect of testosterone propionate on aggression in male and female C57BL/10 mice. *Brit. J. anim. Behav.* **4**, 147–149 (1956).

Tolman, E. C. The inheritance of maze learning in rats. *J. comp. Psychol.* **4**, 1–18 (1924).

Tolman, E. C. *Purposive Behavior in Men and Animals.* New York: Appleton-Century-Crofts, 1932.

Tomasson, H. Investigation on heredity of manic-depressive psychosis in Iceland. *Proc. 7th Int. Genet. Congr. Camb.* 298 (1941).

Trankell, A. Aspects of genetics in psychology. *Amer. J. hum. Genet.* **7**, 264–276 (1955).

Tredgold, A. F. *A Textbook of Mental Deficiency,* 7th ed. Baltimore: Williams & Wilkins, 1947.

Trimble, H. C., and Keeler, C. E. The inheritance of "high uric acid excretion" in dogs. *J. Hered.* **29**, 281–289 (1938).

Tryon, R. C. Studies in individual differences in maze ability. II. The determination of individual differences by age, weight, sex and pigmentation. *J. comp. Psychol.* **12**, 1–22 (1931).

Tryon, R. C. Studies in individual differences in maze ability. VI. Disproof of sensory components: experimental effects of stimulus variation. *J. comp. Psychol.* **28**, 361–415 (1939).

Tryon, R. C. Genetic differences in maze-learning ability in rats. *39th Yearbook Nat. Soc. Stud. Educ.* (Part 1) Bloomington, Ill.: Public School Pub. Co., 111–119 (1940a).

Tryon, R. C. Studies in individual differences in maze ability. VII. The specific components of maze ability and a general theory of psychological components. *J. comp. physiol. Psychol.* **30**, 283–335 (1940b).

Tryon, R. C. Individual differences. In: *Comparative Psychology,* F. A. Moss, ed. New York: Prentice-Hall, Ch. 12, 1942.

Tryon, R. C. Discussion of Hirsch, J. Recent developments in behavior genetics and differential psychology. *Dis. nerv. Syst. Monog. Suppl.* **19**(7), 17–24 (1958).

Tyler, F. H. The inheritance of neuromuscular disease. *Proc. Assoc. Res. nerv. ment. Dis.* **33**, 283–292 (1954).

Ushijima, Y. On the inheritance of intravert and extravert characters. *Jap. J. Psychol.* **10**, 225–239 (1935).

Utsurikawa, N. Temperamental differences between outbred and inbred strains of the albino rat. *J. anim. Behav.* **7**, 111–129 (1917).

Valenstein, E. S., Riss, W., and Young, W. C. Sex drive in genetically heterogenous and highly inbred strains of male guinea pigs. *J. comp. physiol. Psychol.* **47**, 162–165 (1954).

Valenstein, E. S., Riss, W., and Young W. C. Experiential and genetic factors in the organization of sexual behavior in male guinea pigs. *J. comp. physiol. Psychol.* **48**, 397–403 (1955).

Vandenberg, S. G. The hereditary abilities study. *Eugen. Quart.* **3**, 94–99 (1956).

Vernon, M. D. Innate factors as causes of disability in reading. In: *Backwardness in Reading.* Cambridge, Eng.: The University Press. Ch. V., 1957.

Vernon, P. E. Intelligence tests in population studies. *Eugen. Quart.* **1**, 221–224 (1954).

Verschuer, O. v. Twin research from the time of Galton to the present day. *Proc. Roy. Soc. London B* **128**, 62–81 (1939).

Verplanck, W. S. Since learned behavior is innate, and vice versa, what now? *Psychol. Rev.* **62**, 139–144 (1955).

Vicari, E. M. Mode of inheritance of reaction time and degrees of learning in mice. *J. exp. Zool.* **54**, 31–88 (1929).

Waaler, G. H. M. Über die Erblichkeitsverhältnisse der verschiedenen Arten von angeborener Rotgrünblindheit. *Zeitschr. Abstgs. Vererbslehre.* **45**, 279–333 (1927).

Waardenburg, P. J. Character traits in twins. *Mensch. en Maatshappig.* **5**, 17–34 (1929).

Waddington, C. H. *An Introduction to Modern Genetics.* London: Allen & Unwin, 1950.

Waddington, C. H., Woolf, B., and Perry, M. M. Environment selection by Drosophila mutants. *Evolution* **8**, 89–96 (1954).

Wagner, R. P., and Mitchell, H. K. *Genetics and Metabolism.* New York: Wiley, 1955.

Walls, G. L. A branched-pathway schema for the color vision system and some of the evidence for it. *Amer. J. Ophthal.* **39** (Part II) 8–23 (1955).

Walls, G. L., and Mathews, R. W. New methods of studying color blindness and normal foveal color vision. *Univ. Calif. Publ. Psychol.* **7**, 1–172 (1952).

Watson, M. L. The inheritance of epilepsy and of waltzing in Peromyscus. *Contr. Lab. Vert. Biol. Univ. Mich.* **11**, 1–24 (1939).

Weinberg, W. Zur Vererbung bei manisch-depressiven Irrsein. *Zeitschr. ang. Anat.* **6**, 380–388 (1920).

Weinberg, I., and Lobstein, J. Inheritance in schizophrenia. *Acta. Psychiat. et Neurol.* **18**, 93–140 (1943).

Weinberger, H. L. Ueber die hereditären Beziehungen der senilen Demenz. *Zeitschr. Neurol. Psychiat.* **106**, 666–701 (1926).

Weitze, M. *Hereditary Adiposity in Mice and the Cause of this Anomaly.* Copenhagen: Store Nordeske Videnskabsboghandel, 1940.

Weltman, N., and Remmers, H. H. Pupils', parents', and teachers' attitudes, similarities and differences. *Purdue Univ. Stud. Higher Educ.* **56**, 1–50 (1946).

Wenger, M. A. Studies of autonomic balance in Army Air Force personnel. *Comp. psychol. Monogr.* **19**(4) (1948).

Wherry, R. J. Determination of the specific components of maze-ability for Tryon's bright and dull rats by means of factorial analysis. *J. comp. Psychol.* **32**, 237–252 (1941).

Wiener, A. S. Heredity of the agglutinogens M and N. In: *Blood Groups and Blood Transfusions,* 3rd ed. Springfield, Ill.: Thomas, Ch. 14, 1943.

Wildermuth, H. Geschwisterpsychosen. *Zeitschr. Neurol. Psychiat.* **110**, 60–80 (1927).

Williams, C. D. Exploratory behavior of stock and inbred albino rats. *Quart. J. Fla. Acad. Sci.* **19**, 57–60 (1956).

Williams, C. M., and Reed, S. C. Physiological effects of genes: The flight of Drosophila considered in relation to gene mutations. *Amer. Naturalist* **78**, 214–223 (1944).

Williams, R. J. *Biochemical Individuality*. New York: Wiley, 1956.

Williams, R. J., Berry, L. J., and Beerstecher, E., Jr., Individual metabolic patterns, alcoholism, genetotropic diseases. *Proc. Nat. Acad. Sci. Wash.* **35**, 265–271 (1949a).

Williams, R. J., Berry, L. J., and Beerstecher, E., Jr. Biochemical individuality. III. Genetotropic factors in the etiology of alcoholism. *Arch. Biochem.* **23**, 275–290 (1949b).

Williams, R. J., Berry, L. J., and Beerstecher, E., Jr. The concept of genetotropic disease. *Lancet* **258**, 287–289 (1950).

Williams, R. J., Pelton, R. B., and Rogers, L. L. Dietary deficiencies in animals in relation to voluntary alcohol and sugar consumption. *Quart. J. Stud. Alc.* **16**, 234–244 (1955).

Willingham, W. W. The organization of emotional behavior in mice. *J. comp. physiol. Psychol.* **49**, 345–348 (1956).

Willoughby, R. R. Family similarities in mental test abilities. *Genet. psychol. Monogr.* **11**, 234–277 (1927).

Wilson, P. T., and Jones, H. E. Left-handedness in twins. *Genetics* **17**, 560–571 (1932).

Wingfield, A. H., and Sandiford, P. Twins and orphans. *J. educ. Psychol.* **19**, 410–423 (1928).

Witschi, E. Modification of development in sex. In: *Sex and Internal Secretions*, E. Allen, ed. Baltimore: Williams & Wilkins, Ch. 4, 1939.

Witschi, E., and Mengert, W. F. Endocrine studies on human hermaphrodites and their bearing on the interpretation of homosexuality. *J. clin. Endocrinology* **2**, 279–286 (1942).

Witt, G. M., and Hall, C. S. The genetics of audiogenic seizures in the house mouse. *J. comp. physiol. Psychol.* **42**, 58–63 (1949).

Witterman, E. Klinische Psychiatrie und Familienforschung. *Zeitschr. Neurol. Psychiat.* **105**, 459–493 (1926).

Woods, F. A. *Mental and Moral Heredity in Royalty*. New York: Holt, 1906.

Wood-Gush, D. G. M. Genetic and experiential factors affecting the libido of cockerels. *Proc. Roy. Soc. Edinb.* **27**, 6–7 (1958).

Wood-Gush, D. G. M., and Osborne, R. A study of differences in the sex drive of cockerels. *Brit. J. anim. Behav.* **4**, 102–110 (1956).

Woods, J. W. Some observations on adrenal cortical functions in wild and domesticated Norway rats. *Doctoral thesis: Johns Hopkins Univ.* 1954.

Woodworth, R. S. Recent results on heredity and environment. *Trans. N. Y. Acad. Sci. Ser. 2.* **3**, 30–35 (1940).

Woolf, B. Environmental effects in quantitative inheritance. In: *Quantitative Inheritance*, E. C. R. Reeve and C. H. Waddington, eds. London: H. M. Stationery Office, 1952.

Wragg, L. E., and Speirs, R. S. Strain and sex differences in response of inbred mice to adrenal cortical hormones. *Proc. Soc. Exp. Biol. Med.* **80**, 680–684 (1952).

Wright, S. The relative importance of heredity and environment in determining the piebald pattern of guinea pigs. *Proc. Nat. Acad. Sci.* **6**, 320–332 (1920).

Wright, S. Systems of mating: I. The biometric relations between parent and offspring. *Genetics* **6**, 111–123 (1921).

Wright, S. Mendelian analysis of pure breeds of livestock. I. The measurement of inbreeding and relationship. *J. Hered.* **14**, 339–348 (1923).

Wright, S. The results of crosses between inbred strains of guinea pigs differing in numbers of digits. *Genetics* **19**, 537–551 (1934).

Wright, S. The genetics of quantitative variability. In: *Quantitative Inheritance,* E. C. R. Reeve and C. H. Waddington, eds. London: H. M. Stationery Office, 5–41, 1952.

Wright, S. Summary of patterns of mammalian gene action. *J. Nat. Canc. Inst.* **15,** 837–851 (1954).

Wright, S. W., and Fink, K. The excretion of beta-aminoisobutyric acid in normal, mongoloid and non-mongoloid defective children. *Amer. J. ment. Defic.* **61,** 530–533 (1957).

Yeakel, E. H., and Rhoades, R. P. A comparison of the body and endocrine gland (adrenal, thyroid and pituitary) weights of emotional and non-emotional rats. *Endocrinology* **28,** 337–340 (1941).

Yerkes, A. W. Comparisons of the behavior of stock and inbred albino rats. *J. anim. Behav.* **6,** 267–296 (1916).

Yerkes, R. M. *The Dancing Mouse.* New York: Macmillan, 1907.

Yerkes, R. M. The heredity of savageness and wildness in rats. *J. anim. Behav.* **3,** 286–296 (1913).

Yule, E. P. The resemblance of twins with regard to perseveration. *J. ment. Sci.* **81,** 489–501 (1935).

Zehnder, M. Ueber Krankheitsbild und Krankheitsverlauf bei schizophrenen Geschwistern. *Monatschr. Psychiat. Neurol.* **103,** 231–277 (1941).

Zilian, E. Ergebnisse psychologischen Untersuchungen an erbgleichen und erbunglei-chen Zwillingen. *Beih. Zeitschr. angew. Psychol.* **79,** 42–50 (1938).

Author index

Subject index